The Flowering World of
"Chinese" Wilson

THE
Flowering World
OF
"Chinese" Wilson

EDITED AND WITH AN INTRODUCTION

AND BRIEF BIOGRAPHY BY

Daniel J. Foley

The Macmillan Company

Collier-Macmillan Ltd. LONDON

Frontispiece: Regal lilies in a Vermont garden
(P. E. GENEREUX)

Chapters II, VII, XI, and XIV are from Wilson's *If I Were to Make a Garden* (1931); chapters VI, VIII, IX, and XII are from *More Aristocrats of the Garden* (1928). Chapter XIII is taken from *Aristocrats of the Garden* (1926), and chapter XV is from *Aristocrats of the Trees* (1930).

All other chapters are from Wilson's major work, the two-volume *Plant Hunting* (1928).

Library of Congress Catalog Card Number: 69-12646

FIRST PRINTING

The Macmillan Company
Collier-Macmillan Canada Ltd., Toronto, Ontario

Printed in the United States of America

For

HARRIET MOSELEY BODLEY

whose garden at Chailey

in Newburyport, Massachusetts,

contains many of

E. H. Wilson's plant treasures

Acknowledgments

AN IMMEASURABLE DEBT of gratitude is due Dr. and Mrs. George L. Slate for checking biographical details, supplying photographs, and delineating E. H. Wilson's everyday life. I am most grateful also to a number of persons, now deceased, who frequently recalled incidents portraying the warm humanity of the greatest plant hunter of the early twentieth century. Among them were Edward I. Farrington, Harold Ross, Ernest Borowski, John S. Ames, Walter Hunnewell and others.

For assistance with photographs, typing, reading, editing, and clarifying the manuscript, I am most grateful to:

Mr. and Mrs. Moses Alpers   Mrs. Helen Snow Wilson
Mrs. R. V. C. Bodley   Goddard
Mr. John Burton Brimer   Mrs. Laura Hatton
Alfred Fordham   Mr. Heman Howard
Mr. Paul E. Genereux   Mr. and Mrs. Philip H. Lord

Miss Marie L. Lynch
Mrs. Wilfred Marchand
Mr. Richard Marek
Miss Dorothy S. Manks
The Massachusetts
  Horticultural Society
Catherine E. Meikle

Mr. and Mrs. Arno H.
  Nehrling
Mrs. James A. O'Shea, Jr.
Mr. Donald Robinson
Mrs. Gifford P. Scott
Dr. and Mrs. George L. Slate
Mr. George Taloumis
Mr. Joseph Vaitch

Salem, Massachusetts   DANIEL J. FOLEY

Contents

Foreword

THIS IS A BOOK FOR PLANT-LOVERS who garden with a purpose—to grow those ornamentals which are superior for their flowers, their fruits, and their foliage, as well as the unique forms which they assume. It is the right plant for the right place that lends distinction to any garden, large or small. When Ernest Henry Wilson, the most intrepid plant hunter of the early twentieth century, had completed his search for new plants, he launched a great crusade for more and better gardens all across America where his treasures might be utilized. He joined the staff of the Arnold Arboretum in Jamaica Plain, Massachusetts, in 1906, serving that institution as plant hunter and succeeded Charles Sprague Sargent, its first director, in 1927. Although his knowledge of plants was almost beyond compare, what was even more significant was his capacity for popularizing his finds. Since he could visualize their use with other exotics and native kinds, he could literally make them grow as he talked and wrote about them. He could write, "at times with the pen of angels," as Richardson Wright, long-time editor of *House and Garden,* once expressed it. He could talk with vigor and enthusiasm, and he did. He was first, last, and always a plantsman with an uncanny sense of the landscape effects to be achieved with woody plants. Aside from his family and a small circle of intimate friends, the vitalizing force of his life was the plant world to which he was entirely dedicated.

Although nearly forty years have passed since his death, "Chinese" Wilson's writings, volume for volume, chapter for chapter, are as timely, as inspiring, and as informative as they were when written. In the twenty-five chapters selected for inclusion in this anthology, only a few sentences have been deleted. These refer to the culture of rhododendrons, which had not been widely tested and were not grown commonly in gardens and nurseries when Wilson was writing. All of his books have been long out of print so that the present generation of gardeners has lost touch with an inspired writer on gardening.

This book is offered in an effort to recall the achievements of the greatest benefactor of American gardens in our time and, for that matter, of the gardens of Europe and those in other parts of the world. It contains a biography of sufficient length and detail to give some concept of the era in which "Chinese" Wilson worked as a plant collector. The twenty-five chapters from his books serve as a sampling of the world of plants he knew so intimately. Finally, the chapter on his plant treasures is an attempt to evaluate those which are widely cultivated today as well as those which deserve more attention.

When I became editor of *Horticulture* magazine in 1951, Edward I. Farrington, formerly secretary of the Massachusetts Horticultural Society and editor of *Horticulture*, tossed to me a challenge: "Keep E. H. Wilson's name green. Every gardener in America owes him a debt of gratitude." Then he went on to enumerate some of the plants which Wilson called his aristocrats.

Having worked with a goodly number of them at the Breeze Hill Test Garden of Dr. J. Horace McFarland, in Harrisburg, Pennsylvania, having paid many a visit to the Arnold Arboretum, where countless numbers of them flourished, and having seen them embellishing gardens in various parts of the country, I was minded to accept the challenge. In any event, as long as men and women who tend gardens and cherish a love of flowers plant at least one of the hundreds of plant treasures which he brought home, "Chinese" Wilson's name will remain forever green.

DANIEL J. FOLEY

September, 1968
Salem, Massachusetts

The Flowering World of
"Chinese" Wilson

Introduction

CHINA, THE MOTHER OF GARDENS, was for many years the home of a young English plant hunter in the early years of this century. Later, he traveled in Japan, Korea, and Formosa, and still later, circled the globe; but China was his first love. This intrepid explorer greatly enriched the gardens of America in addition to those of his homeland and other countries as well with the handsome ornamental trees and shrubs he gathered. For nearly half a century, every gardener worth his salt has grown at least a few of his introductions.

Ernest Henry Wilson was no ordinary plantsman. He ranked at the top of the list with the great discoverers of previous centuries, not so much because he brought home flamboyant flowers like the geranium, the tea rose, the orchid, and the camellia, but rather for the choice and extensive collection of ornamental woody plants which he garnered, practically all admirably suited to some region of our American landscape. Not all of them have been truly evaluated as yet; others, in addition to those now commonly grown by nurserymen, undoubtedly will come into prominence in the years to come.

A plant hunter, like a game hunter or an explorer, is a man endowed with exceptional traits, including a large measure of courage, for without special attributes he could not succeed in the untamed wilderness. The price paid for such a calling is exceptionally high even when success crowns his ventures, and success is not always achieved. E. H. Wilson possessed all the needed traits, and his exploits were notably successful. He was quick to learn what it meant to be a hunter of plants and he described every facet of his profession in the introduction to *Plant Hunting*, his two-volume record of all the leading plant hunters who had preceded him:

Like any other vocation, plant hunting calls for certain qualifications. First and foremost it is the work of youth for it takes heavy toll of strength and endurance, patience and enthusiasm. A sound constitution and an eminently sane mind are fundamental requisites. An optimistic temperament and abundance of tact are essential in dealing with the difficulties and delays incident upon travel and the idiosyncrasies of native peoples. The more knowledge the hunter has of plants already in cultivation, of gardening, and of botany, the greater the chance of success. Some business acumen, ability to mingle freely and pleasantly with all sorts and conditions of men are added qualifications of no mean order. But above all else tact and a sound physique are needed in the rough and tumble of plant hunting.

Hunting plants presents difficulties over and above those connected with hunting big game. The game hunter after finding, stalking, and shooting his quarry has but to remove the pelt, dress it, and the trophy is won. The same is true of collecting birds or insects. The plant hunter having found his plant must abide the proper season for securing ripe seeds, roots or small plants or, failing these, wood for cuttings or scions. His quest may be found in blossom in spring or summer when it must be marked down for another visit in the autumn. Often several visits are necessary before the actual season of harvest is determined.

The weather greatly influences the harvest of seeds and often several fickle seasons pass before success is attained. Having secured his seeds, roots, small plants or cuttings, many difficulties have to be overcome before they are safely transported to the homeland. The plant hunter is dealing with living things not dead museum trophies, and he must find means of properly conserving the life in his finds so that they reach their destination without undue exhaustion. To transport plant material hundreds of miles overland and then safely dispatch it across the seas is no small task. And having succeeded in this, success or failure of his labor is in the hands of those who take possession of the material in the homeland. Carelessness, indifference, lack of proper knowledge in the art of raising plants from seeds or of nursing them in sickness and youth, spells failure to the plant hunter's enterprise. Full and sympathetic cooperation on the part of hunter and agent at home alone ensures success. Then comes the test. Will the new arrivals adapt themselves to alien climates and novel conditions of life? Will they acclimate themselves? Will they reproduce under alien skies the beauty of flower, of leaf, or form of growth that was the hunter's admiration in their native land? There are many "ifs" and often months and years of anxious moments pass before the truth is known.

Neither must the plant hunter expect strangers to view his finds through rose-hued glasses. Enthusiasts will prattle over any new thing and skeptics will scoff at the finest of jewels, for it is the nature of such to so behave. But the man who knows is the man whose opinion is really worth having. Merit alone counts with this calm, deliberating type and often much time is needed for this decision. Often the plant hunter has to fight with tongue and pen for the plants he has won and which are the children of his heart. He will probably suffer more rebuffs and vexations in the homeland than in the wilds in which he hunted. However, if a true plantsman he will appraise his finds judiciously and time will see his faith triumphant. Beauty is a potent force in disarming skepticism and disrupting opposition.

If new plants possess real merit sooner or later they will come into their kingdom. Experience has shown that, dependent upon the ease with which they may be grown and increased, it may take anywhere from five to twenty-five years for a new plant to become popular. If they are real additions to gardens, if they possess any meritorious quality superior to plants already known, novelties are certain of winning their proper place. Unfortunately, it often happens that the time necessary is greater than that vouchsafed to those who journey forth, content with hardships of all sorts to win plants from their distant homes. But there is fun in the game, much fun, and conquest of difficulties of any sort always gives zest to life. And if health stays with the plant hunter he may in the autumn of his life enjoy the deep satisfaction of seeing in gardens large and small, in that of the cottager and of the wealthy, in gardens private and public, the children he won from many a rough spot flourishing and happy and with their beauty giving pleasure to thousands. They are still his, but the greater the number who tend them as their own the greater and deeper is the joy of the plant hunter. They are tangible proofs of useful accomplishment and with gratitude and pride he can point to them as evidence of a life not altogether selfish nor lived in vain.

Plant hunting, by no means an ordinary occupation, has nevertheless had its devotees through the ages. The craving for exotic plants is an ancient one.

Dating from the late eighteenth century when trade between the two countries was strictly limited, the flora of China held a very special kind of appeal in England. At the time, visions of far-off Cathay were largely clouded by fancy, since comparatively few Englishmen had ever set foot in that strange land. Those that did were greatly restricted as to where and how far from a treaty port they might travel. Europeans were neither welcome nor allowed to travel freely in China then, as was the case in Japan at a later time. Exclusion and seclusion were the order of the day. The governing officials of China displayed feelings of pride and insolence, considering all outsiders as inferior. Despite their willingness to trade with foreigners, the average Chinese looked upon all Europeans as Western devils, who could not be trusted, and the notion persisted until the end of the nineteenth century. All Europeans conformed to the generally accepted Chinese idea of a demon. The average Englishman,

Frenchman, or Dutchman, although of average height, was tall by Oriental standards, sometimes fair-haired and blue-eyed, and when in the wilds, grew a beard. It is a strange fact that men with red hair possessed a curious attraction for the Chinese, or so it was believed. One English traveler, recording his experiences, reported he got ahead of his party on a mountain with an eerie reputation and met a group of natives who at the sight of him dropped all they were carrying and fled.

Portuguese traders had established a settlement in China in 1547. With the marriage of Catherine of Braganza, the Infanta of Portugal, to Charles II, in 1662, England was given entrée to the China trade. Yet, from 1755 to 1842, such trade was, for the most part, limited to Canton and the township of Macao, where the Portuguese had originally settled. There were located the *Hongs*, or warehouses, where trading with various nations took place under strict Chinese surveillance. Foreign merchants were required to live in Macao. Regulations for trading were so rigid that foreigners had to deal with a dozen specified Hong merchants who were licensed for the purpose. Also, foreign traders were forbidden to learn the Chinese language and could hire only licensed interpreters. They were forced to channel all inquiries for commodities and communications to government officials through the Hong merchants.

Enthusiasm for chinoiserie, as it came to be known, reached a high point of fashion in England. Furniture and furnishings of every conceivable kind became highly ornate in the Chinese manner. When the fever spread to gardening, the ultimate result was what has been described as delightful nonsense.

One gardener developed a yellow serpentine river in a valley only twenty yards long and spanned it with a picturesque Oriental bridge. Pagodas loomed in English parks. From *A Dissertation on Oriental Gardening*, published in 1772, we learn: "Their gardeners are not only botanists, but also painters and philosophers, having a thorough knowledge of the human mind, and the arts by which its strongest feelings are excited."

The first Chinese plants brought to England had been collected by ship surgeons of the East India Company. From 1812 to 1831, John Reeves, who served the company as inspector of tea, collected many choice kinds which found their way into English gardens. He maintained a notable garden in Macao where he grew Western plants and showed the Chinese something of the practices of English gardeners. As early as 1821, the Royal Horticultural Society began to send collectors to China for the express purpose of gathering plants.

From 1740 through the late nineteenth century, a number of French Jesuits and priests from other countries contributed their share to horticulture by collecting and writing about plants which they discovered and observed in the course of their travels. Nicholae d'Incarville, who was stationed in Pekin from 1740 to 1756, complained bitterly about traveling privileges. However, he managed to send plants to Paris and London by the circuitous caravan route via St. Petersburg. Jean Denis Attiret wrote an account of the Emperor's garden at Pekin which was published in 1752. Others who were active in plant collecting in the later period and whose names are linked with exotic species include Paul G. Farges, Jean M. Delavay, Jean P. A. David, E. Bodinier, J. A. Soulie, Joannis de Louriero, and G. Giraldi.

In 1842, five months after the signing of the Nanking Treaty, which opened up a number of Chinese ports to the British for trading, the Chinese Committee of the Royal Horticultural Society, eager to exploit the floral riches of this little known country, appointed Robert Fortune as its collector. John Reeves, having retired from his post in China, spearheaded the expedition, knowing that English gardeners were eager to grow exotics from the Orient.

In many ways Fortune's career paralleled that of Wilson's, and, half a century later, Fortune's mantle was to fit Wilson's shoulders. A Scot, born at Kelloe in Berwickshire in 1812, he was early apprenticed in private gardens and then moved on to the Edinburgh Botanic Garden. Not too long after, when he had hardly became established as superintendent of the hothouse at Chiswick, operated by the Royal Horticultural Society, the opportunity to go to China presented itself. The assignment charged him with collecting hardy plants as well as aquatics, orchids, "plants producing very handsome flowers," certain kinds of peaches, "the plants that yield tea of different qualities," and nearly two dozen other kinds of plants of ornamental and economic importance. In all, the detailed set of instructions given him was some 2,000 words in length. In essence, the wordy missal revealed how little was known, or even dreamed of, at the time, about the floral treasures of China.

On this, his first trip, Fortune was even equipped with a Chinese vocabulary. Although never allowed to venture more than 30 miles from a treaty port, he was amazingly successful in collecting plants of high ornamental value from gardens and nurseries. His enthusiasm, although unbounded, was tempered by sound judgment. He at once terrified and charmed Chinese nurserymen who ultimately sold him whatever he wanted. He encountered more than his share of dangers; he even fought off pirates single-handed, and battled high fever. In all, Fortune made four trips to China. The first lasted three years, from 1843 to 1846; the second extended from 1848 to 1851; the third, from 1853 to 1856; his last trip was made in 1861. His second and third trips were financed by the East India Company, which commissioned him to acquire what knowledge he could about growing tea. As a result of his travels and observations, he is credited with establishing the tea industry of India. His final trip was made on his own behalf and included Japan.

Robert Fortune was a keen observer with great knowledge. Of him Wilson wrote, "His industry was great, his judgment of the garden value of a plant infallible, and his ability to pack his collections so that they successfully withstood the vicissitudes of the long voyage home round the Cape of Good Hope calls for the admiration of all who have tried this none too easy task."

In all, Fortune introduced nearly 200 species and varieties of plants, of which more than half were entirely new to botanists and horticulturists. When Fortune died in 1880, Ernest Wilson was but four years old, but as he grew and studied, he soon came to be familiar with Fortune's work through four popular books which Fortune wrote about his travels.

Wilson's immediate predecessor in plant collecting was Charles Maries. In 1879, he had been dispatched to China by James Veitch and Sons, a leading firm of English nurserymen, but had turned back at Ichang, when he was at the very entrance to the paradise of plant collectors. Unable and unwilling to understand the Chinese and possessed of an unstable temperament, Maries incurred their emnity to such a degree that they destroyed his collections. Furthermore, he doubted that any new plants of importance or value could be found in China, and he so informed his employer. Within a few years, Dr. Augustine Henry was to disprove this conviction by shipping to Kew numerous rare and unknown plants. For a time, however, Maries' opinions were generally accepted not only by the Veitches but also by most horticulturists in England.

1

Ernest H. Wilson:
A Brief Biography

"MY BOY, stick to the one thing you are after and do not spend time and money wandering about. Probably almost every worthwhile plant in China has now been introduced into Europe." This was the forthright command given to a handsome young Englishman, then twenty-two years old, as he was hired to make an expedition into the interior of China to find a rare flowering tree called the dove tree, *Davidia involucrata*, and to collect ripe seed for propagation. The man who issued the order to his new employee was Harry James Veitch, one of England's most noted nurserymen, whose establishment was widely known to plant-lovers the world over. He sought the rare and the unusual in plants, since the family business, for several generations, had been established along these lines.

It was a dried specimen of davidia sent to the Royal Botanic Gardens at Kew by Dr. Augustine Henry in 1891 that started the quest. The botanists at Kew became as excited about it as did Henry when he found it. This exotic tree had been discovered and described by Père Armand David, a French missionary, in 1869, but it had never been introduced to cultivation. Even the seeds gathered by Henry and sent to England had failed to germinate. Thus, he continued to write letters to the director of the Gardens, Sir William T. H. Thiselton-Dyer, urging him to tell collectors to look for it and to collect seed. Veitch had learned of this rare tree and he wanted it. He told Wilson that Dr. Henry, who had sent the specimen to Kew, was an Irish doctor, who chose service with the Chinese Maritime Customs in preference to practice as a physician in his native land. He pursued the study of botany in China as an antidote to boredom. During his periods of leave, he traveled widely, all the while training native collectors to assist him.

The young plantsman who listened to this challenge was Ernest Henry Wilson, at the time a student at the Royal Botanic Gardens. His aim had been to attend the Royal College of Science and become a teacher of botany. Fortunately, this modest son of Gloucestershire, born there on February 15, 1876, accepted Veitch's offer instead of enrolling at the Royal College. It was on the recommendation of Sir William Thiselton-Dyer, who had observed his work closely, that Wilson was engaged by Harry J. Veitch.

His early training was no different from that of other English boys of his station and time. Ernest was the oldest of seven children. Since his father died when he was young, he was fired with ambition to assist his mother and younger brothers and sisters as best he could. From the outset, apparently, he had developed an intense curiosity for and love of plants. First, he went to work for the Messrs. Hewitt at Solihull, Warwickshire. At the age of sixteen, he obtained a job at the Birmingham Botanical Gardens and found time to study botany in the Birmingham Technical School, where his skill and competence won for him the Queen's Prize.

From the very beginning, despite his youth, E. H. Wilson had fixed his sights firmly on accomplishing what was expected of him by H. J. Veitch. Before leaving for China, he spent six months with George Harrow at the Coombe Wood nursery, one of several operated by the Veitch family. Harrow was a nurseryman of exceptional skill, and under his tutelage Wilson was trained in the policy and practices of the greatest of English nurseries. Having been exposed to the most extensive collection of exotic woody plants in all England, some of them from China, he became fully aware of the importance of his mission, particularly as it related to Chinese flora.

In the space of a few months Wilson was briefed as to the conditions he might expect to find in China. Although Dr. Henry succeeded in gaining the confidence of the Chinese peasants and learned their language, in his numerous letters to friends at Kew and elsewhere, he bemoaned the slipshod ways of the Chinese, the deceit and hypocrisy of the ruling class, and the depressed spirit which prevailed among the poor laborers (whom he employed to help him collect plants). These facts were well known to Thiselton-Dyer and Veitch, and surely both men left Wilson with no illusions as to what he might expect.

Thus, young Wilson was made fully aware that the trip would be a long one, full of uncertainties, pitfalls, and delays due to primitive methods of travel, language problems, and the animosity of the people. It was common knowledge that all foreigners were suspect and that the Chinese could not be trusted. He could lose his life and his remains might never be found. As it turned out, he was to experience every conceivable kind of delay, disappointment, and frustration. Every danger imagined occurred, in-

cluding a few of which he had never dreamed. This trip was to
be in reality, an object lesson—a test by fire.

Wilson left England on April 11, 1899, for America where he
had been instructed to call on Charles Sprague Sargent, Director
of the Arnold Arboretum, which was connected with Harvard
Univerity. Here he was to learn all that he could, in a few days,
about Sargent's techniques in collecting, packaging, and shipping
plants. Obviously, this alert young Englishman made a profound
impression on Sargent who entertained him at his estate in
nearby Brookline, which was one of the horticultural show places
of the day. He also became acquainted with Jackson Dawson,
the Arboretum's noted propagator.

Five days later he boarded the train and crossed the United
States to San Francisco. Of his experience he wrote:

My trip across the continent was delightful; everything was new,
strange, and interesting, and the hours of daylight were not long
enough to drink my fill from the Pullman windows. When crossing
Texas a talkative brakesman told me hair-raising stories of the exploits
of the notorious James brothers and so impressive was his language
that a thrill goes through me now as I recall it. On May 6 I sailed
from San Francisco and on June 3 safely reached Hongkong where
I had letters from friends.

A pleasant interlude amid the comforts of civilization had come
to an end. Wilson's destination was Szemao, a city in the southwestern corner of Yunnan, near the frontier of northern Burma,
where Dr. Henry was stationed. Henry was expecting him, having
promised to furnish Wilson with a map to locate the famous tree
and whatever information he could regarding Chinese flora that
might be helpful to him. It was necessary to go through French
Tonkin, to the Chinese border, and across the great province
of Yunnan, a distance of nearly a thousand miles. Since bubonic

plague was rampant in Hongkong at the time, no Chinese native was allowed to enter Tonkin. Consequently, Wilson was deprived of an English-speaking Chinese servant without whom he could not travel easily. Equipped with a passport and provisions, he finally boarded a steamer and in six days reached Hanoi, the capital of Tonkin. Wilson spoke only English, which proved to be something of a handicap in this French city, but with his usual tact and diplomacy, he met a French customs officer who spoke English and together they headed for Mengtsz.

On the way, at the village of Laokai, they learned that the foreigners in the community of their destination had been attacked by the natives and that the French consulate and customshouse were destroyed by fire. It was claimed that the uprising was occasioned by local residents who objected to a railway that the French government proposed to build. At the time, a survey for the road was in progress. Bitterly unhappy, Wilson settled down in the Hotel du Commerce, a small inn run by a Frenchman with an English wife who made him welcome. On the very same day, he received a note from the French officer commanding the district, warning him against proceeding on his journey. In the afternoon, news arrived of the murder of four men who had left a few days before for Mengtsz. The outlook was decidedly unpromising, but even then Wilson did not realize how many dreary days of waiting lay ahead.

Conditions at Laokai, a very small village, were indeed depressing. Of it Wilson wrote:

It is situated on the left bank of the Red River and separated from Chinese territory by a small tributary stream and is backed by low jungle and tree-clad hills with swamps near by. Across the Red River on the right bank was a large military encampment including barracks where were quartered a battalion of the Foreign Legion and several regiments of Annamese troops officered of course by Frenchmen. Laokai is within the tropics and although some hundreds of miles from the sea is only a few feet above sea level and being shut in by jungle-clad mountains the climate was very unhealthy. . . . The heat during the greater part of the day was intense and I could go walking for a few hours only after sunrise and for an hour or so in the evening. It was the rainy season and nearly every day rain fell in tropical fury. . . . I settled down to make the best of things and amused myself investigating the flora of the immediate neighborhood of Laokai. As my stay lengthened into weeks my hopes of continuing my journey sank lower and lower, and I went so far as to write to both Dr. Henry and my employers advising them that I should have to abandon the effort when, quite unexpectedly, I managed to move onward. Reviewing the affair after a lapse of twenty-six years I rather marvel that I did not abandon the venture. Certain it is that my enforced sojourn and inactivity at Laokai were the most discouraging, the most trying, and the most unpleasant to endure of any experience during my eleven years of travel in China.

To add to his tribulations, Wilson learned that the military authorities were suspicious of him from the very beginning, regarding him as a spy and a captain of the British Army in disguise. Of the incident he wrote: "As a broad hint to quit I received an enlistment notice! Those were the days of the 'Dreyfus retrial' and of the 'Fashoda incident' and before the 'Entente cordiale'— days when a native of 'perfidious Albion' was the opposite of a welcome guest in a French colony where military rule was dominant."

After three weeks of waiting, Wilson was told that the route to Mengtsz was safe for travel, but nowhere could he find a guide or an interpreter who had the courage to undertake the journey in view of the recent riot and the rumors attending it. Finally, a month later, he received a note which read:

My Dear Sir:
  Before I have wish to do a interpreter with you, because I am very sick cannot to going, at now I have a friend he have learned him

English for two years at Hongkong, if you wish to get a interpreter he can do.

Your small servant
Limay.

Wilson wrote later:

Who Limay was I had not the slightest idea but I was grateful to him nevertheless. The bearer of the note was himself the applicant. He was a Chinese of very unprepossessing appearance who smoked opium freely and had been discharged from the telegraph service for incompetency, but he spoke a little English. I engaged him on the spot, for a chance to reach Dr. Henry presented itself. Not being anxious to do more work than he could help, my "interpreter" rounded up an Annamese who could cook and I engaged him, too. On August 23 we left in a native boat for Manhao. The river was in flood.

After three days on the Red River, Wilson recalled:

I was overtaken by Monsieur Marty who owned the line of river steamers between Hanoi and Laokai and another line plying to Hongkong where he resided. Monsieur Marty was anxious for company and induced me to travel in his boat. To other accomplishments he added those of a good cook and I was really most fortunate in joining him more especially as my own boat, in crossing a dangerous rapid, had lost masts and sail and was so nearly swamped that I had to transfer everything to my companion's boat. On September 1 we arrived at Manhao and three days later with no untoward event reached Mengtsz.

The distress that he found there was hardly uplifting, but Wilson did not dwell upon the gruesome details except to record that he "saw suspended from the branches of a tree, wooden cages containing the heads of five of the rioters. Later I met a posse of soldiers bringing in another gruesome-looking head."

The final stretch of the journey to Szemao was seventeen days distant.

My caravan of fifteen or sixteen mules and several muleteers was imposing and included not only my own belongings, but several cases of silver for Chinese officials at Szemao and a number of cases of stores for the customs staff. I left on the morning of September 8, and, being unable to speak any Chinese, traveled very much as a parcel and enjoyed the trip. I received en route a couple of letters of welcome from Dr. Henry and, when two days from my destination, a note from him informing me that a gang of highway robbers had been plying their nefarious calling between the cities of Puerh and Szemao but that the ringleaders had been captured and executed. The officials at Puerh sent ten soldiers as a guard and a few miles beyond that city ten soldiers sent from Szemao joined us, and with these twenty picturesquely clad but grotesquely armed soldiers our caravan looked like a small punitive expedition.

My last night before reaching Szemao was on a Saturday, and about nine o'clock, after all had retired, a barking of dogs and some shouting aroused excitement and my soldier guard began to prepare for an attack when the sound of an English voice sent a thrill of joy through me. The door was quickly thrown open and I rushed to greet two men, Messrs. Carey and Williams, who with rare forethought of my loneliness had ridden from Szemao to bid me welcome.

A house had been arranged for Wilson at Szemao, where Dr. Henry and his associates made him welcome. The doctor opened his notebook and drew a diagram of the exact location where he found the davidia tree and discoursed at length about the flora of China. Wilson reported enthusiastically about his pleasant respite without mentioning any of the weariness or discomfort he had experienced, but the visit was not to last as long as he hoped it might. Dr. Henry had received orders to replace Mr. W. F. Spinney, an American who was Commissioner of Customs in troubled Mengtsz. Wilson accompanied Henry to his new post, since he had to return to Hongkong to begin his search for the coveted tree.

Even that trip was not without its tribulations since the country was in a highly disturbed state. But, Wilson recalled, "Being in blissful ignorance, all murmurings and grumblings left me unaffected, but my companion—fully conversant with the language—endured some anxiety."

Keen-eyed plantsman that he was, even at twenty-two, Wilson collected plants of the primrose jasmine (*Jasminum primulinum*), which he shipped to England along with items collected by Dr. Henry. (This handsome ornamental shrub has been widely planted in Europe, America, and Australia.) Having arrived back in Hongkong, he made preparations for his trip on the Yangtze River to Ichang in the heart of China. As Wilson tells it:

Ichang, where I arrived on February 24, 1900, was to be my head-quarters for two years[1] so I made plans accordingly, I purchased a native boat of good size in which to live and to serve as a base of supplies and engaged some countrymen to assist me in collecting. . . . By the middle of April everything was ready to start in quest of the davidia. On a half page of a notebook Dr. Henry had sketched a tract of country about the size of New York State and had marked the spot where he had found growing a single tree of the davidia, the only example he had discovered in a trip which extended over six months and the only one he had ever seen. The place was among high mountains in the sparsely populated region bordering the provinces of Hupeh and Szechwan and south of the mighty Yangtze River. This locality was my destination and this solitary tree my sole objective.

On the morning of April 15 I left Ichang, in my boat, to ascend the Yangtze as far as the district city of Patung where I arrived on the 21st idem. The journey was exciting, for the rapids which are very numerous were at that season difficult to negotiate. Twice we ran on rocks and had to repair damage. At the worst rapid the boat all but capsized and there were other and numerous incidents which space will not allow me to mention in detail. At Patung the head official

[1] It often requires two full growing seasons to obtain ripe fruits of some woody plants.

did his best to frighten my men and begged me to abandon the enterprise. Finally, his efforts proving of no effect, he promised an escort of six soldiers and washed his hands, as it were, of the business. The man was in earnest and genuinely afraid for my safety.

Curiously enough, as Miles and John Hadfield pointed out in *Gardens of Delight*, the Chinese poet Po Chü-i had painted a vivid picture, a thousand years earlier, of the very area which Wilson traveled. Like Henry, the writer of the following lines was not only a lover of plants but also a government agent who was punished by his superior officer and given an assignment in this remote section of Szechwan. The poem entitled, "Alarm at First Entering the Yan-Tze Gorges," was written when Po was being towed up the rapids to Chung-chow.

> Above, a mountain ten thousand feet high:
> Below, a river a thousand fathoms deep.
> A strip of sky, walled by cliffs of stone:
> Wide enough for the passage of a single reed.
> At Chu-t'ang, a straight cleft yawns:
> At Yen-ye islands block the stream.
> Long before night the walls are black with dusk:
> Without wind white waves rise.
> The big rocks are like a flat sword:
> The little rocks resemble ivory tusks.
> We are stuck fast and cannot move a step.
> How much the less, three hundred miles?
> Frail and slender, the twisted-bamboo rope:
> Weak, the dangerous hold of the tower's feet.
> A single slip—the whole convoy lost:
> And *my* life hangs on *this* thread!
> I have heard a saying "He that has an upright heart
> Shall walk scathless through the lands of Man and Mo."
> How can I believe that since the world began
> In every shipwreck none have drowned but rogues?
> And how can I, born in evil days

And fresh from failure, ask a kindness of Fate?
Often I fear that these untalented limbs
Will be laid at last in an unnamed grave!

Two years prior to Wilson's arrival, rioting between Christians and anti-Christians had resulted in wholesale murder and destruction. The feeling had not subsided to any marked degree, and new trouble was believed imminent. Wilson was fully aware of conditions, but as he wrote, modestly and without affectation, "My mission was to obtain *Davidia involucrata* and in furtherance of this I did not think of causing trouble of any kind." As he traveled toward his destination, word of the unsettled condition of the area was brought again to his attention, more forcefully, this time, by a Belgian priest whose companion, another missionary, had been murdered two years before. He learned that with the exception of these priests and Dr. Henry, he was the only foreigner who had visited the area. On April 25, he stayed at the same house where Dr. Henry had lodged two years earlier. As he made inquiries, Wilson reports what he found:

Did the people remember Dr. Henry? Did they know the *K'ung-tung* (local name of davidia)? To these and similar questions they pleasantly answered in the affirmative. Would some one guide me to the tree? Certainly! We sallied forth, I in the highest of spirits. After walking about two miles we came to a house rather new in appearance. Near by was the stump of Henry's davidia. The tree had been cut down a year before and the trunk and branches formed the beams and posts of the house! I did not sleep during the night of April 25, 1900.

Surprisingly enough, instead of being discouraged, Wilson was more determined than ever to find full-grown specimens of the object of his mission. He decided to collect all the plants that he might find worthy of sending home, and to travel westward a thousand miles or more to the region where Père David had discovered davidia in 1869. A little more than three weeks elapsed and,

with this resolution made I let the subject drift from my mind. . . . On May 19 when collecting near the hamlet of Ta-wan, distant some five days southwest of Ichang, I suddenly happened upon a davidia tree in full flower! It was about 50 feet tall, in outline pyramidal, and with its wealth of blossoms was more beautiful than words can portray. When figuring Henry's fruiting specimens in Hooker's *Icones Plantarum* (XX, t, 1961, (1891)) the Keeper of the Kew Herbarium wrote: 'Davidia is a tree almost deserving a special mission to western China with a view to its introduction to European gardens.' On beholding this extraordinary tree for the first time I no longer marveled at the keeper's strong language. And now with a wider knowledge of floral treasures of the Northern Hemisphere I am convinced that *Davidia involucrata* is the most interesting and most beautiful of all trees which grow in the north temperate regions. The distinctive beauty of the davidia is in the two snow-white connate bracts which subtend the flower proper. These are always unequal in size—the larger usually 6 inches long by 3 inches broad, and the smaller 3½ inches by 2½ inches; they range up to 8 inches by 4 inches and 5 inches by 3 inches. At first greenish, they become pure white as the flowers mature and change to brown with age. The flowers and their attendant bracts are pendulous on fairly long stalks, and when stirred by the slightest breeze they resemble huge butterflies or small doves hovering amongst the trees. The bracts are somewhat boat-shaped and flimsy in texture, and the leaves hide them considerably, but so freely are they borne that the tree, from a distance, looks as if flecked with snow. The bracts are most conspicuous on dull days and in the early morning.

Wilson was not content merely to collect seed, herbarium specimens, and living plants or roots (when feasible). He also made photographs, often under extremely hazardous conditions. The cameras used in the early 1900's were large—awkward and cumbersome to handle, especially when the photographer worked on steep slopes or in the branches of trees. The plates were made of glass and even a dozen could be a burden. Since practically every step connected with the finding of davidia required more than ordinary effort, making photographs of the tree was no exception, as witness the following notation from Wilson's journal:

Ascending a precipice with difficulty, we soon reach the davidia trees. There are over a score of them growing on a steep, rocky declivity; they vary from 35 to 60 feet in height, and the largest is 6 feet in girth. Being in a dense wood they are bare of branches for half their height, but their presence is readily detected by the numerous white bracts which have fallen and lie strewn over the ground. By climbing a large tetracentron tree growing on the edge of a cliff and chopping off some branches to make a clear space, I manage to take some snapshots of the upper part of the davidia tree in full flower. A difficult task and highly dangerous. Three of us climb the tree to different heights and haul up axe and camera from one to another by means of a rope. The wood of tetracentron is brittle, and the knowledge of this does not add to one's peace of mind when sitting astride a branch about 4 inches thick with a sheer drop of a couple of hundred feet beneath. However, all went well, and we drank in the beauties of this extraordinary tree.

Augustine Henry had seen the lone davidia on his first long expedition for plants. Fifty years later he declared that it was one of the strangest sights he saw in China, "waving its innumerable ghost handkerchiefs." From this description came the common name handkerchief tree which is sometimes used in England. Wilson never refers to the greenish-white bracts in this manner. Sheila Pim, author of Henry's biography, *The Wood and the Trees,* wrote: "The natives regarded it with veneration. In those rugged wastes, it might well seem a supernatural vision. The mind's eye would create a nimbus round the branches hung with white in the sun."

Wilson wrote afterwards of finding davidias in quantity:

Later I found two other trees in the same neighborhood and, in localities varying from 50 to 100 miles apart, eight others. These eleven trees were carefully watched through this anxious year of the Boxer trouble; they fruited freely, and in November I garnered a rich harvest of seeds which were dispatched to England where they safely arrived in due course. In 1901, when on an expedition through the northwest of Hupeh, I discovered the davidia in quantity and more than a hundred trees became known to me. From these hundred trees I did not secure a hundred seeds, and during subsequent visits to China extending over a decade I never again saw davidia fruiting in the manner it did in 1900. The fruit may be likened to that of a walnut, but is more or less ellipsoid, or, more rarely, roundish in shape and about 1¼ to 1¾ inches long. The color is greenish russet and slightly reddish on one side and the flesh is very thin and gritty. The "nut" consists of a number of seeds arranged around an axis and embedded in woody tissue as hard as flint and absolutely unbreakable.

When the "nuts" arrived in England, in the early spring of 1901, they were sown in a number of ways since little was known about the germination habits of this tree. Warm greenhouse temperatures were utilized for some; others were sown in pots and boxes and placed in varying degrees of temperatures. The greater number were sown in the open ground. Every known procedure was followed to hasten the softening of the woody tissue surrounding the seeds. A year later, by the time Wilson arrived home, not a single seed had germinated. Upon investigating, the young plant hunter discovered that those sown in the open showed signs of cracking due to frost action over winter. A month later thousands had germinated; Wilson and an assistant potted 13,000 precious small plants. The seed sown indoors was a failure.

Wilson brought home several small plants also, which were set in Veitch's Coombe Wood nursery. The first seedling bloomed in 1911, and upon being exhibited, received the Royal Horticultural Society's highest award, a First Class Certificate. In 1903, on his second expedition to China, he traveled to the site of Père David's discovery where he obtained a sizable number of fruits and from these more than a thousand plants were raised.

Maurice de Vilmorin, the leading nurseryman in France in the early 1900's, had received seeds of davidia which Père Farges, a French missionary, had gathered in China in 1897. Like Veitch, he, too, was eager to cultivate the dove tree, but neither nurseryman had been willing to divulge trade secrets until the seed had germinated. A single plant was grown in Vilmorin's arboretum at Les Barres, from which several cuttings and a layer were rooted. As a result, cuttings were sent to Kew Gardens and to the Jardin des Plantes in Paris. The rooted layer found its way to the Arnold Arboretum in Jamaica Plain, Massachusetts, where it still flourishes. Shortly after E. H. Wilson had left England on his first trip to China, his employer, Harry Veitch, learned of this incident, but Wilson was not informed. Accordingly, his was "a little cup of bitterness to drain," as he expressed it, for Monsieur Edouard André published the story in *Revue Horticole* in August 1902. Vilmorin's plant bloomed in 1906, and proved to be the smooth-leaved form of the species.

The young plant hunter's early life was not without another heartache when in the late summer of 1906, he learned that a deranged person destroyed by fire several thousand young plants raised from the seed he had gathered in 1901. Such were the "vicissitudes and difficulties" which beset Ernest Wilson's path "in the introduction of every seedling plant, but one, of this remarkable tree."

Had Wilson's life not been tragically shortened in the autumn of 1930, when he was at the very height of his writing and lecturing career, he might have succeeded in persuading nurserymen to propagate the davidia widely in America and amateurs to grow it. At the Arnold Arboretum, the dove tree has been shy in flowering, performing spectacularly only every fifteen years. However, the few old specimens in milder climates in the eastern United States have bloomed more frequently. Apparently, severe winters have taken their toll of flower buds. Yet, those who have been fortunate enough to see this tree in flower have been enthralled by its beauty. In the right setting, where winters are not unduly severe, preferably sheltered by an evergreen background, it may yet prove to be all that Augustine Henry, Ernest Wilson, and all the Chinese peasants claimed for it. It is estimated that it takes about twenty years to obtain a tree of blooming size.

Until recently, the dove tree has been a distinct rarity in the American horticultural trade. Within the past few years, one of America's best known nurseries, Wayside Gardens of Mentor, Ohio, has propagated it in quantity so that it is more easily available and deserves the attention of plant-lovers who enjoy uncommon plants, and are willing to cater to its needs.

Wilson returned to England early in April in 1902. Two months later, on June 8, he married Helen Ganderton of Edgbaston, Warwickshire, whom he had met several years earlier at the home of his friend Sydney Hales, director of the Chelsea Physic Garden.

Nellie, as he always referred to her, had spent a long vigil awaiting Ernest's return. Less than a year after he departed on his first trip to China, word of the Boxer Uprising reached England. The Boxers, otherwise known as the "Society of Patriotic Harmonious Fists," were one of many more or less secret societies in China who held all foreigners in contempt and wished to remove them from the country. Magic and mysticism dominated the thinking of this group who convinced their followers that society membership assured them immunity from death as well as other supernatural powers. Even the Empress was impressed and the Chinese press supported the movement to such an extent that important government officials joined its ranks. A price was put on the head of every foreigner. Little wonder that Nellie Ganderton, Wilson's family, his friends at Kew, and Veitch, his employer, were seized with anxiety and frustration over his safety. To make matters worse, communication between China and Great Britain, at the time, was exceedingly slow and uncertain. Yet, hardly had his bride erased the memory of this experience from her mind before she learned that her husband was to leave for China again.

Wilson's 1903 trip to China was also for the Veitch firm, this time in quest of the yellow poppywort, *Meconopsis integrifolia*. This choice alpine had been described by Antwerp E. Pratt, an English naturalist interested primarily in zoology and entomology who explored the wilderness of China in 1887, and remained in the country for more than two years. He traveled in a leisurely manner and was accompanied by a German collector named Kricheldorff. Being a person of means, he took his family with him and quartered them in Ichang while he went about collecting. In his travels, he met Dr. Henry who persuaded him to hire a Chinese plant collector whom Henry had trained. His peregrinations took him to the famous gorge at Ichang, which Henry had explored, to Shanghai, and up the Yangtze and Min Rivers. He even sent his collector to Mupin, a remote region near the Tibetan border, which Père David had explored some years earlier. Pratt's quest produced several noteworthy plants.

A quarter of a century later, Wilson followed Pratt's footsteps in pursuit of the poppywort. In addition to the usual hardships, he encountered no end of bad weather and nearly starved to death along with his "followers."

However, on July 18, 1903, in the mountains beyond Tachien-lu, at 11,000 feet above sea level, he found the first plant of the yellow poppywort, though it was past flowering. A thousand feet higher in the alpine regions of this same Chino-Tibetan border-land, he located specimens in bloom. Of the experience, he wrote:

I will not attempt to record the feelings which possessed me on first beholding the object of my search in these wild mountains. My journey was for the sole purpose of finding and introducing this, the most gorgeous alpine plant extant. I had traveled some 13,000 miles in five and a half months and to be successful in attaining the first part of my mission in such a short time was a sufficient reward for the difficulties and hardships experienced. The second part of my mission was easily accomplished in due season, and today this plant, with 8-inch broad flowers, blossoms every year in British gardens and is known to all readers of horticultural journals.

Further pursuit led to the discovery of the red poppywort.

At 11,800 feet above sea level on August 31, 1903, amongst scrub and long grass, I stumbled on the first plants of my Red Poppywort (*Meconopsis punicea*). As if to assure me of its identity, a couple of plants were in flower! Now, since I had deliberately traveled from Tachien-lu nearly 600 miles in search of this plant, guided solely by the following scrap of information, culled from a label on a specimen of this plant preserved in the Kew Herbarium, "Potanin, China borealis, Prov. Szechuan septentrionale, '85," I will leave it to the reader to imagine and appreciate my delight. From 12,000 feet to the head of the pass (12,200 feet) this Meconopsis was abundant; the capsules were just ripe and a rich harvest of seed rewarded the day's labor. The seeds were transmitted to England and many plants were successfully raised. It flowered for the first time under western skies in September, 1905, but did not take kindly to cultivation, and the original stock with its descendants are now lost to gardens. This is to be regretted, for it is beautiful with solitary, dark scarlet flowers, 6 inches in diameter, nodding from stalks 2 feet tall. The flowers are produced in quantity but the petals are rather flimsy in texture. The storm-swept mountains have claimed it back but the memory of its loveliness still

E. H. Wilson
at the age of twenty-three

Wedding picture, 1902,
of E. H. and Nellie Wilson
(COURTESY MRS. GEORGE L. SLATE)

gladdens his heart who first bore it forth on that memorable August day.

Methods of travel were not only primitive but extremely tedious and the time element was always uncertain. Wilson summed it up concisely when he wrote:

There are no mule caravans, and scarcely a riding pony is to be found. For overland travel there is the native sedan chair and one's own legs; for river travel, the native boat. Patience, tact, and an abundance of time are necessary, and the would-be traveler lacking any of these essentials should seek lands where less primitive methods obtain. . . . China alternately charms and fascinates, irritates and plunges into despair all who sojourn long within her borders. . . . The Chinese do not see time from the Westerner's viewpoint, and for the traveler in the interior parts of China the first, last, and most important thing of all is to ever bear this in mind.

Regarding roads he declared: "Chinese roads make a lasting impression on all who travel over them, and the vocabulary of the average traveler is not rich enough to thoroughly relieve the mind in this matter. The roads are of two kinds, paved and unpaved. . . . it is nobody's real business to look after the roads, and nobody does." Traveling in the mountainous regions and among the cliffs meant up and down climbing of the most exhausting kind. Sometimes the only way to get up was to hang onto the tail of a mule and be towed. Crossing streams was another matter.

According to Chinese custom, a white man traveling in the unpopulated regions of China on foot was without caste. Conversely, a sedan chair made him a superior being even though he seldom, if ever, rode in it. It simply had to be visible in the caravan as a symbol of the traveler's rank and authority. It was a cumbersome trapping at best, especially for a vigorous young explorer like Wilson, but he knew full well its significance and always had one with him.

He and his party crossed wide streams by means of a cable or rope bridge which he admitted was a fearsome task until he got used to it. "It is speedily accomplished and there is practically no danger so long as one keeps a cool head and the ropes do not break."

Frequently, he spoke of the "sublime beauty" of the gorges in the Yangtze River. The scenery in the savage chasms was "all and more than any writer has described." The rapids, the swift currents, the great rocks, and other difficulties which impeded navigation evoked these comments on river travel:

The native boats are perfectly fitted for the navigation of these difficult waters; they are the outcome of generations of experience, and the balance-rudder and turret-build have been used in these craft long before their adoption by Western nations. The men, too, who earn their livelihood in navigating these boats, understand their business thoroughly. . . . These Chinese boatmen are careful, absolutely competent, and thorough masters of their craft, and the more one sees of them and their work the more one's admiration grows. Oriental methods are not Occidental methods, but they succeed just the same!

This trip required two and one-half years, during which the eager young plant hunter traveled more than 2,000 miles inland. He gathered other treasures including four species of evergreen barberries; the cut-leaf crab apple, *Malus toringoides*; the Yunnan meadow rue, *Thalictrum dipterocarpum*; several species of primroses; two notable shrub roses, *Rosa moyesi*, and *R. willmottiae*; a half dozen different rhododendrons; a new viburnum; and many other uncommon plants.

On his return to England in March, 1905, Wilson was occupied with organizing his collection of plant material, herbarium specimens, and photographs. Early the following year, he was ap-

A good bag, shot by E. H. Wilson in Western China
(COURTESY MRS. GEORGE L. SLATE)

Hotel where Wilson lodged in western China.
The plant hunter is standing at the right.

pointed a botanical assistant in the Imperial Institute in London.

On May 21, 1906, a daughter was born to Ernest and Helen Wilson. She was christened Muriel Primrose. The name Primrose was chosen in tribute to the first plant named for her father, a dainty violet-colored species, *Primula wilsoni*, which he had discovered in Ichang while tracking down the davidia. He shared the seed which he had gathered with Kew Gardens and with Miss Ellen Wilmott, an extraordinary Englishwoman, a devotee of horticulture who not only grew plants but painted their portraits. This little primrose bloomed for the first time in cultivation in Miss Wilmott's garden the day Muriel was born at Kew, and she sent some of the blossoms to the Wilsons on that day. Wilson's primrose was later lost to cultivation.

Hardly had the Wilsons settled down to what had seemed like peaceful domesticity when a bid came from Professor Charles Sprague Sargent of the Arnold Arboretum in suburban Boston which he accepted. A third trip to China was in the making. Thus, Wilson crossed the Atlantic to America a second time in 1906, stopped long enough to obtain instructions, and was soon on his way back to the limestone gorges of western Hupeh. His mission was to collect plants of prime value for American gardens.

Previous visits had given him the opportunity to survey the great wealth of unknown flora in China. Already, his knowledge of cultivated plants was extensive and, coupled with his almost daily contact with the vast quantities of exotic shrubs and trees that surrounded him on his travels, he was able to train his eye and fix his sights on what was unusual and worthy. Working for an educational institution rather than a commercial enterprise, he had greater freedom. The wild, lonely, inaccessible regions of the country that he was approaching were obviously a challenge. On his second visit, he had explored Mount Omei, "one of the five ultra-sacred mountains of China," and Wa-wu-shan, its sister mountain. Of all the plants he saw, the rhododendron had the strongest appeal.

The gorgeous beauty of their flowers defies description. They were there in thousands and hundreds of thousands. Bushes of all sizes, many fully 30 feet tall and more in diameter, all clad with a wealth of blossoms that almost hid the foliage. Some flowers were crimson, some bright red, some flesh-colored, some silvery pink, some yellow, and others pure white. The thick rugged stems, gnarled and twisted into every conceivable shape, are draped with pendant mosses and lichens. . . . How the rhododendrons find foothold on these wild crags and cliffs is a marvel.

On this trip he ascended Wa-wu-shan, being the first foreigner to go to the summit. Viewed from the summit of another mountain, it resembled "a huge ark floating above clouds of mist."

In climbing Mount Wa-wu, he was forced to find shelter in an ancient wooden temple over night: "The rooms, though dingy and damp, were alive with fleas. But since there is no other accommodation between this place and the summit it was necessary to make the best of things. I had my bed arranged in a large hall where three huge images of Buddha looked down benignly upon me."

As a result of this trip, he introduced the white form of the summer lilac, *Buddleia asiatica*, the common name he preferred to butterfly bush. The Chinese variety of the kousa dogwood, *Cornus kousa sinensis*, several cotoneasters, the Wilson pearl bush, and a sizable number of other trees and shrubs were included in his pack of treasures.

Returning from China, he stopped first in England in May, 1909, for a visit, and four months later was back in the United States. He had seen the regal lily but had not collected it, and although his travels had been extensive it was not the year for cones on some of the conifers he most wanted.

Bamboo suspension bridge,
200 feet long,
which Wilson photographed
in western China

E. H. Wilson
on the steps of the
administration building,
Arnold Arboretum
(COURTESY MASSACHUSETTS
HORTICULTURAL SOCIETY)

Gathering specimens of a variety of plants is only part of a plant collector's job. Drying the plants requires placing each specimen between sheets of blotting paper, often an irksome task; especially is this the case with those having fleshy parts, for in wet weather, the specimens have to be examined daily and the paper changed to prevent molding. Some sort of marking or labeling is needed and notes must be made in the field regarding habitat, characteristics of growth, and countless other details. The care with which each step is taken and the amount of information recorded is of vital importance. Regardless of weather, traveling conditions, and general fatigue, even the most knowledgeable person cannot rely entirely upon memory.

Transporting the collected material to a seaport for shipment is another phase of the work. Gathering seed was often the only means for sending home a new treasure, since roots, bulbs, cuttings and the like posed problems of collecting, packing, shipping, and, most important of all, survival. It was practically impossible to anticipate all the things that could happen to a precious cargo of plants. Which plants to select and which to ignore were questions that arose in the plant hunter's mind. Would they have garden appeal? Would they grow easily from seed? Would they prove hardy? Would nurserymen collect them? Would the public like them? At best, it was a gamble.

Wilson's fourth venture to China began early in 1910. This time he would use the Trans-Siberian Railway during part of his travel. With each visit to the country he loved, he penetrated deeper into unexplored territory. Possessed of a rugged constitution and unlimited energy and enthusiasm, he could face almost any form of hardship imposed by weather or rough roads. But this time, it was more difficult than ever to make a headway, even though his "followers" were largely the coolies who had accompanied him on previous expeditions. Passing through the limestone regions in western Hupeh on to the red sandstone of Szechwan, he traveled one stretch of 200 miles that consumed twenty-two days of walking.

Wilson was seeking again the source of a beautiful, fragrant lily in the Min Valley, which he had discovered on his second trip to China. In *The Lilies of Eastern Asia*, he wrote:

This lily has a surprisingly limited distribution being confined to about fifty miles of the narrow semiarid valley of the Min River in extreme western Szechwan between 2,500 and 6,000 feet altitude—a region where the summers are hot and the winters severely cold and where strong winds prevail at all seasons of the year. I never saw it wild outside of this valley, which is walled in by steep mountain slopes culminating in perpetual snows. There it grows in great plenty among grasses and low shrubs and in niches on the bare cliffs. From the last week in May to the first in July, according to altitude, the blossoms of this lily transform a desolate lonely region into a veritable garden of beauty. Its fragrance fills the air and 'tis good to travel there when the regal lily is in bloom, though the path is hard and dangerous as personal experience and notices in Chinese characters carved in the rocks, urging all not to loiter save beneath the shelter of hard cliffs, testify.

It was my privilege to discover this lily in August, 1903, and in the autumn of the year following I sent about three hundred bulbs to Messrs. Veitch. These arrived safely in the spring of 1905, flowered that summer and were afterwards distributed under the erroneous name of *Lilium myriophyllum*. In 1908 I shipped with indifferent success bulbs of this lily to the Arnold Arboretum and to some friends, but in 1910 I succeeded in introducing it in quantity to America and the stock passed from the Arnold Arboretum to Messrs. R. and J. Farquhar and Co., Boston, Mass. Under cultivation in Europe and America the regal lily has behaved royally, being equally indifferent to winter colds, summer drought and deluges, and has flowered and fruited annually. It is the only lily of its class that ripens seeds in the climate of New England. The seeds germinate freely and many millions of bulbs have been raised. It forces well even after cold storage and there seems no reason why it should not become the "Easter lily" of

A characteristic pose—
welcoming visitors
to his garden

E. H. Wilson,
M.A., Harvard;
D.Sc., Trinity College.
Study of Wilson
against a background
of Regal lilies.
(COURTESY MASSACHUSETTS
HORTICULTURAL SOCIETY)

the future. The pollen is very cohesive, which makes shipping the plants in flower a comparatively easy matter, and the fragrance of the blossoms is pleasant, being not so strong as that of related species. The canary-yellow of the inside of the funnel contrasts well with the lustrous and translucent, marble-white upper part of the segments, and often the rose-purple is pleasingly tinted through, more especially if the flowers are allowed to open indoors or in light shade as under cheesecloth. Some critics object to the colored flowers, some to the narrow leaves, but in adding it to Western gardens the discoverer would proudly rest his reputation with the regal lily; he pleads with all who possess or will possess this treasure not to ruin its constitution with rich food.

Of more than 1,000 plants which "Chinese" Wilson introduced, none was more warmly received by American gardeners than the regal lily. In fact, had he introduced nothing else of garden value, his fame would be secure for having brought back from the wilds of China the hardiest and most adaptable of white trumpet flowers. But there is much more to the story. Its introducer nearly lost his life—he broke his leg in a landslide in the wilderness, far from medical aid. The account of how it happened and what followed is told in Wilson's own inimitable manner in chapter 10, one of the few detailed reports of his career describing the hazards encountered when hunting plants in the wilderness. He seldom spoke, even to his most intimate friends, of the dangers to which he had been exposed constantly on his various missions.

The problem of shelter while traveling and the lack of cleanliness everywhere probably plagued Wilson to a far greater extent than all the unforeseen dangers that he met and faced during his eleven years of wandering in China.

He always traveled with his own bedroll and would never sleep in a Chinese bed. In the field, the legs of his camp bed were set in containers filled with insect repellent. Fleas were a constant plague, as were cockroaches and every kind of crawling insect. He contracted malaria on his first trip and fought it all his life. On more than one occasion he had severe recurrences requiring his wife's constant care. No profanity appears anywhere in his writings but the experiences, described in the following passage, occurred again and again and were sufficient to evoke it.

We found lodgings for the night at Wang-tung-tsao, alt. 1,350 feet, having covered our usual 60 li [18 miles]. The day was terribly hot, making the journey very fatiguing. The inn is beautifully situated in a grove of bamboo and cypress, but is poor and abominably stinking. Really, it is a pity that such a vile house should defile such a charming spot.

The next day was also grilling hot, with no signs of a storm to cool the air. Descending a few li [10 li equal 3 miles] we struck a rather broad stream with many red sandstone boulders in its bed. The road ascends this stream to its source, and steep ascents and descents were all too frequent. We lunched at the village of Kao-chiao, and a more hot, fly-infested, stinking hole, with people more inquisitive, I have not experienced. Savage, snarling, yelping dogs abounded, and these, with the other discomforts, did not add relish to the meal. My followers seemed to share my views of this village, and grumbling and malediction were loud on all sides. Our meal did not occupy long, and we all felt better when clear of this filthy, pestiferous place.

Despite the trying experiences of some missionaries and many adventurers, including plant hunters, over more than a century and a half, Ernest Wilson was singularly blessed in his travels in China. In addition to a level head, a calmness of spirit, and great tact, he obviously had a large measure of compassion for the Chinese, and especially his "followers" as he often referred to his aides, interpreters, and servants. His sentiments toward them were tersely expressed in *China, Mother of Gardens*:

In my travels about China I have been singularly fortunate in never having any trouble with the Chinese. In the spring of 1900 I engaged about a dozen peasants from near Ichang. These men remained with me and rendered faithful service during the whole of my peregrinations. After a few months' training they understood my habits thoroughly and never involved me in any trouble or difficulty. Once they grasped what was wanted they could be relied upon to do their part, thereby adding much to the pleasure and profit of my many journeys. When we finally parted in February, 1911, it was with genuine regret on both sides. Faithful, intelligent, reliable, cheerful under adverse circumstances, and always willing to give their best, no men could have rendered better service.

To Wilson, China was more than a great storehouse of ornamental plants. His appreciation of the way of life of the Chinese people, their customs, their beliefs, their folkways, and the wisdom they had garnered over the centuries were revealed in the great variety of photographs he made. Temples and sculpture fascinated him no less than the marvelous bridges which they made of bamboo. Chinese architecture, waterwheels, irrigation systems caught his eye with the same enthusiasm as did mountain peaks, trees, and flowers. His was a rare sense of perception. Although he makes little or no mention of Chinese art, the treasures he brought home to his wife and daughter reveal his innate good taste. These included a handsome silk screen embroidered with a wisteria motif, a superbly carved blackwood corner cabinet, a Ming plate and other choice porcelains, a Chinese silver tea set similar to those made in the days of the China trade, handsome bronzes and brasses, embroideries, jewelry, Mandarin clothes, and other Chinese garments.

Professor Charles Sprague Sargent, whom Wilson called "the chief," was himself a plant hunter. Known throughout the world for his knowledge of woody plants, he was ever on the alert for new ornamentals that would prove hardy in the Boston area. In 1892, he had made a trip to Japan and brought back the torch azalea

(*Azalea obtusum kaempferi*), the Sargent crab apple, and a number of other items of notable garden value. In 1914, Sargent sent Wilson to Japan for the express purpose of studying the flowering cherries of the country, and two years later, the fruit of Wilson's labor appeared in *The Cherries of Japan*. He also wrote a fascinating summary of these handsome spring flowering trees, making of it a chapter in *Plant Hunting*. It is chapter 3 in this anthology.

It was on this trip that he first saw the Kurume azaleas at Hatagaya, a few miles north of Tokyo. The story of this experience which he recounted in *Plant Hunting* appears in chapter 4 in this volume. His wife and daughter accompanied him on this trip which was far less strenuous than his previous expeditions into the wilderness of China. Because of her chronic bronchitis, Nellie Wilson was unable to travel with her husband and spent most of her time in hotels where the social life was limited, for the most part, to the activities of the British Embassy. Often, in the inland cities of Japan where they stayed, the Wilsons were the only guests in the hotel. However, when not attending an English missionary school, a Japanese school, or a French convent, Muriel traveled with her father. Dressed in knickers, she carried the tripod for her father's camera or some other precious bit of baggage needed for the journey.

Again in 1918, "Chinese" Wilson went to Japan, this time to the city of Kurume on the island of Kyushu to see the marvelous azaleas which were cultivated there. A year earlier, he had urged John S. Ames of North Easton, Massachusetts, a noted connoisseur of horticulture and later president of the Massachusetts Horticultural Society, to import small plants from this great collection and grow them in his greenhouses. Several years later, when these novelties were exhibited for the first time at the Society's spring flower show in Boston, they created a sensation and for many years brought great joy to the thousands who beheld them. Boston was the appropriate place for the "Princess Kurume" (to Wilson these azaleas symbolized Oriental royalty) to make her debut in America since the Museum of Fine Arts and the nearby Peabody Museum in Salem had assembled outstanding collections of Japanese art. Yet, the honor of being the first to show these superb flowers had been usurped by San Francisco.

Although Wilson has been credited with their introduction to America, a group of thirty plants shipped from Japan made their appearance at the Panama Pacific Expedition in San Francisco in 1915, but the original collection was soon lost, due probably to lack of knowledge regarding their care. However, to E. H. Wilson is due the honor of successfully establishing these showy flowering shrubs in American horticulture circles in the eastern United States. Wilson selected fifty varieties and shipped them to the Arnold Arboretum. Collections of these varieties are now maintained at Wisley in Surrey, at the gardens of the Royal Horticultural Society, and in the garden of Thomas Wheeldon at Richmond, Virginia. Apparently, Wilson was not aware that the Akashi nursery had sold plants to Domoto Brothers, nurserymen, of Hayward, California, in 1917, and also the exclusive rights to their distribution in the United States. In any event, in the early 1920's, these new azaleas were offered by several East Coast nurserymen and today are widely grown outdoors where winters are not as severe as those in Boston. Florists throughout the country continue to sell them by the thousand in winter and they are enjoyed by thousands of amateur gardeners who grow them in private greenhouses. Wilson would have been exceedingly happy had they proved hardy in New England, but he lived long enough to see them become established in gardens from New York south.

Voyage number six to the Far East was begun early in 1917, again with his wife and daughter accompanying him. He went first to the islands of Liukiu and Bonin and then to Korea and its adjacent islands. In Formosa, he climbed Mount Morrison, 13,072 feet above sea level. This island, then little known, provided several exciting experiences with the natives, including a group of head-hunters who served as guides. Wilson's account of his travels in Formosa is one of his most fascinating narratives (see chapter 20). His quest was for a rare tree, the taiwania, Oriental counterpart of the California sequoia. Quantities of seeds were gathered, but none of them germinated at the Arnold Arboretum where the seed was sown. However, a few small trees which were collected managed to survive and, today, a number of specimens flourish in the milder sections of the eastern United States, including one at Fairmount Park in Philadelphia.

When Wilson returned to America in 1919, Professor Sargent appointed him assistant director of the Arnold Arboretum. A great team these two men made—Sargent and Wilson. Dedicated to their task in every sense of the word, both possessed ency-clopedic knowledge and were well on their way toward making the Arnold Arboretum "America's greatest garden." Professor Sar-gent was eager to extend contacts with the other great botanical gardens of the world, thereby broadening horticultural knowl-edge. Accordingly, he dispatched his assistant director on a global tour, not so much to collect plants but to make some estimate of the holdings of other institutions.

Wilson left the Arboretum in July, 1920, with Australia as his first stop. He visited the botanic gardens at Perth, Melbourne, Sydney, Adelaide, and Brisbane, making photographs everywhere. Naturally, he could not resist plant collecting in the forest. He followed a similar procedure in New Zealand and Tasmania and then was off to Singapore, Ponang, Rangoon, and Calcutta. He traveled to Ceylon, East Africa, and Kenya, on down through Rhodesia to Durban and Capetown. Few men of his time were better suited to the task and fewer still had his rich background.

In later years, E. I. Farrington, editor of *Horticulture,* wrote: "Probably there was no man in all the world who could write a personal letter to so great a number of people in so many corners of the globe." Wilson had an extraordinary memory for people as well as for plants, which supported him well in all his junkets.

Late in the summer of 1922, Wilson returned to the Arnold Arboretum where his duties encompassed a major share of the administrative work of the institution as well as an extensive program of lecturing and writing. He succeeded in making garden enthusiasts and the general public fully aware of the notable collection of plant treasures which he, Professor Sargent, and others had assembled over a period of more than half a century. He told the story vividly in his book *America's Greatest Garden,* which appeared in 1925.

His beloved chief, Professor Sargent, died in March 1927, and a month later Ernest Henry Wilson succeeded him with the title Keeper, which he preferred to that of Director. At the same time Professor Oakes Ames, noted orchidologist, was made Supervisor of all the botanical departments of Harvard University.

Charles Sprague Sargent's death marked the end of a great era in American horticulture. He had been a man of enormous ability, whose varied interests spanned America and the world. He lived in an era when men dared to be individualists and his idiosyncrasies were as unique and marked as he was. His reputation as an authority on woody plants was indisputable and he possessed the ability to record his vast knowledge in many ways. For eleven years he edited *Garden and Forest,* a weekly paper devoted to horticulture and forestry. He wrote *The Silva of North America,* which was published in fourteen volumes and later condensed into the authoritative *Manual of the Trees of North America.* The Arnold Arboretum had been established in 1872, and Sargent was appointed director the following year. For fifty-six years he guided its destiny, starting with the modest income of $3,000 a year. When he died in 1927, the *Outlook*, a national weekly, published the following tribute:

The Arnold Arboretum is his monument. He took an inadequate fund, a worn-out farm, a willing spirit, and "in a few years," as it seemed to him, transformed them into the greatest arboretum on earth. That it is the greatest is indicated by the fact that a few years ago a Chinese came there to make an exhaustive study of the trees of China. . . . Thousands of gardens in America and in Europe are his monuments. They have been made lovely by the trees and plants which he searched the world for and propagated.

The wooded sides of the Adirondacks are his monuments. He laid the foundation of the New York State forestry work and saved the mountain woods.

The redwood forests of the Pacific coast are his monument. His was the leading spirit in the movement which saved the giant trees.

Glacier National Park is his monument. He made the first proposal for the setting aside of that region as a park—thirty years before it was actually set aside.

The multiplied millions of acres of National Forests are his monument. Establishment of the National Forest policy resulted from the study of the National Academy of Science Commission, of which he was chairman. He took the leading part in inducing President Cleveland to make the first reservation of 21,000,000 acres. Later, when pressure against the policy was heavy and President McKinley was ready to turn the Forest Reserves back into the public domain, he took the leading part in inducing the Chief Executive to change his mind.

No monument that can be erected will equal the least of these, for, as commemorating the achievements of such a man,

Marble is dust,
Cold and repellent,
And iron is rust.

This was the full stature of the man whom Ernest Wilson succeeded.

Now that the "Chief" was gone, Wilson's duties multiplied, but he was no stranger to the demands made on his office. The stream of visitors from all parts of the world was constant, as was the correspondence attending it. In addition to his duties, he was actively engaged in lecturing, and writing had become a solid commitment. He was beginning to see his plants offered in the trade, and home gardeners all over America were enjoying them. All the while, he was observing other plants, still languishing in their trial plots, awaiting the day when these treasures would find ready acceptance and be made available to the public. The regal lily was firmly intrenched, and so, too, were a number of his other favorites.

He knew that not all of his discoveries and introductions would prove hardy in New England, but America was big enough and varied enough in climate to accommodate, in some region, all the plants he had found. But, time is required to acclimate them and an even longer period to popularize them.

Wilson looked forward to another ten years of writing when he became Keeper of the Arnold Arboretum. He had plans, too, for the further development of the Arboretum. His Kew background made him aware of the importance of the public's acceptance of arboretums and public gardens, for it was during his time of apprenticeship there that Sir William Thiselton-Dyer had revitalized Kew for the pleasure, inspiration, and instruction of all England. Furthermore, Wilson was able to relate his own contributions in the field of plant hunting to all who had preceded him in the profession. Then too, he realized that the niche a man made for himself in this profession was only significant insofar as the results of his efforts were utilized and enjoyed.

His masterful work, *Plant Hunting*, in two volumes, appeared in 1927. The following year the Royal Horticultural Society and the Rhododendron Society of England awarded him the Loder Cup for the extensive group of new species of rhododendrons which he had introduced. That same year, *More Aristocrats of the Garden* was published, a companion volume to *Aristocrats of the Garden* which had appeared earlier. In 1929, he was made a fellow of the American Academy of Arts and Sciences; the Massachusetts Horticultural Society gave him its Centennial Gold Medal; his book *China, Mother of Gardens* appeared. This volume, a complete account of his four expeditions to China, was greatly enriched by the observations he made of Chinese life, customs, religious monuments, travel, and the like.

The nickname "Chinese" that was frequently associated with him could not have been linked more appropriately with any other living person than it was with Ernest Henry Wilson. Whether this reserved Britisher actually liked what the publicists had dubbed him, I cannot say, but E. I. Farrington always claimed that he did. As a child, Wilson's daughter Muriel was made most unhappy at Miss Seager's School in Brookline by her father's nickname. Her classmates used to taunt her by saying that she had a Chinese father. To prove that he was a dyed-in-the-wool Englishman, she gave one of the boys in her class such a trouncing that her father was summoned to the school as a result. While he maintained his severe British sternness toward Muriel in the teacher's presence, she felt that he was truly proud of her defense of her father's status.

It is one of life's strange ironies that danger often lurks in unexpected places. During his five extensive expeditions into the Chinese wilderness, Ernest Wilson had been exposed to practically every kind of danger imaginable. He had survived the Boxer Rebellion when there was a price on every foreigner's head. He overcame a serious attack of malaria and fought off recurrences of the fever for nearly thirty years. He emerged from a treacherous landslide, which could have cost him his life, with only a broken leg. Yet, while returning from a visit with their daughter Muriel, now Mrs. George L. Slate of Geneva, New

York, the Wilsons' car skidded on a wet highway near Worcester, Massachusetts, and both were killed. Legend has it that the road was strewn with leaves. Rain had been scarce that autumn until a prolonged storm occurred, but on that fateful day, October 15, 1930, there were no leaves on the road, nor any trees near by the site of the accident. Wilson had a great fondness for dogs and always had one with him on his peregrinations in China. Curiously enough, his Boston terrier Buddie survived the accident.

Nellie Wilson was by nature shy and reserved. Among those who knew her best were Alfred Rehder and his wife. Alfred and Ernest had been long-time associates at the Arnold Arboretum. Rehder knew well the loneliness that was hers during the long periods her husband was collecting plants in the Orient and the ill health that plagued her. In the memorial he wrote on Wilson, he described Nellie as "quiet and unassuming." She "found her highest pleasure in making the happy atmosphere of the home in which he loved to write." Daughter Muriel recalled that her mother best displayed her pride in her father's accomplishments in the warm and gracious manner in which she entertained the innumerable horticulturists and botanists who visited the Wilsons.

Honor and recognition came to E. H. Wilson in the prime of life. Harvard University conferred upon him the honorary degree Master of Arts in 1916. The Royal Horticultural Society had awarded him its two coveted medals, the Victoria Medal of Honor and the Veitch Memorial Medal (on two occasions). The Massachusetts Horticultural Society gave him its George Robert White Medal, the most coveted horticultural award in America, and there were other honors as well, all of which brought into sharp focus his contribution to the garden world. Unlike a number of his confreres whose "bones lie scattered along the trail they blazed," Wilson was spared long enough to record in words and pictures what he had achieved and to enjoy some measure of satisfaction that his endeavors had been worthwhile.

Few men reach their goals without the help of others, but, all too often, there is an unwillingness to acknowledge interdependence. Not so with Wilson, who graciously recognized where and how he stood in his profession and the world in which he worked. "He could tell, and he could be told—a combination not always in evidence," as J. Horace McFarland expressed it.

He was fortunate in having several associates of superior competence at the Arnold Arboretum. Otherwise, many of the choice plants which he collected might have been lost to cultivation. Jackson Dawson, as superintendent and propagator, once described as one of the greatest gardeners in the world, watched carefully and devotedly the plants raised from the seed which Wilson had gathered. When Dawson died in 1916, William H. Judd, a Kew-trained horticulturist who served under him, took charge of propagation. He was a person of broad knowledge and a highly skilled propagator. As a result, he aided materially in increasing the stock of plants which his associate, Wilson, wished to promote. In the matter of taxonomy, he was ably supported by Alfred Rehder, who was born in Waldenburg, Germany. Rehder came by his enthusiasm and knowledge of plants by virtue of family inheritance, since both his father and grandfather were professionals in the field. At the age of twenty-five, he came to America to pursue the study of fruit culture and forestry for *Möller's Deutsche Garten-Zeitung* of which he was associate editor. Professor Sargent, who was an uncommon judge of men and their talents, found a place for him. Rehder worked closely with Wilson on the botanical aspects of his introductions, and also wrote extensively and authoritatively. In addition, he became an accomplished photographer. John G. Jack was another of Wilson's contemporaries with a rich and varied background. Rehder, Judd, and Jack all outlived Wilson.

Of all the Chinese peasants or "followers," as he called them, who made up his caravan, only his interpreter or "number-one boy" spoke English. Nowhere in his writings does Wilson give his readers the slightest notion of what these men thought of his plant-collecting projects and his picture taking. But on more than one occasion he wrote of their loyalty, their devotion, and their intelligence, and in a similar vein, he spoke of the Chinese people as a whole. An abiding love of flowers had been an integral part of their tradition for centuries, as Osvold Sirén reminds us in *Gardens of China*: "The Chinese saw in flowers something more than simply decorative and useful objects; they sought a meaning and expressiveness in these silent beings, and if the meaning was in many cases rather freely constructed, it was nevertheless calculated to strengthen and deepen the appreciation of the living symbols of the vegetable kingdom. . . . The connection between the cultivation of flowers and their representation in art has therefore been intimate in China." Whatever the sentiments of his coolies, they were undoubtedly favorable because this Westerner was pursuing an interest which they not only understood but respected profoundly.

Practically all plant hunters kept records and wrote letters, but few had Wilson's skill in recording, reporting, and interpreting information about plants. On the one hand, he wrote as a scientist in preparing material for *The Cherries of Japan*, *The Conifers and Taxads of Japan*, and *A Monograph of Azaleas* (with Alfred Rehder). *Plantae Wilsonianae*, edited by Professor Sargent, and written largely in collaboration with Alfred Rehder, contains the record of most of his introductions, written from the botanical point of view. *The Lilies of Eastern Asia*, although technical in its approach, has had wide appeal for dedicated amateur gardeners.

On the other hand, Wilson was a great popularizer, describing, evaluating, and recommending plants with style and charm, for the home gardeners of America, for whom he turned out *America's Greatest Garden*, a vivid description of the Arnold Arboretum; *The Romance of Our Trees*; *Aristocrats of the Garden* and *More Aristocrats of the Garden*; *Plant Hunting*; *China—the Mother of Gardens*; *If I Were to Make a Garden*; and *Aristocrats of the Trees*. Each was warmly received by amateur and professional gardeners and, today, among connoisseurs, they are collector's items. Wilson always visualized plants in the landscape, as units or masses in a planting. He had a landscape designer's eye, for his profound knowledge embraced the architecture of nature. To him plants were not to be considered merely as horticultural specimens, but rather as part of a man-made landscape, to be placed and arranged in gardens in a natural manner. Obviously, he enjoyed writing about them for he projected himself on countless pages of print.

His readers liked what he said and the way he said it. When he wrote his last book, *If I Were to Make a Garden*, he started off with this thought:

If I were to make a garden, another garden, a new garden, I should probably make mistakes, as I have done in the past, mistakes like every reader of this has made and will make. There is no royal road or clean-cut path to the making of a garden. It depends so much on circumstances, on area, on climate, on the topography of the site, and on the soil. One should, of course, have ideals, but one must always realize that they are ideals and that practice can only approximate to them.

His many contributions to scientific journals and popular magazines included more than a hundred for *Horticulture* alone. He was strongly devoted to this magazine and enjoyed reading the proof for each issue. For six years, month to month, he turned out stimulating articles for Richardson Wright, editor of *House and Garden* who, more than once, declared his mingled admiration and wonder at a man who could write with a flare and at the same time be as accurate as he was inspiring. In addition, he had made more than 5,000 photographs. As Wright expressed it: "For all his sixteen thousand contributions to herbariums, he was never a dry-as-dust scholar."

The late Edward I. Farrington, his first biographer, remarked that, socially, Wilson was never a good mixer among strangers. Yet, in his travels he was a true cosmopolite, at ease and at home with all whom he met. There was about him a manner of reserve and aloofness, partly inherent. He had the bearing and the manner of an aristocrat and such he was. He achieved this status by virtue of his accomplishments and the discipline needed to attain them. Curiously enough, he gave the title "aristocrat" to those plants which he thought worthy and the basis on which he made his selections was as thorough as the man himself. Not only did he dislike heroics, but he never even wasted adjectives in describing plants, people, or situations. His humor was subtle.

To one of his secretaries, "little Miss Kelley," as he called her, Wilson was "a very happy man full of humor, kind and generous." She came to work for him fresh from Jamaica Plain High School in 1924, and she still remembers puzzling over her shorthand book during lunchtime, but she soon learned to wrestle with Latin binomials. Heman Howard, assistant horticulturist, and Alfred Fordham, propagator, long-time staff members at the Arnold Arboretum, were trainees in Wilson's day. Both recalled that he had a habit of whistling instead of calling when he wanted them to perform a specific task. They were conscious of his Kew training as well as of the discipline and the wit with which he directed "America's greatest garden." They were expected to do what was required, whatever the task, and few words were wasted. As Howard put it, "If you didn't 'catch on' in two years, that was it."

His circle of intimate friends was limited, but among those

who knew him the feeling toward him was one of genuine admiration and love, and this devotion was mutual. His close friends included the jovial Jackson Dawson, propagator at the Arnold Arboretum who died in 1916; Fred A. Wilson and Thomas Roland, noted horticulturists, who lived in Nahant; Edward I. Farrington of the Massachusetts Horticultural Society; Ernest Borowski, a highly skilled grower of azaleas from Norwood; John K. M. L. Farquhar, leading nurseryman in the Boston area; Harlan P. Kelsey, plantsman, conservationist, and garden designer of Boxford, Massachusetts; W. Ormiston Roy who came to Boston frequently from Montreal; and several others. All were members of the Horticultural Club of Boston, a small select group of amateurs and professionals, which met regularly at a leading Boston hotel, to discuss the affairs of the plant world, over the best of food and drink. On such occasions, among close friends, he was at ease and talked freely, but the essence of this side of the man is unrecorded since there were never any published reports of the meetings and all of Wilson's contemporaries have passed away.

Dr. David Fairchild, longtime plant explorer for the United States Department of Agriculture, spoke of Wilson's "systematic dragnet methods" but comparatively little is known or recorded regarding these methods—the details of his amazing skill in organization, his capacity for collecting, or his ability to endure the hardships that led to the success with which he delivered his finds.

"'Chinese' Wilson was the robust, lusty, alert and forthright middle-class Englishman. There was no patchouli about him." This was Richardson Wright's description of the man with whom he worked closely for six years, preparing articles for *House and Garden*. The word "patchouli" belongs more commonly to an earlier generation than ours and denotes an essential, fragrant oil derived from an Oriental odoriferous plant, somewhat subtly sweet. Wilson would have enjoyed the subtlety of this compliment, for there was nothing saccharine about him. He greatly admired Wright, who served as editor of *House and Garden* for thirty-six years, and dedicated *Aristocrats of the Trees* to his friend "whose literary genius, pleasantly flavored with the salt of humor, has greatly advanced the love of plants and gardens in America." This tribute meant more to Wright than many an honor that was given him later. These two men shared many interests in common for, as a young man, Richardson Wright had traveled extensively in Siberia and Manchuria and wrote three books based on his travels. Gardening was his chief hobby and he championed Wilson for his achievements and the way in which he shared what he knew. What is more, Wright was urbane, witty, and a bon vivant in the best sense of the word.

Perhaps nothing reveals the spirit of these two boon companions better than Wright's account of how Trinity College came to award E. H. Wilson an honorary degree.

I had been elected a trustee of my college and was as yet unacquainted with procedure. While glancing through old records, my interest quickened when I found, among the graduates of Trinity College, Hartford, in the class of 1842, the name and subsequent career of Dr. George R. Hall. No recognition had been made of his accomplishments. Colleges then paid little attention to botanical hunters. However, it set a train of thought going. I brashly submitted to the Committee on Honorary Degrees the name of Ernest Henry Wilson, plant hunter, together with a dossier of his accomplishments, suggesting that he measured up to a Doctor of Science.

Now, making an Honorary Doctor of a man who is not fabulously wealthy or in the headlines, I found, can be about as difficult as canonizing a saint. The chairman of that committee, a stern-faced and incredulous magnate, shot at me, "Wright, why do you want to give a Doctorate of Science to a nurseryman?"

In my best pleading, which is my worst, I began extolling "Chinese" Wilson, his great travels, his learned and popular books, his discoveries, his high standing in his particular world. Apparently I wasn't getting to first base. Then I thought of George R. Hall—told the assembled trustees about the various new Japanese plants he had brought to our gardens and how this college, in his time, never thought to honor him. Here was our chance to make reparation! Somehow that quixotic notion stung the chairman's collegiate pride. He and his fellow members went into plenary session and Wilson was voted the degree. He received it in June, 1930, a few months before he was killed.

After the meeting, the magnate had the graciousness to acknowledge that, now he came to think of it, Hall's honeysuckle did grow on his estate—and a damned nuisance it was—but he was proud of the way the auratum lilies and *Malus halliana* seemed to thrive.

At nine o'clock on the morning of the ceremony I went down to his hotel to fetch Wilson back in state. I found him and Arthur Osborn, Curator of the Arboretum at Kew Gardens, whom he had brought along to support him through the ordeal, comfortably seated in deep armchairs smoking large cigars and between them, nesting in its cooler, a bottle of champagne. What a noble way of preparing one's self to become Doctor in Scientia Honoris Causa! As Wilson labored over the cork, I told them the story of how he came by the degree. Our glasses charged, he gave the toast, "To Dr. George Rogers Hall—good old George."

J. Horace McFarland, the nation's greatest champion of the rose, used to tell a favorite story about Wilson in which "humor and indignation marched together. He was telling me of a certain very notable oak, new to America, of which he had, he said, 'a hatful of acorns. I debated,' he went on, 'whether to send them all home through the quarantine,[1] or to smuggle a handful. The smuggling instinct prevailed. When I got home, the quarantined shipment was at hand, and with it the tag showing that while the acorns had had two precautionary 'treatments' with some gas, no bugs or diseases were found. I sowed them, but not one germinated. Of my smuggled pocketful, all grew.' And he laughed!"

[1] The United States Department of Agriculture had passed a law, effective in June 1919, restricting the importation of plants which proved to be a bugaboo to plant hunters.

In summing up Wilson's achievements, E. H. M. Cox wrote: "If he had collected after the war when gardeners became enthusiastic about exotics—and unless you have a general enthusiasm there is no incentive toward intensive propagation—many of his introductions would have been far more popular than they are today. His best work was undertaken just a generation too early."

Maybe so, but the scholarly Scot who made this statement has overlooked the full impact of Ernest Wilson's reputation as a popularizer of the plants he introduced. Wilson actually died too young. As Richardson Wright so ably put it:

Wilson . . . had a marked gift for salesmanship which few plant explorers possess. . . . He most enjoyed popularizing his finds. He believed in his plants. He hit on the popular tag of "aristocrat" for the best of them. He tramped up and down the countryside "selling" them in lectures to all who would listen. He bludgeoned American nurserymen—notoriously slow in accepting new things—into growing them for popular trade. His tragic death in 1930 cut short a valiant effort to bring more of his treasures from the back lots of China, Korea, and Japan into the back gardens of England and America. We can be thankful that he lived long enough to see his beauty-bush, *Stewartia koreana, Clematis montana rubens,* tea crab, Chinese dogwood, and regal lily well distributed and accepted.

Wilson was at heart a true gardener. In the introduction to *Plant Hunting,* he wrote his own epitaph: "There are no happier folk than plant-lovers and none more generous than those who garden. There is a delightful freemasonry about them; they mingle on a common plane, share freely their knowledge and with advice help one another over the stepping-stones that lead to success. It is truly said that a congenial companion doubles the pleasures and halves the discomforts of travel and so it is with the brotherhood who love plants."

2

Spring Beauty in the Garden

SPRING, real spring with its radiant beauty, belongs especially to the colder climes. To the tropics it is unknown, and even in the warm temperate regions its charms are few. We of the north find in spring ample compensation for the long winters, although at times we grow impatient. Since the year began, the study of seedsmen's lists and nurserymen's catalogues has been the gardener's chief delight. Possibly, envy of those who garden in warmer climes has not been entirely absent from the mind, for we are very human. But, with the arrival of spring, no gardener would change his own plat for any other, be it ever so fair. Here in the north, spring is our own season of blossom—rich, varied, inspiring, and invigorating.

With its changeful landscapes rich in bursting buds, spring is indeed a gladsome season. Vegetation awakens refreshed from a long winter sleep, yawns, stretches itself, springs up, and commences the season's work. Roots, never profoundly asleep, be-

The dove tree (*Davidia involucrata*) (GEORGE TALOUMIS)

Regal lilies growing among astilbe and other perennials (GEORGE TALOUMIS)

come wide awake and energetically active, drawing from the enveloping earth water and food salts in solution which are transported through specially organized tissues to the growing points of tree, shrub, and herb. The sap commences to rise and, like warm blood coursing through the veins, gives to twig, shoot, and stem a fresh and healthy hue like blushes suffusing a maiden's cheeks. Starch and other reserves of food are transformed into sugars for immediate use. Growth commences. The bud scales, which have so valiantly protected the vital growing points of leafy shoots or shielded embryo flowers, are thrown aside, hastily, and without a show of gratitude by some plants, tardily in others where they enlarge considerably and often become highly colored and conspicuous. Where the flowers take precedence over foliage, the naked stems are rapidly festooned with blossoms. In other plants, leaves, green and naked or swaddled in down of varying hues, peer forth to bask in the sunshine and bathe in the dew and rain. In orderly haste, vegetation robes itself in clean and fresh apparel and vigorously commences the season's work of elaborating food for the growth of new leafy shoots, for the development of the flowers, and for the perfecting of fruits and seeds.

A variety of explosive bulbous plants are the first to strew the earth with spring blossoms. Snowdrops with their white bells and crocuses, white, yellow, blue, and lavender, star the ground ere the grass changes to green. The scillas are drifts of heavenly blue, surpassed in loveliness only by their relatives the chionodoxas, well-called glory-of-the-snow. The favorite blue *Iris reticulata* and *I. stylosa*, the latter with fragrant flowers, are the first of their clan to blossom. Snowflakes, too, and arabis in sparkling, foaming sheets, and sprawling masses of aubrietia of uncertain colors are conspicuous. Yellow alyssum is everybody's friend, and in sheltered nooks coy hepatica and cyclamen add beauty to the scene. A winter aconite shines here and there, as do blossoms of its more aristocratic relative, adonis. The first adventurous daffodil spreads its cup and chalice and is speedily followed by a host of friends. White anemones are worthy foils to the exquisite blue *Anemone blanda*. Another windflower, *A. fulgens*, supplies red of various shades, color rare in early spring. Of fritillarias, charming little things with flowers of varied colors, there are many, but none excel the majestic *Fritillaria imperialis*, the crown imperial. No plant responds more swiftly to the stir of early spring than does this gallant herb. It thrusts fat, ruddy noses through the soil, rushes its stems aloft and in amazing rapidity crowns them with a ring of hanging, honey-laden yellow, orange-to-crimson bells. A favorite of centuries, the crown imperial is an essential part of spring beauty. Simple bulbs and low herbs in endless variety are the delights of early spring, and they are spendthrifts in color and wealth of blossom. They are everybody's flowers and no tyro can fail with them any more than the most fastidious can resist their charms. And let us not forget grass, emerald green carpet that it is, restful and enhancing the glory of the landscape on every hand.

Yellow is a prominent color among spring flowers, occurring in many bulbs, herbs, and shrubs. In woody plants it features winter jasmine (*Jasminum nudiflorum*), cornelian cherry (*Cornus mas*), spicebush (*Benzoin aestivale*), leatherwood (*Dirca palustris*), witch-hazels and their kinsfolk the corylopsis, but in greatest riot the goldenbells (*Forsythia*). These amazingly floriferous shrubs are known to all who garden, for they have been planted far and wide. Everybody loves these children of the Orient, but many do not correctly understand their needs. If people did, they would not shear off their heads in early spring just as these glorious shrubs are about to push forth bells of lovely yellow from every joint. One of the distressing sights of spring is the gross mutilation of these and other early-flowering shrubs wrought by ignoramuses in their well-meant efforts at spring cleaning in the garden. Let these and all other spring-flowering shrubs alone until their blossoms are spent, and then cut and carve them as necessity or fancy dictates. All the forsythias are good, very good, but that known as *spectabilis* is best. The hardiest of all is a Korean sort named *F. ovata*.

The garland flower (*Daphne cneorum*), with gray-green leaves and clusters of rose-colored, fragrant flowers terminating each of its slender, tufted, foot-long stems, is a well-known and deservedly popular plant. Not all are successful with this gem from the Caucasus, although many of us can grow it easily in the rockery and open border. A relative is the mezereon (*D. Mezereum*), a woodland shrub, but when once established thriving in a cool, open border. It is a sturdy bush seldom more than 4 feet high, with erect branches and twigs whose whole length is covered with rose-colored, or, in the variety *alba*, with white, fragrant flowers. Often these are followed by scarlet berries of great beauty but poisonous.

Noblest of spring-flowering trees are the Asiatic magnolias with their large, fleshy-petaled fragrant flowers borne on naked shoots. Great favorites are these, and fine specimens may be seen in thousands of American gardens: the yulan with its great white infolded cups; *Magnolia soulangeana* and its many forms with pink to rose-colored goblets; and the charming star magnolia, *M. stellata*, with snow-white spreading petals. Every spring I find renewed pleasure in watching the star magnolia push off the furry cap which shields the flower and spread its petals white as new snow. That these trees with their splendid flowers should be able to withstand the rigors of a New England winter is a blessing that we should be grateful for.

3

Heralds of Spring

JAPAN HOLDS flower festivals during many months of the year, beginning with that of the plum blossom (*Prunus mume*)[1] in February and ending with that of the chrysanthemum in November, but the most popular is that of the cherry blossom which falls in early April. The floral treasures of the Orient are indeed many, but none are more renowned than the cherries of Japan. And justly so, for no language can exaggerate their loveliness. Some are small, others large trees with wide-spreading crowns; some have pendent and others quite erect branches. All are beautiful. Cherry trees grow wild in the woods and thickets throughout the length and breadth of Japan and they are everywhere planted in vast numbers—in temple and castle grounds, by pond and by riverside. In Japan no peasant is too humble, no prince too proud to plant and cherish the cherry tree.

At Koganei, a village some ten miles from Tokyo, there is an

[1] *Prunus mume* is now known as the Japanese apricot.

avenue three miles long of cherry trees planted in 1735 by command of Shogun Yoshimune. Many of the trees are from 60 to 75 feet tall with trunks 10 to 12 feet in girth and crowns from 50 to 60 feet through. The avenue has been well cared for and when the trees are in blossom the scene presented is a never-to-be-forgotten one. The flowering of the cherries is made the occasion of a national holiday in Japan, annually decreed by the Emperor. And right merrily do the people enjoy the festival. It signifies that spring, the season of gladness, has come. Old and young, rich and poor put on their best raiment, visit and entertain their relatives and friends. There is something peculiarly gay and cheery about these white and pink cherry blossoms, and the prodigality of flowers and joyousness of color is ravishing.

It is sixty years since the first Japanese cherry was introduced into Western gardens, but where are the fine specimen trees that one might reasonably expect to see? Here and there where trees directly imported from Japan have been planted, fair examples are to be seen, but it is only within the last twenty-five years that such trees have been available in any quantity, and they are still all too rare. The early importations were nearly all used for purposes of propagation by budding and grafting on European stocks. This has been a curse. In the practice of gardening the art of grafting and budding is useful, nay it is essential, but it is greatly abused. As a means of perpetuating fruits and certain flowering plants it may be deemed indispensable. By the trade the art is often practiced as a means of quickly producing salable plants, but results in much disappointment to the purchasers. Too little attention has been paid to finding out the right kind of stocks to use, and especially is this true in regard to flowering trees and shrubs. With the Japanese cherries it has been the practice to graft or bud them upon the gean (*Prunus avium*),[2] the wild cherry (*P. cerasus*), and other Western species, and

[2] The common name of *Prunus avium* is mazzard cherry.

the results are far from being satisfactory. In fact, such stocks are quite unsuitable, and the sooner this fact is accepted the better. Many of the Japanese cherries may be rooted from cuttings; all the species and their wild forms may be raised from seeds. The double-flowered and anomalous garden forms should be budded or grafted on their wild prototypes. Planted closely together for a year or two and pruned to a single stem, young trees suitable for any required purpose are soon obtained. Confused nomenclature has also acted as a deterrent. In fact, this and unsuitable stocks for their propagation are largely responsible for the subordinate position Japanese cherries occupy in our gardens at the present time.

I do not recommend indiscriminate or even general planting of the double-flowered forms. Even in Japan they are neither large nor long-lived trees. Short-stemmed, at the most 30 feet tall and as much through the crown is their maximum, and such trees are rarely seen. Prematurely old, lichen-clad, and decrepit trees one often sees, and such the people of Japan admire; not so ourselves. Near buildings and out of the wind—for, being surface-rooting they are easily blown down—an occasional double-flowered cherry is all right: but for avenues, margins of woods, or the pleasure grounds it is the single-flowered species and their wild forms, which grow into large and long-lived trees, that should be planted. The Japanese have a keen eye for detecting points of difference among their favorite flowers. They recognize more than 100 forms of cherries, but for all practical purposes the distinct double-flowered forms may be included in a couple of dozen kinds.

The cherries of the Orient may be used for many purposes in the embellishment of our gardens and parks. For avenues there are no finer deciduous trees with pleasing blossoms than the Sargent cherry (*P. serrulata* var. *sachalinensis*) and the Tokyo cherry (*P. yedoensis*).[3] As a specimen on the lawn or in the park, none is finer than the rosebud cherry (*P. subhirtella* var. *pendula*) —I mean real trees, not the stunted apologies one usually sees. For any purpose where small trees are in request none could be more beautiful than the spring cherry (*P. subhirtella*)[4] with its myriad soft pink blossoms. Seen in the early morning against a blue sky, with the dew still in evidence, it is a vision of perfect beauty. The cult of the rhododendron is vastly on the increase and devotees should plant cherry trees in association with their broad-leafed favorites, for these give just the requisite amount of shade and are added beauty. Raise the cherry trees from seeds —plant them in quantity—there will be no regrets. In central China cherry trees are a feature of mixed woods and beneath them luxuriate evergreen rhododendrons. Often have I fondled the opening flower trusses of *R. sutchuenense* intermingled with the white and pink petals of *Prunus conradinae*, *P. serrulata* var. *spontanea*, its pretty sister, var. *pubescens*, and *P. subhirtella* var. *ascendens*.

Cherries are sun-loving trees and enjoy a warm, light, loamy soil. Against a foil of evergreens the flowers are seen to best advantage. In the forests of evergreen oaks and laurels, which clothe the higher mountains of interior Formosa, the red-flowered *Prunus campanulata* is indigenous, and, as I write, the picture it presented in February, 1918, with its perfect setting comes vividly to mind. But this cherry, most richly colored of all, is only for those who garden on the Pacific slope and other favored spots. . . .

In Japan nine species with several varieties are indigenous. All are worthy, most of them excellent. Several kinds grow also in the forests of Korea and China, but their distinctiveness and the garden merit of those introduced have yet to be fully demonstrated. Such as *P. concinna*, *P. pilosiuscula*, and *P. conradinae*,

[3] Tokyo cherry is now called Yoshino cherry.
[4] Spring cherry is now called Higan cherry.

Primrose jasmine (*Jasminum mesnyi*)
grown as a standard at the
Isabella Stewart Gardner Museum,
Boston. A tender vine,
grown under glass in the Northeast,
it is one of the most
ornamental of all the
jasmines with soft,
semievergreen foliage and
single, or semidouble,
tubular yellow flowers.
(P. E. GENEREUX)

Henry's lily (*Lilium henryi*),
discovered by Dr. Augustine Henry
and introduced to cultivation
by E. H. Wilson. The willowy
stems, 4 to 6 feet tall,
which support the yellow-orange
blooms, usually need support.
A long-lived, hardy lily,
it has been the source of
numerous hybrids. (P. E. GENEREUX)

all small trees, are undoubtedly acquisitions, while *P. serrula* is
worth growing for its handsome yellow-brown bark; but the rank
and file are inferior to those about to be described.

The first Oriental cherry introduced into the Occident came
from Canton in 1819, and was named *P. pseudocerasus*. This
species is wild in Hupeh and is cultivated in many parts of
China for its fruit. Long ago for the same purpose it was introduced into Japan where it may occasionally be seen today; there
is also an old tree in the Cambridge Botanic Gardens, England.
The flowers are white, freely produced, and pretty, but the tree
is tender and of no outstanding merit as an ornamental. I would
not mention it here but for the fact that its name has been pro-
miscuously applied to the flowering cherries of Japan, with which
it has absolutely nothing to do. The next cherry introduced also
came from Canton and had double white flowers. This was named
P. serrulata in 1830. Good trees of this kind I have not seen in
America but in the Cambridge Botanic Gardens, England, and
also at Kew there are fine specimens. These are low, thanks to
grafting, with rigid, horizontal, spreading branches and, out of
blossom, are more remarkable than beautiful in appearance. This
cherry is simply a double-flowered form of a species common in
the woods and forests of central China and of northeastern Asia
generally, and now known as *P. serrulata* var. *spontanea*. In the
north of Japan it is replaced by the larger-flowered variety
sachalinensis. Associated with both, and having a wider distribution than any other Asiatic cherry, is the variety *pubescens*, distinguished by its hairiness. Where and when the double-flowered
P. serrulata originated is unknown and the same is true of its pink
counterpart var. *rosea*. They are well distinguished from all other
forms by their smaller flowers crowded with narrow petals.

The wild varieties *spontanea* and *pubescens* are the common
cherries of the Far East and in Japan are both called Yama-
zakura, that is, mountain cherry. The trees grow to 75 feet in

height, with a trunk sometimes 12 feet in girth; they have stout ascending branches and pale-to-rose-pink blossoms 1 inch or less across. The young foliage is a bronze, metallic green and in the autumn changes to shades of yellow, orange, and crimson, which adds much to the attractiveness of these trees. The more northern form (var. *sachalinensis*), the Sargent cherry, is distinguished by its larger flowers, each from 1 to 1¾ inches across, often rose-pink, rarely white, in color. This is the most hardy and the largest growing of all Asiatic cherries, and if one kind only can be planted it should be this. The finest of the pink and rose-colored double-flowered cherries are forms of this variety. The six best are "Kirin," "Horinji," "Ichiyo," "Fugenzo," its white form "Shirofugen," and the late-flowering "Sekiyama" (or "Kanzan," as it is usually called in Japan).

The principal parent of the cultivated Japanese cherries is *P. lannesiana* var. *albida*, which is native to the volcanic Seven Isles of Idzu, the Boshu peninsula, and elsewhere in the warm parts of Japan. It is a tree of moderate size with pale bark and white or pale pink, fragrant flowers. It is not a very hardy tree nor long-lived, though of rapid growth. Of the scores of named forms of this cherry the following dozen are among the best: 'Amanogawa,' 'Sirotae,' 'Ariake,' 'Jonioi,' 'Sumizome,' 'Senriko,' 'Ogon.' 'Yayeakebono,' 'Botanzakura,' 'Miyako.' 'Hatazakura,' and 'Grandiflora,' known to the Japanese as 'Ukon' or 'Asagi' and remarkable for its pale yellow flowers. Another species with double flowers is *P. sieboldi*, often called in the trade Waterer's cherry,[5] which is characterized by the soft, appressed, fulvous-gray hairs which clothe the leaves. This is a tree of moderate size, and, though commonly cultivated in Japan, has not yet been reported in a wild state. Like *P. lannesiana* and its forms, this cherry may also be rooted from cuttings.

Of the spring or rosebud cherries there are four distinct types.

[5] Waterer's cherry is now known as the Naden cherry.

The wild form is *P. subhirtella* var. *ascendens*, which is indigenous in the woods of central China, Formosa, and Japan. It is a large
tree with a wide-spreading crown, but is less beautiful in blossom
than its sisters. The variety *pendula* is well described by its name,
and the tree in size equals that of the wild form. What has to bear
the specific name of *P. subhirtella* is a small tree, probably of
garden origin, and is the most floriferous and, perhaps, the most
pleasing of all Japanese cherries. It is the "Higan-zakura" or
spring cherry. The fourth form has semidouble flowers which
are sometimes most freely produced in the autumn and, in consequence, is named var. *autumnalis*. Very often it flowers sparsely
in the spring and freely in the autumn; in other seasons the very
opposite prevails. All the forms of *P. subhirtella* should be
worked on the type; they will also root from cuttings. From seed
a percentage come true, but the tendency of the varieties is to
revert to the wild form, *ascendens*. All have pink blossoms,
deeper in the bud, hence the name rosebud cherries. They are
very hardy and remarkably floriferous and, with their branchlets
more slender than those of other species, they have a grace and
charm peculiarly their own.

A quick-growing and handsome tree is the Tokyo cherry (*P.
yedoensis*), whose opening blossoms herald the cherry festival.
Though abundantly planted in Tokyo and elsewhere this cherry
is of unknown origin, and is, very possibly, a hybrid. It has a
short but thick trunk and large spreading branches which form
a broad, rounded crown. The flowers are white to pale pink and
are characterized by their hairy, cylindric cupula and flower stalk.
It is a magnificent tree for avenue planting and may be readily
raised from seed. Three other Japanese species, *P. maximowiczi*,
P. nipponica, and *P. apetala*, are of less merit.

The chapter may well end with mention of *P. incisa*, a species
abundant on the lower slopes of sacred Fujiyama and one of the
most pleasing of all, yet virtually unknown to Western gardens.

Usually a bush from 5 to 15 feet tall, it will, under favorable conditions, form a small tree from 25 to 30 feet tall with a neat crown of spreading and ascending twiggy branches. The flowers are usually nodding and vary in color from white to pale pink; the cupula and sepals are vinous red and the stamens are tinged with the same color; the anthers are golden. No cherry is more hardy, more floriferous, or more lovely than this, the "Mame-zakura"—pigmy cherry—of Japan.

4

The Princess Kurume

WE HAVE the honor to announce that Princess Kurume, reigning beauty of the azalea kingdom, is in town and will hold court throughout Easter. Further, I have to declare the Princess' intention of becoming a permanent resident, also, that in each succeeding year her court will be held continuously from Christmas to Easter. The doors are open to all. Her handsome debonair Chinese cousin, under the pseudonym of Indian azalea, has been long a favorite in the floral courts of America and Europe and so, too, have other relatives, but endowed with radiant beauty this youthful, winsome Princess is bound to capture and hold the stronghold of public affection and esteem. She first came to these shores as a baby in 1916, and in 1920 a few favored folk were permitted to peep at this charming damsel in conservative Boston. The effect was magical, all who saw forthwith became her devotees. Her first lover in this part of the world, her sponsor and guardian, I immediately found myself a mere atom in her universe. A crown of gold was by unanimous consent placed on her head and with loud acclamation she was proclaimed mistress royal of her clan. Pleasing speeches were made and nice things said of me for the part I had played in prevailing upon her to leave her island home of the Rising Sun to grace these Western shores. Her conquest was too spontaneous and complete for jealousy to wing dart. Hardheaded nurserymen fell in love with her at first sight even as I had done, and she was surrounded by chaperons intent upon providing for her well-being and proper education into Western modes of life. I relinquished my trust and went abroad not disconsolate, however, since I knew she was in safe hands.

Since that epoch-making date Princess Kurume has, except on rare occasions, remained in the seclusion of educational cloisters. Her education completed, the pleasant task of announcing the coming of age of this royal debutante has fallen to me.

More than royal is this lovely Princess, for is she not descended from Ninigi, grandson of the sun-goddess, Amaterasu? History tells that her ancestors sprang from the soil on which Ninigi alighted when he came down from heaven to found the Empire of Japan. If skeptics there be, they have but to visit Mt. Kirishima, in south Japan, where they themselves can see in wondrous beauty the kinsfolk of this damsel in countless thousands, embellishing the slopes of this sacred and still active volcano. How many generations of the Princess' family displayed their beauty to the sun, the moon, and the stars, to the birds of the air and the four-footed friends that walk the earth, we do not know. But about a century ago a wandering pilgrim of the genus Homo became enraptured with them and lovingly carried a few away to his home in the town of Kurume and a new era in the family history dawned.

I was first introduced to the Kurume family in 1914 when, at the invitation of my lamented friend, the late Mr. H. Suzuki, the foremost Japanese horticulturist of his time, I accompanied him on a visit to the nursery district of Hatagaya, a few miles north of Tokyo. There in a garden I saw thousands of tiny plants bearing white and colored flowers of nearly every hue. With the courteous consent of the owner I secured a set of fragments and dried them for the Arnold Arboretum. In 1917, at my suggestion, Mr. John S. Ames secured a number of small plants from this collection and these were the first ever brought into the eastern States. They were midgets, indeed, but grew amazingly and flowered profusely and soon became one of the floral delights of the Ames estate, a joy to the owner and his friends.

What I saw in 1914 whetted my appetite and I was hungry to see and learn more about these delightful plants. Opportunity came in 1918, and to my great good fortune my friend, Suzuki, was able to accompany me to the headquarters of the family, the city of Kurume. This city is on the island of Kyushu, situated some 800 miles south by west of Tokyo and is quite an important place. But the fame of its azaleas will make it universally known. There we arrived on a fine May morning, to find the azaleas in the pink of perfection. I went prepared to see a display of blossoms, but the entrancing beauty of myriad delicately colored flowers clothing a multitude of shapely, grown plants surpassed my most sanguine expectations. The gardens of two leading specialists were veritable fairylands and I gasped with astonishment when I realized that garden-lovers of America and Europe knew virtually nothing of this wealth of beauty. Most of the plants were trained into low standards, each about 20 inches high with flattened or convex crowns some 24 inches through, and were monuments to the patience and cultural skill of the Japanese gardener. Other shapes there were but this was the favorite and most effective. The flowers, each about one-half to three-quarters of an inch across and borne in clusters of from two to several at the end of the twigs, were in such profusion as to almost completely hide the leaves. If a fault could be found, it was that the flowers were too numerous! Some have bizarre-colored flowers but such I do not favor. A great many have the calyx petaloid and the flowers are hose-in-hose. The stamens, always five, and pistil are perfect and there is no malformation as in ordinary double flowers. The anthers are light to dark, varying with the color shades, tip the straight filaments and add not a little to the pleasing appearance of the flowers. They are, in truth, the roguish eyes of laughing, dimpled, and blushing blossoms.

At Kurume the azaleas are grown in a number of gardens but the oldest and best collection is that of Mr. Kijiro Akashi, who for more than forty years has assiduously devoted himself to the development of these charming azaleas. He has raised from seeds and perpetuated by cuttings nearly all the kinds in cultivation. In his garden is the finest of all collections, and the loving pride with which this grand old gardener pointed out to us the particular merits of this or that pet can be appreciated only by those whose lives have been lived in close companionship with plants. In this garden I made a selection in duplicate of fifty of the best kinds. Making the selection was much easier than persuading Mr. Akashi to part with them, though, with true old-time Japanese politeness, he had offered me any or all that he had. He loved his plants and I fully understand his diffidence when the time to part with them actually came.

I think that Kurume azaleas are the loveliest of all azaleas. Small of stature but sturdy, they are rich in attractive features. The branches are very numerous and twiggy, clothed with small, neat, rich, green leaves and crowned with clusters of small, slightly fragrant flowers, which on different individuals embrace all the delicate shades of color familiar to us in sweet peas. The individual flower suggests the frilled petticoat of a dainty lady. In many, the calyx, green and inconspicuous in ordinary flowers, grows to the same size and has the same color as the corolla, and here we get two frilled petticoats, one over the other, of exquisite grace and finish. Such arrangement is called hose-in-hose, that is, one flower within another. These hose-in-hose flowers have none of the ugliness usually associated with the double flowers and, moreover, last in perfection much longer than the ordinary sorts.

The colors, so pure and exquisite, are of every hue and shade—pure pink to rose-color, cerise, lavender, vermilion, salmon, bright red to scarlet, crimson, and the richest magenta; others the purest white.

At Kurume the plants are often trained as low standards with a compact, umbrella-shaped crown; less commonly they are dense and globose or open and irregular in form. They are extremely floriferous, and in season the blossoms often completely hide the leaves. The leaves are of two forms and they vary considerably in size, in shades of green, in their autumn coloring, and in their degree of persistence. In a great measure these variations are correlated with the color of the flowers, and experts in Japan can with ease distinguish each variety by its foliage and general appearance.

Japanese experts recognize by name more than 250 kinds of Kurume azaleas, but the differences are often infinitesimal. The two leading experts, Messrs. Akashi and Kuwano, at my suggestion named six as the pick of them all: 'Takasago,' 'Azuma-kagami,' 'Kirin,' 'Kumo-no-uye,' 'Kurai-no-himo,' and 'Kureno-yuki.'

For the sake of completeness I give a full list of the sorts I brought over. The Japanese names have priority and in all fairness should be kept as the proper names for these azaleas. Unfortunately, however, it is well-nigh impossible for the Western tongue to pronounce them accurately; moreover, they are untranslatable, being as a rule picturesque phrases. As a compromise, therefore, I propose to add to the Japanese name an English name, and I hope this will be acceptable to friends both in the Orient and Occident.

Double flowers
characterize many of
the Kurume azaleas
(P. E. GENEREUX)

A handsome specimen
Kurume hybrid azalea
grown by Ernest Borowski
of Norwood, Massachusetts,
who obtained his original
stock from the
John S. Ames collection
at North Easton,
Massachusetts
(P. E. GENEREUX)

Seikai	Madonna	white, hose-in-hose
Kureno-yuki	Snowflake	white, hose-in-hose
Shin-seikai	Old Ivory	cream-white, hose-in-hose
Yoro-zuyo	Purity	white
Nani-wagata	Painted Lady	white suffused lavender
Tancho	Seraphim	flesh-color, hose-in-hose
Hachika-tsugi	Prudence	white suffused lavender
Iro-hayama	Dainty	white margined pale lavender
Hoō	Appleblossom	white tinged with pink
Sui-yōhi	Sprite	flesh-color
Takasago	Cherryblossom	cherryblossom pink, hose-in-hose
Kasumi-gaseki	Elf	pale pink
Bijinsui	Little Imp	pale pink
Asa-gasumi	Rosy Morn	rose-pink, hose-in-hose
Kimigayo	Cherub	pink
Azuma-kagami	Pink Pearl	deep pink, hose-in-hose
Osaraku	Penelope	white suffused and margined lavender
Otome	Maiden's Blush	blush pink
Aya-kammuri	Pinkie	rose-color
Shintoki-no-hagasane	Rose Taffetas	rose shading to pink, hose-in-hose
Saotome	Peachblossom	rose-color
Kirin	Daybreak	deep rose shading to silvery rose
Tamafuyo	Fancy	white striped peach-color
Kiritsubo	Twilight	rosy mauve
Omoine	Dame Lavender	pale lavender
Oinō-mezame	Melody	deep rose-color
Katsura-no-hana	Ruth	rose-color
Shin-utena	Santoi	pale salmon
Kumo-noito	Betty	pure pink
Kumo-no-uye	Salmon Prince	pure salmon
Benifude	Sunbeam	salmon
Kasane-kagaribi	Rosita	dull salmon-red
Tsuta-momiji	Cardinal	bright red
Suetsumu	Flame	crimson

Fudesute-yama	Poppy	light red
Ima-shojō	Fascination	bright red, hose-in-hose
Rasho-mon	Meteor	scarlet
Waka-kayede	Red Robin	red
Yaye-hiryu	Scarlet Prince	bright scarlet, hose-in-hose
Kurai-no-himo	Carmine Queen	carmine, hose-in-hose
Agemaki	José	carmine
Hinodegiri	Red Hussar	bright crimson
Aioi	Fairy Queen	almond-blossom pink, hose-in-hose
Sakura-tsukasa	All-a-Glow	rosy mauve
Tama-no-utena	Flamingo	pale salmon
Gosho-zakura	Vanity	white striped peach-color
Ukamuse	Princess Delight	vermilion, hose-in-hose
Hinode-no-taka	Ruby	crimson
Osaraku seedling	Winsome	white suffused lavender
Hana-asobi	Sultan	red

As to the origin and history of these plants, Mr. Akashi kindly furnished me with the details. They were originated by a Japanese gentleman named Motozo Sakamoto, who lived in the city of Kurume about one hundred years ago. The parent stock came from sacred Mt. Kirishima, but whether brought from there by Sakamoto or given to him by some pilgrim is uncertain. At any rate, he cultivated several varieties and raised and selected seedlings, including one he named "Azuma-kagami" from which it is claimed have descended all the pink-colored forms. After his death, Sakamoto's collection passed into the hands of Kijiro Akashi. The original plant of "Azuma-kagami" is still healthy. I photographed it but failed to purchase it, though I tried hard to do so. Mr. Akashi showed us a gold medal awarded to him for an exhibit of thirty plants, in a dozen kinds, of Kurume azaleas at the Panama Pacific Exposition, San Francisco, in 1915. The plants were afterwards sold, and Akashi's pride in the gold medal seemed a little saddened when he thought of the loss of those thirty plants.

Next it was determined to visit Mt. Kirishima, the place tradition says the parents of the plants came from. I had visited this mountain early in March, 1914, and remembered that an azalea grew there and that I had gathered leafless specimens. We spent a night near the base of Kirishima, and starting early the next morning soon reached an altitude of 3,000 feet above sea level, where forests abruptly give place to grassland, and saw before us the mountain slopes dotted with blossoming azalea bushes in quantity. They grow in volcanic soil on wideswept grassy slopes and among rocks. In size the bushes are from nearly prostrate to a yard high, and hardly two plants have flowers of the same shade of color. We gathered specimens of forms with pink, salmon, mauve to rich magenta-colored flowers and at a little higher altitude red-flowered forms and an occasional white one. We found much variation in the size and shape of the flowers and leaves and also that the anthers varied in color. The evidence was complete in every detail, and no shadow of doubt as to the origin of the wondrous race of azaleas we had seen in Kurume remained in our minds.

To a place so sacred as Kirishima pilgrimages have been made by the Japanese from immemorial time. With their profound love for flowers some of the pilgrims would certainly take back as souvenirs living plants of this charming azalea. Naturally it was named for the mountain, and in the course of time was distributed widely in the gardens of Japan. It is easily understood that a plant bearing flowers of an unusual color would be that selected as a souvenir by the average pilgrim. It is such forms that reached gardens first, and so we find the red *obtusa*, the magenta *amoena*, the white *alba* to be the earliest known.

The reader may think it strange that a race of azaleas so rich in forms and of such decorative value should have remained so long unknown to us, yet the explanation is simple. Interior Kyushu is little known to the Western world, and even to those Japanese whose homes are on the other islands. The feudal system of government which until comparatively recently obtained in Japan created and preserved this aloofness. Further, Kurume is remote from the horticultural centers of Osaka and Yokohama, from whence we have drawn the bulk of our garden plants and where business is made of growing for export. Nagasaki is much nearer, but in the days of early explorers, intercommunication was difficult and, for foreigners, impossible. And so it has resulted that the product of Sakamoto's hobby, richly developed by Akashi, has remained hidden from the outside world until now. During the last fifteen years the fame of the Kurume azaleas has reached Osaka, Tokyo, and other places, and growers have obtained stocks and are propagating them apace. Unfortunately, every grower and enthusiast names the plants according to his fancy and the result in a few years will be chaos. And this is helped by the fact that every slight sport or variant is kept and named and no attempt at selection made. I do not see how it is possible to improve upon the strain grown in Kurume unless yellow could be injected. What is needed is rigorous selection and the reduction of the named forms to fifty or less. In the past, seedling selection and preservation of sports by vegetative propagation have been the sole means employed in the evolution of the race of Kurume azaleas, but now attempts at hybridizing them with the large-flowered "Indian" and "ledifolia" types are in progress. This may result in a new race, but whether it will be as lovely and fascinating as the present one is doubtful.

Just how hardy this race will prove remains to be seen, but I am of the opinion that under the genial influence of the Gulf Stream from Cape Cod southward many places will be found where they will be at home and flourish in perfection. They root readily from cuttings and in conservatories may be had in blossom from Christmas until Easter. Good-natured, adaptable, at home in any surroundings, brightening and cheering us with a glow of color and beauty—the divine Princess Kurume is assured of a lasting welcome in the land of her adoption. Proud am I of being the fortunate one to introduce this exquisite damsel to the gardens of eastern North America.

5

Crab Apples of the Orient

DIFFERENT SPECIES of crab apple grow wild in the temperate regions of Asia, North America, and Europe. The greatest number are native of the Orient, where they are a feature of the margins of woods, thickets, and valleys in China, Manchuria, Korea, and Japan. Indeed, of the many floral gifts the East has lavished on the gardens of the West few, if any, excel the Oriental crab apples, which possess all the qualities necessary in hardy woody plants. No trees flower more profusely in spring or fruit more abundantly in autumn. Moreover, the fruit is beautiful in itself, hangs long on the trees, and is much appreciated by birds. I propose limiting this chapter to the Oriental species, but before dipping properly into our subject just a word about the generic name of crab apples. It has become a custom with many to unite the apples, sorbs, and pears under the name pyrus which, properly speaking, belongs to the pears alone. Such classification is both cumbrous and misleading. No good purpose is served by this drastic lumping together of trees which are obviously distinct, and there are good and sufficient technical characters distinguishing them. In the European records that have come down to us from the earliest time, the apple is known as malus and this name from every viewpoint is correct.

Many of the Oriental crab apples are essentially trees for the larger garden and park, but there are sorts well suited for the flower garden and the suburban lot. Their great merits, notwithstanding, crab apples are far from occupying the position they are entitled to hold in gardens. Odd trees or bushes are often seen and there are a few notable collections. Fitly enough there is one in the Arnold Arboretum and another at Kew where, in an unpromising sandy soil, the returns the trees give are nothing short of marvelous. A good loam, rather on the stiff side, is ideal and crab apples do not by any means object to lime. As to site, provided it is open and exposed, they are not particular, though a hillside or slope is preferable. The common pests of crab apples are scale insects and a white woolly aphis known as American blight. The former may easily be kept down by spraying in late winter with lime-sulphur or imperial soap (one gallon to eight gallons of water).[1] The blight is destroyed by spraying in summer with imperial soap (one gallon to thirty gallons of water). Several of the Oriental crab apples can withstand greater cold than the common apple tree and where this thrives its Oriental relatives will be found to flourish. They love to have the wind and sunlight play freely through them and under these conditions are long-lived and suffer little from pests of any kind.

[1] Control methods for crab apple pests have changed considerably since E. H. Wilson wrote this chapter. Scale insects are controlled with miscible oil applied in late winter or early spring when the temperature has reached 40° F. Borers are best controlled by inspecting trees in spring and fall and using a wire to kill them at their work. Fire blight and cedar apple rust, which frequently attack apples, are not serious or common with most Oriental crab apples. The white wooley aphis can be checked with any of several insecticides.

Near the house no tree could be more attractive than the shapely *Malus halliana* with flustered rose-pink, pendent, more or less double flowers; on a bank with its bottom branches hugging the ground the low, broad, white-flowered *M. sargenti* is a jewel above price. For the flower garden many sorts are good, none more so than the old favorite *M. spectabilis* with pink semidouble blossoms, and the new *M. theifera*[2] with white flowers, rose-pink in the bud. As a flowering tree in the park, the Siberian *M. baccata*, especially its hairy variety *mandshurica*, with an oval crown full 50 feet tall, the lower branches sweeping the ground and pure white, fragrant flowers, cannot be excelled. This and other tall kinds may also be planted with advantage on the edges of woods and copses, especially where oak and maple trees predominate. An occasional pine, fir, or spruce well to the rear adds greatly to the landscape effect.

All crab apples are deciduous and most of them mentioned here open their blossoms before the leaves unfold, though in some the foliage is partially developed ere the petals fall. The flowers are followed by an abundant crop of small fruits, in most species scarcely larger than a good-sized marrow-fat pea, either crimson, wine-red, yellow, or red and yellow, but in a few dull greenish red. To those who breed pheasants or love birds in general, crab apples have double or rather treble values, since to the aesthetic qualities of flowers and attractive autumn fruits they add the utilitarian value of providing winter food in quantity for feathered friends.

The flowers of many Oriental crab apples are bright rose-pink in the bud, changing to white as they expand. Such are those of *M. floribunda* and *M. theifera*. Some, like *M. sargenti*, *M. toringoides, M. baccata* and its forms, are pure white. In *M. spectabilis* the flowers are pink, fading to nearly white, and in *M. halliana* they are bright rose-pink, becoming slightly paler as they age. All

[2] *Malus theifera* is now classified as *M. hupehensis.*

are slightly and pleasantly fragrant, but this pleasing quality is most highly developed in the delightful *M. baccata* var. *mandshurica*. The flowers last about a week, the fruits for several months; indeed, in several species they remain fresh in appearance throughout the winter. Intense productiveness tends to exhaustion and so crab apples have their off years like everything else. In a good season, and that is usually every other one, the branches from tip to base are densely studded with flower clusters and are transformed into plumes or wands of blossom. About mid-May I have in many years reveled in the beauty of *M. theifera* with 12-foot-long plumes of flowers, the blossoms so densely set on all sides of the branches that it was not possible to insert a finger without touching the petals.

Crab apples are so susceptible to pollen from their neighbors and hybridize so freely that few breed true from seeds. Some beautiful chance hybrids, like *M. arnoldiana*, have originated this way, but the danger of worthless mongrels arising from attempts to raise them from seeds is very great. Fortunately they may be propagated easily and quickly by budding and grafting, and in so far as the Oriental species mentioned here are concerned the common apple is a good stock. But I would warn garden-lovers against using this stock for such anomalous east Asiatic species as *M. yunnanensis, M. pratti, M. kansuensis,* or *M. tschonoski,* or, for any of the American species. To use the common apple tree for these is to court disaster.

The first of the crab apples to open its blossoms in the spring is *Malus baccata* var. *mandshurica*. This is a native of Manchuria, Korea, and northern Japan, where it is a common and striking feature of the landscape. Where it has proper room to develop, this is a tree about 50 feet tall with a broad, bell-shaped crown and branches sweeping the ground. The flowers are pure white, an inch or rather more across, and are more fragrant than those of any other Old World species of malus. The fruit is yellow or lustrous red. The typical *M. baccata* is native of the more interior regions of northern Asia and is distinguished by being everywhere glabrous. There are forms with erect branches (*fastigiata*) and with slender, semipendent branches (*gracilis*).

The typical *M. baccata* with pealike, round, naked fruits was introduced into England in 1784, but the varieties mentioned are comparatively newcomers. With the exception of the fastigiate form, *M. baccata*, its varieties and hybrids, are the best suited of Oriental crab apples for planting in the park, open landscape, or on the edge of woods where there is plenty of room for them to develop to their maximum size and display their full beauty. Many of the so-called Siberian crab apples of gardens are hybrids between *M. baccata* and the Chinese apple (*M. prunifolia* var. *rinki*). The most familiar in gardens is the handsome *M. robusta*, more generally known as *M. cerasifera*, with fruits about one-third of an inch in diameter, some crowned with the remains of the calyx, some quite naked, others are hybrids of the common apple.

The first known of the Oriental crab apples is the well-named *M. spectabilis*. This is a tree of from 25 to 35 feet tall with a vase-shaped crown of numerous rigid, ascending-spreading branches and short branchlets. The flowers vary from pure to pale pink and are more or less semidouble; the fruit is yellow, nearly globose and about three-fourths of an inch in diameter. There are several forms of this old favorite, differing in the number of petals and degree of color; the habit is rather stiff but the wealth of flower clusters is amazing.

Undoubtedly related to the above, and also of unknown origin, is *M. micromalus*, more generally known as *M. kaido*. It is a tree of similar habit but with less rigid branches, darker leaves, slightly larger and deeper rose-pink flowers. Supposed to be of Chinese origin, this crab apple is known only as a planted tree in Japan

(ABOVE LEFT) Detail of the fruit of an Oriental crab apple (GEORGE TALOUMIS)

(BELOW LEFT) Tea crab apple (*Malus hupehensis*) rates high as a picturesque ornamental flowering tree. The flower buds, borne in clusters, are deep pink but fade to white as they open, emitting a pleasant fragrance (P. E. GENEREUX)

(BELOW) Detail of the flowers of the tea crab apple (*Malus hupehensis*). The greenish-yellow fruits which ripen in autumn are tinged with red. (P. E. GENEREUX)

where it is far from common. It is the second crab apple to open
its blossom each season making a close race with the fragrant
mandshurica.

The Japanese and many people in eastern North America consider *M. halliana* the finest of all Oriental crab apples. Certainly
it is the most handsome of all with colored flowers. It is a treelike
shrub sometimes 15 feet tall with a broad bushy crown of ascending-spreading branches and twiggy branchlets and rather sparse,
comparatively thick, dark green leaves deeply tinged with bronze
color when they unfold. The flowers, each on a long, slender stalk,
are borne in clusters and are bright rose-color, but the pealike fruit,
which ripens late, is greenish red and unattractive. The flowers
vary from nearly single to semidouble and the central one of each
cluster is usually male. This favorite of the Japanese has been cultivated by them for many centuries but its origin is unknown.

Widely dispersed in central and western China and a feature of
the thickets and margins of woods on the mountains of western
China is *M. theifera*. This is a small tree, seldom exceeding 20 feet
in height, with sparse, upright spreading crown of rather zigzag
branches which are densely studded with short spurs. The flowers
are rose-pink in the bud and pure white where fully expanded;
the fruit is dull greenish red and not showy. I have told of the
plumes of flowers and will only add that among the many plants
it has been my privilege to add to gardens I count this the most
beautiful of the deciduous small trees. The illustration tells its own
story and grateful am I of the honor of being the fortunate introducer of this crab apple. The specific name is derived from the
fact that in China the peasants collect the leaves and from them
prepare a palatable beverage which they call red tea.

Perhaps the best known and by some considered the finest of
Oriental crab apples is *M. floribunda*. This was introduced from
Nagasaki into Holland by Siebold in 1853, yet its origin remains
unknown and Japanese botanists and gardeners of today are un-

acquainted with this plant. It is a broad, round-topped tree, sometimes 30 feet tall and more in diameter of crown, with a tangle of
branches and masses of slender, arching, and pendent branchlets.
The clustered flowers are white when fully expanded and bright
rose-pink in bud, and as they open in succession the contrast is
singularly beautiful. A cascade of myriad flowers symbolizes this
crab apple when in full bloom. In 1883 there appeared in the
Arnold Arboretum among some presumed seedlings of *M. floribunda*, a distinct plant which has since been named *M. arnoldiana*.
This is probably a hybrid between *M. floribunda* and *M. robusta*.
It has the habit and abundant blossoms of the former but the
flower and ovoid fruit are nearly twice as large.

Another crab apple introduced by Siebold in 1853 is the bushy
M. sieboldi, often known as *M. toringo*, with small flowers which
open late, and lobed leaves on the free shoots.[3] It is really a
dwarf form of a crab apple very common on the mountains of
Japan and on the Korean island of Quelpaert, to which the name
M. sieboldi var. *arborescens* has been given. This is a rather
slender tree often 30 feet tall with ascending, wide-spreading
branches which are densely studded with clusters of white-tinged-
with-rose-color flowers and small fruits, red on some trees, yellow
on others. The flowers though small are produced in great abundance and the tree has the advantage of flowering later than most
of the other Oriental crab apples.

The pigmy of the crab apple family and preeminently suited
for planting on banks is *M. sargenti*. This plant forms a rounded
mass 5 feet tall but is often twice that much through with rigid,
spreading branches, the lowest of which lie on the ground. The
flowers are saucer-shaped, of the purest white with conspicuous
yellow anthers, and are borne in umbellate clusters produced in
utmost profusion. The fruit is wine-red covered with a slight bloom
and is long persistent. This most distinct crab apple is native of

[3] Toringo crab apple is the common name for *M. sieboldi*.

salt marshes near Muroran in north Japan, where it was discovered and introduced into the Arnold Arboretum by Professor Sargent in 1892.

The latest to flower and the most beautiful in fruit of all Oriental crab apples is *M. toringoides*, a recent introduction, having been discovered and introduced by myself in England in 1904 and into America in 1908. At maturity this is a tree from 25 to 30 feet tall with a short trunk and a broad, tangled crown of branches and spiny branchlets. The leaves are partly entire and partly incised and lobed, resembling those of the hawthorn, and are well expanded when the clustered white flowers open. The fruit is conspicuous and handsome, being exactly like a whiteheart cherry only somewhat smaller. This grand acquisition is growing in a few gardens and its fortunate possessors never tire of sounding its praise.

In the garden of the Imperial Summer Palace near Peking the well-known *M. spectabilis* is a planted tree, and I have seen it in a few other old gardens in eastern China. It was introduced into England from Canton about 1780 through the agency of the old East India Company and was the first Oriental crab apple to reach England. Very rare in China and known only as a planted tree and quite unknown in Japan, the origin of this beautiful plant is a mystery.

There are other crab apples of merit and several fine hybrids that have originated in Europe, such as *M. scheideckeri*, *M. atrosanguinea*, the new *M. purpurea*, *M. eleyi*, and *M. aldenhamensis*, but my tale must end with mention of *M. sublobata*. A hybrid of uncertain origin, this tree grows to a large size and has bright yellow fruit an inch in diameter. Its parents are probably the Chinese apple (*M. prunifolia* var. *rinki* and *M. sieboldi* var. *arborescens*), but, whatever its origin, it is in the autumn the finest of the larger fruited crab apples.

No race nor creed have made the crab apple their favorite

flowering plant. I have often wondered why Buddhists have not taken it as an emblem of abundance. Much mystery surrounds the origin of these crab apples; indeed, there is no group of familiar plants concerning which our ignorance is more profound. Of those mentioned here five only are known in a wild state. By devious channels and many agencies the Oriental crab apples have reached our gardens. The first to arrive was *M. spectabilis*, the last *M. toringoides*, both from China. The others came at different times between 1780 and 1904. All are worthy, and, although we cannot tell the origin of many, we can be thankful that such beauty has fallen to our enjoyment.

6

Plants for Shore Gardens

IN GARDEN-MAKING by the sea, the problem is to find trees and shrubs that will withstand the wind's full blast, carrying as it does more or less salt-laden moisture. Everybody realizes that gales blow from the sea and the high velocity of the wind is common knowledge. This has a dwarfing effect upon vegetation and one has but to stroll a mile or two along the coast to realize this, and note how markedly the direction of the prevailing winds is shown. Until a rampart of protective vegetation is established as a wind-break, it is useless to attempt to grow choice herbs, shrubs, and vines. The difficulty is greater in the colder regions of the world than in warm temperate and tropical lands. In the tropics Mother Nature, in mangrove, coconut palm, and others, has evolved types of vegetation that will withstand both wind and salt spray. In the warm temperate regions also there are in rich variety trees and shrubs immune to the effects of gale and spray. A great deal of this vegetation is evergreen, the leaves being relatively thick and capable of withstanding adverse conditions. In the cool temperate regions evergreen trees are almost nonexistent, except the narrow-leafed sorts, what vegetation there is near the cliffs is deciduous, and the young growth in the spring is very susceptible to salt air.

For California and the warmer states there is abundant material that can be used as a screen and windbreak for shore gardens, but in New England and other cold parts of the country creating such a windbreak is a very difficult undertaking, for the conditions are severe. But gales and far-flung salt spray notwithstanding, perseverance can accomplish much and shore gardens protected and filled with the choice plant material can be made. In spite of its harsh and blustering character the sea exercises a moderating influence upon temperature and imparts humidity to the atmosphere. The conditions on the whole are favorable to vegetation. As a matter of fact, around the coasts of every country a greater variety of plants can be grown than in places removed from the sea. As illustrating both the retarding influence of winds and the moderating influence of humidity the sea imparts to coastal climates, the adage so commonly expressed in Cornwall and Devon is very apt. The people of those favored districts in England declare that their trees are bushes and their bushes trees. The paradox is both apt and descriptively accurate.

Since in planning a shore garden a windbreak is the first essential, it is all-important to plant trees and bushes that will withstand gales and salt spray. Their ability to do this must be the first consideration. Where sand dunes, projecting rocks, and gullies are found, some natural protection is afforded which can be utilized to good advantage. In planting on absolutely naked ground the difficulty is greater, and it is a good plan to erect as a temporary windguard low walls, banks of earth, or even wattled hurdles. Behind such ramparts the first plantings may be made. It need hardly be stated that small plants only should be set out and that they must stand thickly together for mutual protection. Thick planting of vigorous young plants is the first essential in the establishing of a windguard, for by such means the plants are the better enabled to get firm hold of the soil whilst enjoying the protection of the protecting rampart. Growth as a rule is very slow but each successive row grows higher than the one in front of it; so ultimately, if the planting be sufficiently thick and broad, a bank of vegetation sloping upwards from the sea is formed and makes an admirable first line of defense. Such a thicket or border will not be a thing of beauty but the aesthetic in this case must give way to the utilitarian. Once we have got our protective belt of vegetation, making a garden by the sea is simple.

However, before we can establish our first line of defense it is necessary that we know the material suited to the purpose. Evergreens are best for such purposes but alas! the number suitable and hardy in New England is exceedingly limited. The best of all is probably the Austrian pine (*Pinus nigra*), which appears to delight in New England's gales and harsh climate. On Long Island and New Jersey the Japanese black pine (*Pinus thunbergi*) is splendid for the same purpose, further south the cluster pine (*Pinus pinaster*), the Monterey pine (*P. insignis*),[1] and others may be used. But we had better concentrate on the colder regions where the problem is so great. In New England the native pitch pine (*Pinus rigida*) is useful, and as an outermost rampart the low-growing *P. montana*, of which the mugho pine is a variety, can be used to great advantage. The red cedar (*Juniperus virginiana*) stands up well under the most adverse conditions and should be used.

Among deciduous trees there is greater variety but nothing really better for New England than the sycamore of Europe (*Acer pseudoplatanus*). Along the shores of Narragansett Bay and on parts of Cape Cod picturesque groups of this tree planted long ago may be seen and their effectiveness as a windbreak gauged.

---

[1] The scientific name for Monterey pine, now in use, is *Pinus radiata*.

Planted thickly they put up a splendid fight against the strongest winds, and though their growth is slow and their appearance ragged they are nonetheless effective. The common willow (*Salix alba*) and the white poplar (*Populus alba*) are also excellent plants for shore plantings, but unfortunately, the satin moth is now a pest on these useful trees and bids fair to wipe them out of existence. The common pear (*Pyrus communis*), the mountain-ash (*Sorbus americana*), and the white beam (*Sorbus aria*) are also very useful trees; hornbeam (*Carpinus caroliniana* and *C. betulus*) and the different hawthorns are also very accommodating. The larches, including the American, Japanese, and European, are all good for such purposes.

As an insurance, the more mixed this type of planting and the more thickly it is planted the better. It ought never to be forgotten that the object of such a planting is, first, last, and all the time, protection from wind and salt spray. It is not to be expected that shapely specimens will result. On the contrary, the trees will be stunted, gnarled, and lop-sided, but if they provide a living, permanent shield, in the shelter of which choice trees, shrubs, and herbs can thrive, they have fulfilled their purpose.

It often happens that the site chosen for house and grounds has but a thin surface layer of soil covering the rocks. In this case it is almost out of the question to establish trees and as a first line of defense one must fall back on shrubs. That there are a good number that will grow under these conditions may be seen by anyone who will take the trouble to traverse a few miles of New England seacoast. Even the most sandy wastes are more or less clad with woody vegetation of sorts. Nearly all this vegetation is deciduous but the inkberry (*Ilex glabra*) is an exception. This round-topped, twiggy bush is dense of habit and clothed with lustrous dark green leaves. It is about the only evergreen shrub of any size that the colder parts of New England boasts. For trailing over rocks or sandy areas or hanging down over the face of cliffs, the bearberry (*Arctostaphylos uvaursi*), with prostrate rope-like stems and dark green evergreen foliage, will grow under very harsh conditions. An excellent groundcover, its little pink urns are bright and cheery in late May and June and its dark scarlet fruits are handsome in the fall. Anyone who has visited Cape Cod must have noticed the large areas clothed with this plant. It is by no means confined thereto; indeed, it is found well north toward Labrador and it circles the boreal regions of the northern hemisphere.

Were I writing for shore gardens in California or the warm states, I could instance scores of evergreen plants that would flourish, such as the evergreen raphiolepis of Japan, the lovely escallonias of South America, and various leptospermums of Australia and New Zealand, not to mention the bottlebrushes (metrosideros)[2] and the pittosporums of New Zealand. In Tasmania *Acacia sophorae* binds the sandy foreshores as firmly as does maram grass those of Europe. It would be easy to describe a hundred broad-leafed evergreen plants for California shore gardens, but in New England choice is limited.

Certain euonymus do well by the seashore and from Long Island south; the maritime *E. japonica* in its various forms is a useful plant. This shrub is much used in the south of England for hedges right on the sea front. More hardy and equally useful is *E. patens*, which flourishes around Newport, Rhode Island. Both are evergreen and ought to be used wherever they prove hardy.[3] The common broom (*Cytisus scoparius*), naturalized on the coast as far north as Cape Neddick in Maine, does remarkably well by the seashore and in spring is a mass of clear yellow. Although its foliage is scarcely discernible, the green, twiggy stems are attractive. Planted

[2] Iron tree is the common name now in use for metrosideros.

[3] Curiously enough, Wilson makes no mention of *Euonymus fortunei* as being useful for seaside planting. It was formerly listed as *E. radicans*. He does mention this species, however, in *More Aristocrats of the Garden*; he was responsible for introducing one of its varieties.

A young specimen of dragon spruce (*Picea asperata*), noted for its closely arranged needles which last seven years before dropping. An ideal seaside evergreen, whose branches become somewhat pendulous as it matures. (P. E. GENEREUX)

thickly and pruned severely after flowering, this will make an excellent thicket and bear salt spray with impunity.

Heather may be grown on cliffs where there is the thinnest covering of soil, always supposing that lime is absent. This plant is much hardier than is generally supposed and given free exposure thrives merrily. Less hardy but also good for seashores is *Erica cinerea* and, so too, is the better colored *E. vagans*. In parts of Europe, especially in southern England, broom, gorse, heather, and heath make a lovely combination. Gorse (*Ulex europaeus*) is less hardy than the broom and can be transplanted with success only from pots. Where it will thrive it is not only handsome but is an excellent defense against marauders.

Among narrow-leafed evergreens two junipers of prostrate habit must be mentioned. One is the Bar Harbor juniper (*Juniperus horizontalis*), which makes a dense mat on cliffs. It is either green or gray-green through the summer months and changes to a lovely vinous purple during winter. The other, an excellent juniper for sandy regions from Cape Cod south, is the Japanese *Juniperus conferta*. This is essentially a maritime plant and I have seen it covered with sea water at high tide. It has an immense distribution along the Japanese littoral, extending far into Sakhalin and will, undoubtedly, be of great value in this country. Though known for a long time, it was not introduced until I sent seeds to the Arnold Arboretum in 1914. It does well on Long Island and is fairly hardy with us.

As to deciduous shrubs, the colder parts of our coasts are much better off. Up and down the coast of eastern North America there is no more beautiful plant in spring than the beach plum (*Prunus maritima*), which is anything from a shrub flattened on the ground to a bush of irregular shape 5 or 10 feet tall. There is much character to this common plant. Its branches are rigid and intricately placed and when laden with a multitude of pure white flowers the bushes resemble irregular drifts of snow. It ought to be much more abundantly used as an ornamental shrub; moreover, its fruit makes an excellent preserve. In parts of Europe it has a counterpart in the blackthorn (*Prunus spinosa*), which is similar in appearance but flourishes much further inland. These two plums could, to advantage, be planted as thickets to brave the elements in any and every shore garden of New England. With them may be associated the common bayberry (*Myrica carolinensis*) with fragrant foliage and fatty fruits, which are used for making the familiar bayberry candles.

Among the bushes or small trees well adapted for seashore planting are the tamarisks, of which *Tamarix parviflora, T. pentandra,* and *T. odessana* are the hardiest. They are familiar plants, with slender branches bearing in great profusion racemose clusters of pink blossoms. After flowering they should be severely pruned to keep them within bounds. Light, airy, and graceful in habit, they are very effective on top of sea walls or in sandy places. The Russian olive (*Elaeagnus angustifolia*) is also a suitable plant but needs shelter from the strongest winds. Its relatives, the bushy, broad-leafed *E. multiflora* and *E. umbellata*, are more satisfactory plants; of denser habit and lower in stature they withstand the gales better. More hardy than any of these is the silvercherry (*E. argentea*)[4] and where lime is present this can be used to advantage.

Low-growing and spreading by means of underground stolons, the aronias form dense masses and in flower and fruit are handsome. Widespread in eastern North America, they will grow in the poorest of soil right on the foreshore. The sumachs, including *Rhus glabra, R. typhina,* and *R. copallina,* do well under adverse conditions and in the autumn give wonderful color effects. Several of the bush honeysuckles, including *Lonicera morrowi*, with flattened, wide-spreading branches, and the variable *L. tatarica*, can

---

[4] Silvercherry, more commonly called silverberry, is now classified as *Elaeagnus commutata*.

be planted thickly as a screen. Both have pleasing flowers in spring and brightly colored fruits in late summer and early autumn.

In the swampy regions near the sea a shadblow (*Amelanchier spicata*) is abundant on Cape Cod and elsewhere. This is a bush sending up in quantity erect stems which grow from 5 to 8 feet tall and in spring are laden with pure white blossoms. The common goat willow (*Salix caprea*) does well by the sea and in early spring its pussies are a never-failing source of delight to young and old. The red dogwood (*Cornus sanguinea*) and the osier dogwood (*C. stolonifera*) form thick masses and in winter their polished scarlet-to-crimson stems give color and brightness to the dingiest landscape.

A few roses find a natural home on coasts, sandy wastes, and in swamps. *Rosa virginiana*, the common seashore rose of New England, is one of the loveliest wildings we boast. Its pink flowers are as pretty as roses can be, while its crimson stems through the winter and its scarlet fruits in late autumn are very handsome. It has erect stems, from 1 to 4 feet tall, spreads by means of underground shoots, and takes care of itself in the poorest of soils. The most widely known and perhaps the best rose for the seaside is *R. rugosa*, known to the Japanese as the sea-tomato, a name which intimates both its habitat and appearance of its fruit. There are a good many varieties of this well-known rose, but none are more handsome than the pure white and pink varieties with single flowers. All the hybrids of this rose do well and for a low fence nothing is more pleasing than the so-called carnation rose, F. J. Grootendorst, with small, fringed, very double, crimson flowers borne in great profusion. In the culture of rugosa roses the old canes should be cut clean away giving the new growth a chance to flourish. For trailing over rocks nothing is more lovely than *R. wichuraiana* with polished, dark green leaves and pure white blossoms; *R. multiflora* does well under similar conditions but forms a more hummocklike mass. The various hybrids of these species are all valuable for shore gardens. The Scotch rose, *R. spinosissima,* in its different forms can also be used; so too can the sweetbriar (*R. eglanteria*).

One of the most beautiful of the viburnums, namely, *V. carlesi,* is naturally a littoral shrub growing wild among rocks bordering the Sea of Japan. It is too scarce and valuable for massed planting but behind the first line of defense a few bushes should be grown. Where the climate is mild the laurustinus (*V. tinus*) is one of the very best of all shore garden plants—evergreen, blossoming in the winter, always of compact habit, it is a thing of beauty at all seasons of the year.

There are a great many other shrubs that could be mentioned but perhaps enough has been said to show that there is no dearth of woody plants available for shore gardens. The important thing is to plant thickly so as to form, either with trees or with bushes, an outer rampart of vegetation. Such planting will not of itself be beautiful; neither will the plants develop into shapely specimens. Their work is to break the winds and if they accomplish this then the next is easy. Behind such a rampart a thousand and one beautiful herbs and shrubs can be grown, often to greater perfection in gardens by the sea than in those far inland. One may have to battle vigorously with the elements, but by starting with small plants, thickly placed, and exercising the necessary amount of patience victory is sure. There is possibly greater fun in making a garden by the sea than elsewhere since it is a fight against nature. Some of the finest gardens in the world are those that nestle behind windguards along the seacoasts.

7

Summer Beauty
in the Garden

SUMMER IS NATURE'S SEASON of greatest endeavor. Bounding bois-
terously into activity in spring, she soon settles down to the calm
of earnestness and wastes not a moment from her task. During
the summer season the earth is clothed in a mantle of rich green
and every leaf on every tree and shrub, vine and herb is a complete
chemical laboratory actively engaged in fashioning foodstuffs for
the plant's present and future development. Plants can do what
animals cannot do: that is, they can increase the sum of their organic substance from inorganic sources. Their supply is drawn,
molecule by molecule, from the gases of the atmosphere, or from
water in which they are dissolved. From daybreak to dark this
labor is energetically pursued. The visible signs are not marked
as in the explosive development of spring growth or the autumn
robing in brilliant colors, but the work is unceasingly carried on.
Every plant organ from the tip of the most outlying rootlet to the
topmost leaf is making maximum effort in the path of duty. Water

and food salts absorbed from the soil by myriad rootlets are conveyed by a perfect transportation system to the leaves. The leaves
absorb carbon dioxide from the air, break it up and recombine
the elements with those of the food salts to form sugar for immediate use in the growth of shoot and root and the maturing of the
fruit and seed. Surplus water is evaporated and excess of sugar is
converted into starch and stored away. All this orderly business,
though hidden, is carried on in the leaf canopy, whose cool shade
we seek from the heat of the day.

From the blossoming of the last lilac bush to the coming of
stately gladiolus may be reckoned the summer season—from June to
mid-August. This is to every garden-lover the most enjoyable of the
four seasons. Gone is all fear of frosts, and a halt is called between
the planting activities of spring and the planning and preparing
of autumn. Light labor with the hoe and free use of hose and
watering pot succeed the heavier task of digging with spade and
fork; staking and tying, trimming and thinning there is aplenty,
but clad in light raiment, one may sit or stroll in full enjoyment
of the garden one has made. Summer is the season to which we
look forward in all the different processes of cultivation; it is the
season of enjoyment; the season of hopes now ended in the reality
of sight; the season when we may feast our eyes on the beauty we
have created and in which we cheer ourselves with the delightful
feeling that our labors have not been in vain. Yes, summer in the
garden is a season of rich content.

June is the month of roses, favorites in every land where flowers
are grown. Pampered, petted, and exalted on high, there are
many races of the rose rich in form, color, and fragrance. Often a
special garden is set aside for these aristocrats, and all who garden
make some effort to grow roses. Not all of us can boast success
with the hybrid tea, fashion's present favorite that long labor has
produced. Exquisite she is and we love her, but where winters are
severe, her cost is greater than many of us can afford. Her more

robust half-sister, the hybrid perpetual, in late years has been thrust into the shadow, but she has merits of fragrance, color, and hardihood that are lasting, and sooner or later she will again meet with proper recognition. Dear to the hearts of all are the wonderful rambler roses of modern origin and worldwide favor. In white, pink, and shades of red and crimson these vigorous plants with myriad clustered flowers grace the gardens of all sorts and conditions of people. Whether on fence or pergola, on bank or over boulders, they reign in joyous beauty and gladden the heart. Folk of simple tastes may at little expense enjoy roses with single blossoms, white, pink, red, and yellow in rich abundance. First of such to bloom is Father Hugh's rose, with arching stems clothed with broad, yellow flowers; the large white flowers of the Altai rose, Queen of the *spinossissima* clan, follow soon. The common seashore rose of eastern North America (*Rosa virginiana*), upright of stem, from 3 to 4 feet tall and rich in pink blossoms of good size, is of more than summer value, for its scarlet fruits are delightful in autumn and its crimson stems splendid through the winter. For those who garden by the sea, *R. rugosa* and its hybrids have exceptional merit, for they laugh at salt spray, and after abundant blossoms in white, pink, and red, are gay with large tomato-like nodding fruits. Last of the summer roses is that of the prairies (*R. setigera*), with vigorous, arching stems bearing in profusion clusters of pink blooms when those of exotic favorites are past. The rose and summer are inseparable; few flowers are so deeply entwined about human affections and none will chide the rose for the position it has won.

The azalea family, rich of color and abundantly floriferous, ushers in the spring, and its members deck our gardens with beauty well into July. Some of the most fragrant sorts blossom late; the yellow *Azalea pontica*, the multicolored Ghent hybrids, *A. arborescens* with crimson pistil and stamens set within its white funnels, and latest of all, the pure white *A. viscosa*, which is excelled by none in delicious perfume. A bush, a clump, or a border of azaleas gives color, fragrance, and blossom in rich abundance. They intoxicate with their charm and should be denied no garden where lime is not present in the soil. Broad-leaved rhododendrons, with large and handsome leaves and splendid flowers in many shades of color, are the noblest of their clan. . . .

The mountain-laurel (*Kalmia latifolia*) comforts and consoles at all seasons of the year. This is the broad-leaf evergreen par excellence for northern gardens, where it is cheery and happy throughout the year. Native though it be, and, strangely, this is ever a disadvantage, it has won respect, and the exquisite compelling beauty of its blossoms can neither be disputed nor ignored. The flowering time is about the end of June or early in July and forms a last floral pageant of our eastern countryside. Every shoot on every plant terminates in a broad, rounded cluster of white or pink blossoms, each bloom a fluted chalice with stamens bent backward, tense and ready to spring forward and dust with pollen every honey-seeking bee. No flower on close inspection reveals more beauty of construction and none in mass or individually is more lovely. A clump of restful green for eleven months of the year, then an unmatched wealth of loveliness, a myriad of blossoms artfully fashioned burst into clouds of white and delicate pink.

Among that most useful group of shrubs we know as viburnums there are several kinds that blossom around midsummer. Such as *Viburnum canbyi*[1] and *V. dentatum* are broad, rounded bushes of good height with plenteous foliage and myriad heads of white flowers. Of all our native shrubs, these and the spicebush (*Clethra alnifolia*)[2] best typify summer luxuriance.

Most of our native trees have insignificant blossoms produced in early spring, but few there are with conspicuous blooms that

[1] *Viburnum canbyi* is now listed as *V. pubescens.*

[2] The common name spicebush is associated with *Benzoin aestivale*, whereas summersweet and sweet pepper bush are common names for *Clethra alnifolia.*

flower in summer. Among these may be instanced the yellow-wood (*Cladrastis lutea*), with pendent racemes of pure white, pea-shaped flowers which hang amidst its divided green leaves. Still more conspicuous is the Indian bean tree (*Catalpa speciosa*)[3] with large, heart-shaped, pointed leaves and erect trusses of large flowers. In shape like a foxglove, these lovely flowers are white, with lip spotted and streaked with yellow and purple, and emit a fragrance reminiscent of sweet peas.

In July the basswoods or lindens put forth their scented, honey-laden, pendent blossoms, cream-color or white and clustered at the ends of a long, hanging stalk which is supported by an oblong shield. The flowers draw the bees from near and far, and the trees are filled with the sound of bee-life in intense activity. At any time of the day it is good to stroll among these trees and feast on draughts of honeyed fragrance, but the early morning, before the dew is spent, is best.

If lindens are the last large group to blossom, there are individual trees and shrubs which produce their flowers in the summer season. The so-called varnish tree (*Koelreuteria paniculata*),[4] an Oriental with clear yellow blossoms, small, but produced many together in broad pyramids at the end of every shoot, is unique at this season in the color of its flowers and later in its bladderlike, top-shaped fruits filled with jet-black seeds, round and resembling buckshot. Another is the pagoda tree (*Sophora japonica*), which has in quantity, pealike, cream-colored flowers, also in clusters, at the ends of the shoots. By the waysides in rich plenty grows the fragrant pepper bush (*Clethra alnifolia*), in summer alight with erect spikes of the purest white. In July the last of the buckeyes, the shrubby *Aesculus parviflora*, holds aloft its white candles with out-thrust, brushlike masses of stamens, each of which is tipped with a rose-colored anther. August is the season of charming

[3] Northern catalpa is the present-day common name for *Catalpa speciosa*.
[4] *Koelreuteria paniculata* is often called the golden rain tree.

(ABOVE) White butterfly bush, a cultivar of *Buddleia davidi* of which Wilson introduced several forms. He preferred the common name summer lilac for this showy summer-flowering shrub, now valued not only for its extensive color range, but also for its distinctive fragrance. (P. E. GENEREUX)

(BELOW) Veitch cinquefoil (*Potentilla fruticosa veitchi*) in flower. A useful small shrub with creamy white blooms, which appear in early summer. (GEORGE TALOUMIS)

heather, with pink and white flowers densely clustered on every shoot. Nestlike in habit, of strong social instinct, heather strives to cover the land in a carpet of growth, loving the sunshine and wind, resenting the presence of other plants, and sulking bitterly when tall bushes invade its domain. Fruits, ripe and luscious, appear in summer on many a honeysuckle bush, the first of shrubs to ripen its berries which are borne in such profusion as to weigh down the arching branches.

Iris of a hundred forms add beauty to the garden from the earliest days of spring. At midsummer blossoms Kaempfer's splendid sort, the idol of Japan. Vigorous of habit, its broad-petaled flowers, pure white through pale and deep blues to royal purple and often variously veined and flushed with color, are reared aloft on yard-high stems. The petals, almost translucent, are delicate as silken tissue. Fond of moisture and rich food, this iris is a worthy product of centuries of care and skill and, like many other worthwhile flowers, is a gift from Japan to the gardens of the world.

For sheer luxuriant splendor, the peony is not excelled and small wonder that it counts its admirers in increasing millions. Easy of culture and yielding abundant returns, this is a flower for the multitude even as for the connoisseur. Pure white through all shades of pink to red and glowing crimson are its blossoms, either single in form or double and in some kinds as large as a child's head. A clump, a border, or a bed of peonies in flower is a gorgeous sight.

Narcissus and other bulbous plants in rich variety add largely to the pageant of spring, but lilies keep their charms for summer's love. "Torn by his father Jupiter from the flowing breast of Alcmena, his earthly mother, and borne through the heavens to the bosom of the goddess Juno, so that, son of a mortal woman, he may be nurtured by an Immortal and become himself a god, the boy Hercules, his mouth o'er full of milk, lets fall the drops which form

the Milky Way and star the earth with lilies." So runs the legend
of the origin of one of the fairest groups of flowers. But not all
lilies have white blossoms, for some are yellow, others orange,
some pink and many are glowing shades of red to scarlet. However, all are beautiful but none surpass the chaste madonna lily,
of which the legend speaks and which has been a favorite in
gardens from early times. It is one of the first to blossom, sending
up stately stems carrying a score and more glistening white cups.
In mid-June the regal lily (*Lilium regale*) flaunts its richly fragrant trumpets, each six inches long, a rich yellow within, rim and
lips glistening white and stained with rose-purple hues without.
Later white, purple and scarlet martagons, with spikes of flowers
shaped like a Turk's cap, are in season. So, too, is *L. auratum*, with
huge, heavily scented, bowl-like flowers banded with gold and
freckled with crimson. Other sorts keep up the procession until
L. speciosum, with white to crimson-pink blossoms, each with segments bent boldly back, rings down the curtain late in August.
Most of us who garden love the lily over much and do it harm un-
wittingly. Some sorts love woodland soils and the shelter of trees,
others love the sun, but all need good drainage and none a rich
soil. They are best massed in beds by themselves in association with
low-growing shrubs. Keep them away from the heavily manured
rose bed and herbaceous border if ye would keep lilies in health
and vigor.

Old-fashioned phlox, pink-eyed and of many hues, add fragrance
as well as beauty to the garden. Delphiniums in wondrous shades
of blue stand stalwart among summer flowers and each year claim
increasing hosts of admirers. To list a tithe of the plants that deck
the summer garden in a blaze of color and fill the air with fragrance would be but a dictionary of names. For vigorous perennials and annuals alike, it is the climax season of the year and
flowers of every kind riot on all sides. Long days with abundant
heat and moisture incite the maximum of growth in vegetation at

large. The kine are knee-deep in meadow grass and fragrance; on all sides exuberant health and luxuriance dominate garden and landscape. A rich content fills the garden-lover as he idles among the thousand-and-one pretty things he has caused to shed beauty around him. With less fortunate folk he delights to share his treasure trove of flowers. Within house and hospital ward the product of the garden sheds hope and cheerfulness, brightens lives, and through radiance of color and fragrance of blossom restores health. The bountitude of nature is both infinite and infectious; selfishness and miserliness cannot abide a garden. Contact with garden beauty sets free the better impulses of human nature and generosity and gentleness take free reign.

It is in the summer season that the garden-lover enjoys moments of supreme happiness, moments he would not barter for gold untold. How much the making of a garden, no matter how small, adds to the joy of living, only those who practice the art can know. And the advice to the less fortunate is to go and do likewise; learn for thyself how great a thing a garden is in rounding out and making life worthwhile. In a garden, beauty flourishes and its influence develops the best traits of human nature. To the Jews of old, man's history began in a garden, and many there are who think that in no better place could it end this side of Paradise.

8

Clematis: Blossoms
of Every Hue

CLEMATIS ARE cosmopolitan plants rich in virtues of surpassing merit.[1] A few of the members are little more than herbaceous perennials but the vast majority are plants which, climbing by means of twining leafstalks, grow from 6 to 60 feet tall. In general they are free-flowering, many sorts extraordinarily so. Some blossom in the spring, quite a number in the autumn, but by far the greatest number bloom continuously throughout the summer to early fall. No other group of climbing plants produces blossoms so

[1] Wilson's enthusiasm for plants, his firsthand knowledge of species and their origins, together with his eagerness to share what he knew so that they would be more widely grown and enjoyed, resulted in lengthy articles like this chapter. No writer in the popular vein, before his time, had written more knowledgeably. In the years following his death, the attention he had focused on clematis led to a widespread interest on the part of amateur gardeners. It, in turn, spurred nurserymen to propagate little-known species and hybrids. Wilson's own *C. montana rubens* remains a true aristocrat and so does *C. armandi* in the warmer sections of America where it can be grown successfully and in certain parts of Europe as well.

large and none boasts such a wide range of color. The flowers vary in size from about one inch (*Clematis paniculata*) to eight inches (*C. henryi*); in form they may be tubular (*C. davidiana*), starlike (*C. apiifolia*), platterlike (*C. jackmani*) or urn shape (*C. viorna*). The colors range from bright red (*C. texensis*), clear yellow (*C. tangutica*) and pure blue (*C. patens*), through varying shades of red and magenta to rich purple tones (*C. viticella*). In a great number the flowers are white, in some they are pure pink (*C. montana* var. *rubens*), and in others lilac to lavender (*C. lanuginosa*). What many species lack in size of blossom they make up for in quantity, whilst a pleasant fragrance is an attribute of the rank and file. Some are evergreen (*C. armandi* and *C. indivisa*) but the greatest number lose their leaves in the autumn. Certain species are handsome when past flowering on account of the large fluffy heads of silken fruit. The common name virgin's bower portrays their graceful habit of growth and wealth of wreathing blossoms. That of old-man's-beard denotes the characteristic appearance when in fruit, but that of traveler's joy symbolizes them best since it conjures up the pleasure they give in decking wayside bushes, tree trunks, boulders, and stone walls with a multitude of pretty flowers and fruits.

They are indeed joyous plants and as befitting such demand that their upper parts at least bask in the sun's full presence. In planting it is best to place them on the west or southwest side of wall or tree stump so that they may enjoy some protection in early spring, but, as they burst into growth they should not lack free air and sunlight. One other, and a very important point indeed, clematis are lime-loving plants. When this mineral is not naturally present in the soil it should be added. Some of the sorts grow well in ordinary garden soils but all are benefited by a dressing of lime.

Nurserymen should grow for sale clematis plants in pots since they are more easily and successfully transplanted this way. When once established leave clematis severely alone for they resent root interference. When pruning is done it should have relation to controlling the plants within the space available. In the spring-flowering sorts the necessary trimming should be done immediately after they have blossomed. The large-flowered kinds should wait until the plants commence to sprout into growth in the spring when all dead wood can be removed and straggling shoots shortened to a healthy vigorous bud. The rampant-growing, autumn-flowering species can be more severely dealt with in the spring as growth shows signs of commencing.

Clematis, like human beings, object to drafts about their feet and ankles. They are best accommodated against walls, tree trunks, or trellises attached to buildings; also, they make a glorious tangle over rocks or old tree stumps and, aided by twiggy branches, form hummocklike masses in borders. In nature clematis are mostly denizens of thickets and margins of woods; some court the shelter of boulders and cliffs, whilst a few luxuriate midst screes in high alpine meadows. They are gross feeders delighting in rich, well-drained loam and abundance of leafmold. To this farmyard manure should be added as a mulch against summer's drought and winter's cold. Bone meal is an excellent food for clematis since to them lime is so essential. They are propagated readily and simply from seeds, also by cuttings and by grafting on pieces of root, but these methods to be successful demand professional knowledge, skill, and equipment.

Apart from the ubiquitous *C. paniculata*, whose ubiquity is warranted by its floriferous qualities, its fragrance and graceful beauty, very few clematis are really grown in American gardens. The large-flowered hybrids have many admirers but seemingly they are not very successful with these gaudy blossomed aristocrats. In and around Montreal I have seen in greater quantity and perfection the glorious *jackmani* types than elsewhere in North America. Does the natural limestone soil of Montreal give the clue? Only in part, I think, since if it did these plants ought to be in equal evidence throughout western New York.

The large-flowered clematis are of mixed parentage and obscure origin. It is doubtful if some of the printed stories concerning them have foundation in fact. The original clematis of this class is supposed to be *C. hendersoni*, which is said to have been obtained about 1830 by crossing *C. viticella* and *C. integrifolia*. It is still a popular plant which grows from 6 to 8 feet tall and produces from July to September bluish purple flowers, each from 2 to 3 inches across and borne singly on 4-inch-long stalks. A slender not very woody plant, it dies almost to the ground level each year. In truth *C. hendersoni* is not far removed and is probably a form of *C. viticella* which is native of southern Europe and grown in gardens since the sixteenth century. This has bluish-to-rosy-purple flowers solitary on long stalks and each about one and one-half inches in diameter. There is a nearly white flowered form (*alba*) and an ugly double-flowered one also. But *C. viticella* and *C. hendersoni* best claim fame as part parents of *C. jackmani*. The other parent is said to be the oriental *C. lanuginosa*. The *jackmani* race of clematis, with flowers of varying shades of purple and each from 4 to 5 inches across, has been a prime favorite for more than half a century. Where happy they are vigorous growers delighting in sunshine and blossoming freely from July to October on the current season's shoots. The part-parent *C. lanuginosa* is native of China and from that land and also Japan we owe *C. patens* and *C. florida*, both with large flowers. Hybrids and seminal forms of these three species with flowers white, pale lilac, blue to deep violet-purple in color, and each from 4 to 8 inches in diameter, have been raised in gardens. Taken collectively the large-flowered clematis form a most gorgeous group with platterlike blossoms produced in rich abundance from midsummer to late September. Among the named sorts listed by our nurserymen are *henryi* with white, eight-inch-broad flowers, Duchess of Edinburgh with large,

The beautiful *Clematis montana wilsoni* (GEORGE TALOUMIS)

double, white blossoms, Ramona with light blue and Mme. Edouard André with dark crimson flowers. Altogether there are a score or more of these named varieties but many are difficult to obtain in this country.

A vigorous climber producing luxuriant fascicles of white flowers in spring is *C. montana*, widespread in China and on the Himalayas. It is scarcely hardy north of Rhode Island but south to Washington it ought to be widely grown. There is a summer-blooming sort (var. *wilsoni*) and another (var. *rubens*) with dark foliage. These two varieties I discovered and introduced from China some twenty-five years ago and experts acclaim them to be among the most notable additions to gardens in recent times. The type and its varieties are sturdy growing vines with trifoliolate leaves and blossoms in great plenty. The variety *rubens* is hardier than the typical *C. montana*, flowers regularly every season, and is readily increased by cuttings. Two closely related species are *C. chrysocoma* with white flushed with pink and *C. spooneri* with white blossoms. Both have soft silky leaves and are free-flowering. Already the French hybridists have been busy with these clematis, and the future will see a fine race of spring and early summer blossoming vines evolved from these orientals. Somewhat resembling these is *C. fargesi*, a hardy species with many foliolate leaves and ternate, clustered masses of two-inch-broad flowers produced freely about midsummer.

There is a prominent group of clematis represented by species in many parts of the Northern Hemisphere, which flowers in August and September. In this part of the world it is featured by *C. virginiana* and in western North America by *C. ligusticifolia*; in Europe *C. flammula* and *C. vitalba* represent this group whilst in the Orient there are *C. apiifolia*, *C. grata*, *C. gouriana*, and several others. In general appearance all are much alike with white or cream-colored, fragrant flowers and variously incised leaflets. The individual flowers are small but the wealth of blossom completely hides the foliage. Allowed to ramble freely, these vines drape and garland bush, tree, and trellis in billows of white and are conspicuous from afar. After the flowers are over, the feathery heads of fruit are singularly pleasing. The most hardy and satisfactory of these is *C. apiifolia* and in the Arnold Arboretum, where on walls and gate pillars it is freely used, it never fails to excite the admiration of September visitors. More beautiful than any of this particular group, however, is the favorite *C. paniculata* with pure white fragrant blossoms and dark green, almost lustrous, foliage. So well known is this charming vine that description is superfluous but of the thousands who love this plant few know that, like Thunberg's barberry, it is a gift of the Arnold Arboretum to American gardens. In 1877 seeds of this clematis were received from Russia by the Arnold Arboretum. They germinated freely and later plants were distributed. Nurserymen soon realized the value of this useful garden plant and it has been propagated and distributed by the million.

A closely related but not woody species of clematis is the European *C. recta* of which a superior form (*mandshurica*) is widespread in eastern Asia. Both may be regarded as herbaceous plants which, dying down each autumn, give rise in the spring to vigorous shoots that grow 4 to 5 feet tall, and form tangled, balloonlike masses of white blossoms in July and August. They are easily accommodated in the flower border and are very hardy.

There are half a dozen different species of clematis that have yellow flowers, all of them native of different parts of temperate Asia. In these the flowers are nodding, more or less urnlike and slightly spreading at the apex. The oldest known is *C. orientalis*, which is found from the Caucasus to central Asia and has been known in gardens since 1731. Much more beautiful, however, is *C. tangutica*, native of northwestern China and adjacent Turkestan and introduced into gardens as recently as 1898. This is a very hardy plant, quite happy around Montreal, growing some 10 to

12 feet tall with grayish-green foliage, raggedly cut and lobed, and rich yellow, top-shaped, long-pointed flowers borne singly on 6-inch-long stalks. The flowers arise from the leaf axils of the current season's shoots in June and July and are followed by large feathery heads of fruit of singular beauty. Topping a wall, clothing a trellis, or sprawling over boulders, this plant is exquisite. An equally good plant is the variety *obtusiuscula*, distinguished by having short pointed flowers, which came to our gardens from western China in 1910. A related species with smaller flowers freely produced in August and September is *C. serratifolia*, a native of Korea.

Common in bleak arid parts of Siberia and northern China is *C. glauca* with glaucous green leaves and yellow or bronzy-yellow flowers produced in axillary clusters. This is a variable plant of which several forms have received names. The best of all is var. *akebioides*, plentiful on the margins of subalpine thickets and on rocks and screes in western China. It produces in August bronzy-yellow, urn-shaped flowers in quantity and is a very worthy plant which I am pleased to have discovered and introduced to gardens in 1904. If planted at the base of boulders or low walls and allowed to ramble, it will form a fine drapery crowded with attractive blossoms at the off season. All these yellow-flowered clematis grow where snow abounds in winter and relish its protection.

Native of Texas is the lovely *C. texensis*, a slender vine with urn-shaped, almost closed, thick, fleshy flowers, carmine to scarlet in color. It is better known in gardens as *C. coccinea*, and there is no more brilliant bit of color among the entire clematis tribe than the bright scarlet flowers of the form *major* of this Texan species. This plant rarely exceeds 6 feet in height and produces its blossoms singly from the leaf axils. It has been crossed with *C. jackmani* and the hybrid named *C. pseudococcinea*. Here belong the new creations, Countess of York, Countess of Onslow, and Countess of Albany, much in vogue across the Atlantic. Similar in form of flower is *C. viorna* (leather flower) and *C. simsi* both natives of eastern North America. These have purple flowers and have been known to gardens for more than a century. The last-named lacks the feathery fruits so characteristic a feature of most clematis.

Another very distinct set of clematis is represented by *C. alpina* and a few cognate species, which are characterized by more or less bell-shaped flowers, usually violet-blue to rich violet-purple in color. The typical *C. alpina* is native of Europe and northern Asia; a variety (*sibirica*) has cream-colored flowers. In north China and Siberia grows *C. macropetala*, remarkable for the large size of its rich violet-colored flowers. In Colorado, Utah and New Mexico *C. pseudoalpina* represents the group. All are slender vines, rarely 6 feet tall, which ought to be more extensively grown in gardens. The structure of the flower is rather different from that of clematis proper and for this reason some would place them in another genus under the name of atragene. All are happiest among rocks in associationship with low shrubs over which they delight to ramble displaying their blossoms in late spring.

A partly shrubby, nonclimbing plant is *C. heracleifolia* with blue tubular flowers. This grows about a yard tall and has broad, rather coarse leaves. A much better garden plant is *C. davidiana* with large indigo-blue fragrant flowers, tubular in form with the upper half spreading. Another but less woody species is the Japanese *C. stans* with lavender-colored, smaller flowers. Bearing axillary and terminal flower clusters, these form an interesting and very hardy little group which can be accommodated in the flower border but are most effective under a wall or among rocks.

Since more than 230 different species of clematis are known, it is obvious that only a cursory survey of the genus is possible here. So far attention has been directed to the sorts which lose their leaves at the approach of winter. In conclusion a few words may be devoted to a couple of species representative of a considerable group that retains its leaves through the winter. In central China as spring bursts, the first vine with conspicuous blossoms to enliven thickets and margins of woods is *C. armandi.* This is a strong grower with stems often 30 feet long, clad with dark green, glossy, leathery, trifoliolate leaves from the axils of which arise clusters of white, pink, or white changing to pink, slightly fragrant blossoms, each from 2 to 2½ inches across. The individual clusters are three-flowered but many arise from the same leaf-axil and often a score or more blossoms are bunched together. I have seen ropes of stems bearing hundreds of axillary clusters numbering in all thousands of flowers and have marveled at the beauty presented. It was my good fortune to introduce this plant into gardens in 1900. Unfortunately it is not hardy in Massachusetts, but from Philadelphia south it ought to succeed and around San Francisco it should luxuriate. This and *C. montana* var. *rubens* I count among the finest climbing plants it has been my privilege to add to gardens.

The most beautiful vine that New Zealand has contributed to gardens is the evergeen *C. indivisa* which has shining, leathery, dark green, trifoliolate leaves and axillary panicled masses of milk-white, fragrant flowers. A strong grower, its stems will attain a length of 40 to 50 feet and in season produce myriad blossoms. It is a greenhouse plant for all but California and other warm parts of this country.

9

Wild Roses: Flowers
of the Wayside

EVERYBODY KNOWS and everybody loves the rose.[1] Usually when one speaks of roses the thoughts are of the modern rose—hybrid tea or hybrid perpetual, tea or pernetiana, rambler or rugosa hybrid—products of the untiring skill of enthusiasts in many lands. Some, indeed, the culminating effort of decades, others the fruit of yesterday. Beautiful in form and color, often rich in delightful fragrance, they rank as queens and kings in gardens. To bring them to perfection nothing is spared. Special soil, special care, and often special gardens are the portion of these favored flowers.

---

[1] In Wilson's day, hybrid tea roses were being developed with perhaps less attention to hardiness than has been the case in more recent decades. Double digging of soil and a somewhat rigid ritual were involved in their culture. With these thoughts in mind, his comments on the modern rose in this chapter and elsewhere in his writings fall into their proper niche in the long history of growing the queen of flowers. His emphasis on the beauty and usefulness of wild or species roses paved the way for their wider use in park and estate plantings, thereby enabling the public to become better acquainted with them.

Wonderful is the modern rose, yet its origin was humble and the position it has reached may be surpassed by others of which we know not. But my theme is not of the modern rose. Other scribes may sing its praises, I tell of the wayside roses of this and other lands.

Of wild roses there are a great many species and these vary so much that no two authorities are agreed as to the number. They are found throughout the length and breadth of the Northern Hemisphere from near the Arctic Circle to the Tropic of Cancer. Some are diminutive shrubs, others vigorous rambling plants which climb to the tops of trees. Nearly all have the familiar leaf, prickle, five-petaled flower, usually clustered, rarely solitary, and the characteristic hip or fruit. Their garden value depends largely upon their hardiness. Very few of the climbing sorts can withstand the rigors of New England climate, but of the bush forms a great number are perfectly at home with us. Indeed, some think that the garden rose of the future, so far as the colder parts of the world are concerned, will be evolved by blending these perfectly hardy wildings with the toughest sorts of the modern rose. But apart from interesting possibilities many kinds of wild roses are well worth a place in our gardens. In point of fact, their uses are much greater than is generally appreciated. All have beautiful flowers and many are extraordinarily floriferous. Some have fragrant blossoms and the color is usually pure and refined. They can be grown without any special effort though none object to good soil. Full exposure to sun and wind is essential. Pruning is not the elaborate business it is with the hybrid tea and others. All that is necessary is the cutting away of the old and worn out canes and the shortening back of overvigorous shoots so as to keep the plants within bounds.

Wild roses may be used against pillars, fences, walls, or on boulders to excellent effect. They should be given plenty of room and especially such sorts as the prairie rose (*R. setigera*), so well suited for grouping, and others like the Scotch rose (*R. spinosis-sima*) may be used in beds. For seashore gardens *R. rugosa* is one of the best of all plants. In Japan it is known as the sea-tomato—a very apt name, when its natural habitat and its fruit are remembered. In the Arnold Arboretum the common seashore rose of New England (*R. virginiana*) is much used for planting between the sidewalks and the carriage drives. Borders about 5 feet wide and 100 yards long are a feature and no plant could be more serviceable or effective. In June these strips are lit with thousands of soft rose-pink blossoms; in the autumn they are jeweled in countless numbers of scarlet hips, and throughout the winter and early spring the ruddy, erect stems are cheery to look upon. No protection of any sort is required and this most pleasing plant is attractive at all seasons of the year.

A wild rose of recent introduction that has captured the garden-lovers of America is *R. hugonis* from the mountains of central and western China. At the moment it is easily the most popular species in this country. The habit leaves nothing to be desired. The stems are ascending with the outer ones arching gracefully to form a rounded bush from 4 to 6 feet tall. It is among the earliest of roses to open its blossoms and so freely are these borne as to transform the branches into sprays of flowers hiding the leaves and the whole plant in a bouquet of soft yellow. The fruit is dark scarlet, ripens and, unfortunately, falls early. In China it flourishes on rocky semiarid mountain slopes and valleys reveling in good drainage, hot summers, and cold winters. Its history is interesting. It was discovered by a Welsh priest named Hugh Scallan attached to an Italian mission who sent a parcel of dried plants to the British Museum. When looking the material over, the authorities noticed some rose hips and sent them to Kew Gardens. In course of time these vegetated and later when the plants flowered the rose was named *R. hugonis* for its discoverer. In 1908 it was received at the Arnold Arboretum and soon afterward passed into American gardens. There is another yellow Chinese rose in cultivation named *R. xanthina* with both single and double flowers, but this does not appear to have taken so kindly to this country. At least I have never seen it doing justice to itself here as I have in the gardens of Korea.

From the remote and arid regions of Afghanistan and the tableland of central Asia came the charming *R. ecae*, a rose of rare beauty and perfect hardiness with pale yellow flowers and leaves with the fragrance of sweetbriar. This is a shrub from 5 to 6 feet tall with many erect, reddish stems and neat, shining foliage. As yet it is scarcely in the trade but when properly known all will want it.

A century ago scores of varieties of *R. spinosissima* were grown under the name of Scotch roses. Like others they have largely disappeared from gardens in favor of the modern rose. This is a pity for they are pleasing plants of supreme hardiness preeminently suitable for the colder parts of this country and Canada. As a class they are low, twiggy bushes from 2 to 5 feet tall, suckering freely and form masses of permanent character. They have white, pink, rose-red, and yellow flowers and there used to be sorts with double flowers of varied hues. All are of good habit with small, pleasing foliage and black fruits and the fact that they are native of the coldest parts of boreal Europe and Asia attests their value to northern gardens. The aristocrat of the species is the variety *altaica* from the Altai Mountains of Siberia. It is more vigorous and taller than its sisters, growing fully 6 feet tall with pure white flowers, each 2 inches across, abundantly produced. A well-known rose enthusiast living near Chicago has aptly named it the hardy Cherokee rose. Of hardy white roses it is my favorite and I know of none more worthy, either as a specimen bush, for massing, or for using as a hedge. No northern garden should be without it.

Wild roses are plentiful in northern lands but nowhere are they so abundant as in China, the land of flowers. Everywhere from sea level to mountain top in that land roses luxuriate, and in season the air is redolent with the fragrance of their myriad flowers. As I write memory recalls delightful mornings and evenings in May and early June when I roamed through an Eden of banksian, musk, and other roses and drank my fill of fragrance from festooned bush and tree. And many a tear of cloth and flesh have I suffered from their prickles when gathering specimens to press or seeds to send home. 'Tis good to have lived such memories but better still to have been the fortunate means wherewith others can share the joys by growing in their garden in the Occident some of the gems of far-off western China. Of wild roses it has been my privilege to add some twenty-five species to our gardens. Across the water the one acclaimed above all others is *R. moyesi* which I culled from the austere borderland of China and Tibet and named for a missionary who welcomed me with hospitality in 1903. The beauty of this rose is in the rich, lustrous red shade of its flowers and its brilliant scarlet hips. I prefer to be ambiguous in reference to the color since enthusiasts have quarreled vigorously over it and are still far from agreement. I am fully content that its worth and beauty have won their hearts. Vigorous, hardy, beautiful in foliage, flower, and fruit, this wilding has in critical field won the first-class certificate of the Royal Horticultural Society of London, than which there is no higher award. In the Arnold Arboretum this rose grows well, is perfectly hardy, and fruits in perfection, but the dry, hot air of early summer dims the rich lustre of its flowers.

In the garden of my friend Horace McFarland at Harrisburg, Pennsylvania, flourishes a particularly good form of *R. setipoda*, another of my finds in China and I do not envy any critic who speaks disparagingly of this rose when McFarland is within ear-shot. It is a strong grower with stems arching over and in season a cascade of rosy red flowers followed by brilliant scarlet fruit. A related species with rich red flowers is *R. bella*, a dense, compact shrub about 5 feet tall and as much in diameter and well worthy of its name.

Two pleasing species with gray-green foliage, pure pink blossoms, and orange-red fruits are *R. willmottiae* and *R. multibracteata*. In the former the flowers are usually solitary whereas in the latter they are normally clustered, otherwise they are much alike.

The original musk rose (*R. moschata*) appears to have been native of the Pyrenees but has long been lost to cultivation and its name applied to a vigorous climbing rose (*R. brunoni*) native of the Himalayas and China whose flowers also have the odor of musk. Of this type of rose there are half a dozen species native of China and now in cultivation. The hardiest of all is *R. helenae* named for my wife. This is a strong-growing plant that will make arching canes from 6 to 12 feet long and produces at the end of short shoots large rounded clusters of pure white, delightfully fragrant flowers to be followed by orange-to-red-colored fruits. The flowers, each about 1½ inches in diameter, have conspicuous yellow anthers and are singularly beautiful. This rose grows fairly well in the Arnold Arboretum but does much better on the limestone soil of Rochester, New York, where, in fact, it is not only hardy but flourishes as on its native heath. Closely related but less hardy are *R. rubus* with hairy leaves, *R. gentiliana* with larger flowers and lustrous green leaves, glaucous gray on the underside, and the robust *R. soulieana* with gray stems, gray-green luxuriant foliage and cream-colored flowers.

Widespread in the warmer parts of the United States is the Cherokee rose (*R. laevigata*), and few who bask in the purity of its whiteness realize that it is merely a naturalized plant brought no one knows how or when from China, its real home. Throughout the warmer parts of China there is no more common woody plant than this rose with its lustrous trifoliolate leaves, large flowers, and handsome hips. In eastern China grows the Macartney rose (*R.*

bracteata), which is also naturalized in the southern states. The parents of the tea, monthly and polyantha roses are also Chinese and the direct ancestors of the old seven-sisters and crimson rambler are common especially on the foreshores and banks of rivers. And lovely is this wilding, *R. multiflora* var. *cathayensis*, with its large trusses of pure pink flowers with golden-anthered stamens. Sprawling on the ground and over rocks, hugging other shrubs in warm embrace, or forming of itself a compact bush 5 to 6 feet tall, it is in blossom ever graceful and beautiful, more so in fact than many a named garden form derived from it in Western gardens. It is perfectly hardy in the Arnold Arboretum, where it flowers freely each summer.

The parents of our rambler and wichuraiana roses (*R. multiflora* and *R. wichuraiana*) are essentially Japanese, though they also grow in southern Korea and possibly in coastal parts of China. Like other species of wild roses, these plants are very variable in a natural state and in the hands of the hybridist have been most prolific in results. The polished shining leaves of *R. wichuraiana* and the large trusses of *R. multiflora* have blended well and with color from the blood of the descendants of var. *cathayensis*, hybrid perpetuals, and others have given in recent years a new class of roses without which modern gardens would be strangely incomplete.

One ought to tell of many other wild roses—of the common roses of Europe, the dog rose (*R. canina*), the sweetbriar (*R. eglanteria*), the Austrian briar (*R. foetida*), and many others—but finality is not attempted. My theme may well end with mention of a native species, the prairie rose (*R. setigera*), too much neglected in this country. We grow it in the Arnold Arboretum in a bed of irregular shape; the old canes and weak ones are cut out each year in the spring and the vigorous ones slightly shortened. In early July each year the plants are ablaze with clusters of rosy-pink blossoms. It flowers after other species are past blooming, which is an additional reason for its place in every garden. Some have called it garish but to me it is right worthy of its native land and one of the loveliest of wild roses.

10

Advent of the Lily Royal

How MANY PEOPLE know the size of a mule's hoof? Quite a number have felt the strength of a mule's leg and the sharpness of his teeth; his obstinacy is a proverb. But the size of his hoof is another matter. Frankly, I do not know with mathematical exactness but as I lay on the ground and more than forty of these animals stepped over my prostrate form the hoof seemed enormous, blotting out my view of the heavens. The instinctive surefootedness of the mule is well known and I realized it with my gratitude as these animals one by one passed over me and not one even frayed my clothing.

It happened in the no-man's-land of the Chino-Tibetan borderland and my predicament had been brought about by a rockslide, a common occurrence in that part of the world. I had left Boston, Massachusetts, at the end of March, 1910, and having crossed to Europe reached Peking by way of the Trans-Siberian Railway early in May. From Peking I traveled by devious routes across China to Sungpang Ting, in the extreme west-northwest, which was reached toward the end of August. My quest was the regal lily, which I had discovered some years earlier but had failed to successfully introduce into American gardens. Its beauty of blossom and richness of fragrance had won my heart and I was determined that it should grace the gardens of the Western world. That such a rare jewel should have its home in so remote and arid region of the world seemed like a joke on nature's part. However, there it was and my business in life was to effect its transference to lands where its beauty would find proper recognition.

Throughout an indefinite past, generations of the regal lily had lived unsung and unseen save by the rude peasants of a rude land. But few white men had passed that way when first I made discovery and none had noted my royal lady. This had been preserved for me. And what of the regal lily? Journey in thought with me for a moment or two, westward, until "west" becomes "east," although we still chase the setting sun. Across the broad American continent, across that wide ocean misnamed "Pacific" to Shanghai, gate of far Cathay; onward and westward up the mighty Yangtze River for 1,800 miles, then northward up its tributary the Min some 250 miles to the confines of mysterious Tibet; to that little-known hinterland which separates China proper from the hierarchy of Lhassa; to a wild and mountainous country peopled mainly by strange tribesfolks of unknown origin; to a land where Lamaism, Buddhism, and Phallism strive for mastery of men's souls; to a region where mighty empires meet. There in narrow, semiarid valleys, down which torrents thunder, and encompassed by mountains composed of mud shales and granites whose peaks are clothed with snow eternal, the regal lily has her home. In summer the heat is terrific, in winter the cold is intense, and at all seasons these valleys are subject to sudden and violent windstorms against which neither man nor beast can make headway. There in June, by the wayside, in rock crevice by the torrent's edge and high up on the mountainside and precipice this lily in full bloom greets the weary wayfarer. Not in twos and threes but in hundreds, in thousands, aye, in tens of thousands. Its slender stems, each from 2 to 4 feet tall, flexible and tense as steel, overtop the coarse grasses and scrub and are crowned with one to several large funnel-shaped flowers, each more or less wine-colored without, pure white and lustrous on the face, clear canary-yellow within the tube, and each stamen filament tipped with a golden anther. The air in the cool of the morning and in the evening is laden with delicious perfume exhaled from every blossom. For a brief season this lily transforms a lonely, semidesert region into a veritable fairyland.

Sungpang Ting is a military town situated on the headwaters of the Min River on the very edge of the grasslands of northeastern Tibet. It is a very important outpost of Chinese civilization and a trade entrepôt of considerable magnitude. Medicines in great variety, including the famous rhubarb and musk, are brought in by tribesfolk from the neighboring mountains and bartered to Chinese merchants. I knew the town well and on former occasions had rested within its walls and beneath the clear blue skies it enjoys had recuperated after arduous journeys. So, too, on this occasion. Rested and reprovisioned I and my followers sallied forth and for seven consecutive days plunged down the seemingly interminable gorge of the Min River. The mountains on either side are so high that the summits were usually hidden from view. Here and there, where some tributary stream flows in, a glimpse of snow eternal met our gaze. Habitations are few and far between, but wherever possible patches of the mountainside are under agriculture. It was frightfully hot and traveling was most fatiguing. In many places the narrow track is hewn and blasted from the solid rock and here and there tunneling has been necessary. In several places Chinese characters of huge size carved in the rocks warn those who can interpret them of the dangers of the road and urge all not to tarry in particular places. This road, difficult and narrow as it is, is the artery of ingress and egress to Sungpang Ting from and to the cities of wealthy Szechwan. There was in consequence much traffic, largely coolies, but several mule-trains taking up brick-tea and cotton cloth in particular, and various merchandise in general and bringing down medicines, hides, and deer horns. The road is narrow, sometimes it skirts the edge of the river's turbulent waters, but more usually ribbonlike it winds along from 50 to 300 feet above. The passing of mule trains is a difficult business, often possible only at particular places when one caravan comes to a standstill and allows the other to pass.

I traveled mostly on foot but had with me a light sedan chair made of rattan and my boy or principal servant was similarly favored. A sedan chair is an outward and visible sign of respectability without which no traveler is properly equipped. In those days it was of far more importance than a passport, for it inspired confidence and ensured the respect of the people. Whether one rode in it or walked was immaterial; the important thing was its presence.

On the seventh day we were down to 5,500 feet altitude and the following extract from my diary seems worth recording: "A bad road through barren, desolate country and abnormally long miles sums up the day's journey. Barring absolute desert no more barren and repelling country could be imagined than that traversed today. But it is really only the narrow valley and precipitous mountain-sides that are so desertlike. On the upper slopes trees and cultivation occur and small villages and farmhouses are frequent. In the valley houses are far between and what few there are are in ruinous condition. A fierce up-river wind blows regularly from about eleven o'clock in the morning and it is difficult to make headway against it. The leaves on the maize plants are torn to shreds by the wind's violence. The houses are of mud and flat-roofed, as protection against the winds. The regal lily occurs here and there in abundance on the well-nigh stark slate and mudstone cliffs."

The eighth day I camped and for several days was busy arrang-

Regal lilies as they grew for the man who discovered them

ing to secure in October, the proper season of the year, some six or seven thousand bulbs of the regal lily. Plans completed, we set out for Chengtu, the capital city of Szechwan. The hardship of a four months' journey were beginning to tell on me and dysentery in a mild form had troubled me for days. Yet it was with a light heart and a satisfied mind that I rode in my chair. Soon after starting we passed a mule-train breaking camp and bound our way. With the thoughts of the flesh pots of Chengtu only four days' distance, all were in a cheerful mood. We were making good progress, my chair leading, with personal attendants and the man carrying my large camera immediately behind; my black spaniel dog wagging his tail ahead of us all. The Chinese characters of warning carved in the rocks did not afright us, we had seen so many and passed all well. Song was in our hearts, when I noticed my dog suddenly cease wagging his tail, cringe, and rush forward, and a small piece of rock hit the path and rebounded into the river some 300 feet below us. I shouted an order and the bearers put down the chair. The two front bearers ran forward and I essayed to follow suit. Just as I cleared the chair handles a large boulder crashed into the body of the chair and down to the river it was hurled. I ran, instinctively ducked as something whisked over my head and my sun hat blew off. Again I ran; a few yards more and I would be under the lea of some hard rocks. Then feeling as if a hot wire passed through my leg, I was bowled over, tried to jump up, found my right leg was useless, so crawled forward to the shelter of the cliff, where the two scared chair-bearers were huddled.

It was only a small slide and our lives had had a providential escape. The man carrying my camera could not run back so fast as others and suffered a bad scalp wound. I was the biggest sufferer but, fortunately, was not knocked unconscious. If I had been, the men would probably have deserted from fright; as it was they behaved well. The pigskin puttee on my right leg was cut slantingly as with a knife and forced round my leg; the toe cap of my boot was torn off and with it the nail of my big toe; the right leg was broken in two places below the knee and the side of my calf was badly lacerated. Not a pleasant situation to find oneself in alone with Chinese and four days from the nearest medical assistance!

As soon as it was safe to do so the men came along, terrified and solicitous. My boy with his chair also came soon afterward but was quite ignorant of the whole affair. With the legs of my camera tripod I improvised splints, and while these were being bandaged to my leg the mule-caravan passed in the morning loomed into view. The road was too narrow for them to turn back and they dare not stand still until I could be moved forward, since we knew not when the rock slide would re-commence. There was only one thing to do. I lay across the road and the mules stepped over my body. Then it was that I realized the size of the mule's hoof. There were nearer fifty than forty of them and each stepped clearly over me as if accustomed to such obstacles. Nevertheless, I breathed freely when the last was over!

My own chair being smashed, I requisitioned the boy's, had a piece of wood laid crosswise, and lashed the leg in splints to the right pole. At considerable risk to themselves the men salvaged my wrecked chair and we started on our journey to Chengtu. We made it in three days, marching early and late, and three agonizing days they were for me. At Chengtu I was carried to the house of Dr. Davidson of the Friends' Presbyterian Mission and all that could be done was done. The leg had become infected. In spite of every care, at the end of six weeks there was no signs of the bones uniting. The question of amputation was pressed but somehow I never felt this would be necessary. Other doctors were called in, including a French army surgeon named Dr. Mouillac. Some cutting and slitting was done and the infection stayed. At the end of

three months I was out on crutches. Soon afterward I hired a boat
and started down the river toward Ichang, where steamers were
available for Shanghai and thence for America. At every place
on the river where there was medical missionaries I received attention. On crutches I crossed the Pacific Ocean and the American
continent to spend a couple of weeks in a hospital in Boston. Afterward, fitted with a special boot I was able to limp about with a cane,
and in just a year from the date of the accident walked freely
once again. Owing to the infection it was impossible to fit the leg
in a cast and so the bones just grew together. The leg is crooked,
fifteen-sixteenths of an inch short, but is strong and sound and has
since carried me many, many thousands of miles.

The accident notwithstanding, I got my regal lily and brought
the bulbs safely to Boston. The arrangements I had made with the
local peasantry to dig the bulbs were carried out under the super-
vision of my trained collectors. The bulbs were encased in clay,
packed in charcoal, shipped at silk rates, and reached Boston a
few days after myself. Planted in a garden in Roslindale, Massachusetts, they flowered freely in the June following and some even
ripened seeds. From this stock has sprung the millions now happily
acclimated in American gardens and other gardens across the
seas. Its beauty captured all hearts at sight. Mrs. Francis King,
the well-known enthusiast, wrote to me saying, "Nothing so fair
or so beautiful has ever before blossomed in my garden." A poem on
the regal lily was published in the *Boston Transcript*; Gouverneur
Morris wrote of it aptly as the "Incandescent Lily" in the *Saturday Evening Post*. Its merits have been lauded far and wide by
many scribes. It loves this country and the climate, and from the
Atlantic to the Pacific is grown wherever gardens are loved. Each
year it adds to the pleasure of millions of folk. The price I paid
has been stated. The regal lily was worth it and more.

Royal is this lily and regally it has taken its place and added

luster to gardens. Proud am I to have discovered, introduced, and
christened the regal lily. Did what?

>   "God forgive me! No, I didn't.
>
>   'Tis God's present to our gardens.
>
>   Anybody might have found it but—
>
>   His whisper came to me!"
>
>   (*With apologies to Kipling.*)

11

Autumn Beauty in the Garden

AUTUMN IS THE season royal of fruit and colored foliage and a season of great rejoicing. Of all the festivals, Christian or pagan, that of Harvest Home appeals most strongly to the gardener. It is told that Mother Eve was tempted and fell for the fruit of a tree which she did share with Adam. Her children through all ages have inherited the same weakness. Since I reached the age of understanding, I have ever been comforted by the thought that our Mother succumbed not to the charms of bird or beast, nor to the lure of gold or precious stones but to the fruit of a tree, to something beautiful, useful, healthful, and life-sustaining. The gardener knows all about thorns, thistles, and tares but his love for the fruits of the earth remains strong and unshakable. And what is more pleasant to look upon than an apple tree burdened with russet and ruddy fruit or a vine hung with bunches of luscious grapes? The tree and vine in one's own garden abundantly fruitful through one's own attentive care! No fruit so sweet, no vegetable so tender, no flower so fine in color or so fragrant as those from our own garden. Every mother owns the finest baby in all the world and every gardener grows the finest produce. Loving care assures this miracle.

A garden is marvelously productive. It yields not only flower for the soul's enjoyment and food for the body of man, but food for his feathered friends, also. And what if impudent fur and feather rob it unblushingly, there is always ample to spare. The gardener's unremitting care ensures this; indeed, he labors to this end.

The fruits of service to man are limited in number, but it should be remembered that every plant, large and small, produces fruits, though in general those on tree and bush and vine are most ornamental. If the flowers of autumn are, with few exceptions, those of herbs, it is the woody plants that produce succulent fruits of many colors. In spring and early summer, crab apples, hawthorns, barberries, viburnums, bush honeysuckles, cornels, and many others give a rich display of blossom. Behold them in the fall, their branches bowed down with weight of fruit—white, yellow, blue, orange, scarlet, and crimson. Herbs give a season of flowers, but many, very many, woody plants give one season of flowers and another of fruits. For a brief period, dahlia may reign as king, but the rose is always queen and frequently in autumn outdoes in blossom her high summer effort. Gladiolus, ablaze in shafts of color, strives with dahlia for garden chieftainship, but *Clematis paniculata* in myriad fragrant stars is content to hang a bridal veil on fence and wall, pergola and porch. I love the permanent, but would not ban ephemeral delights. In a well-considered garden every season has its own peculiar feasts of beauty, and autumn is perhaps richest of all. Spring may excel in variety of blossom, summer in lushness of growth; but autumn is supreme in wealth of fruit and brilliance of tinted foliage.

Autumn is indeed a season of great beauty in the garden. Foliage assumes its richest hues and pomp of color shines resplendent.

The leaves have labored since the break of spring and now their task is done. Ere they fall, a well-earned holiday is enjoyed and their mirth and gaiety finds expression in a brilliant galaxy of joyous color.

Autumn tints, even as the explosive development of spring, are peculiar to the north temperate regions, and we who dwell there are doubly blessed and favored of mankind. Did an intelligent native of equatorial regions or of the Southern Hemisphere visit these northern shores in October, he would think himself in an enchanted land. With the trees colored every hue and hung with brilliant fruits, he could not believe that this was but another part of the same old world, for neither torrid nor southern regions know such splendor.

In the garden that I love, pleasant walks abound, and its lure, strong at all seasons, is especially so in autumn. In valleys, on wooded knolls and open places, goldenrod, and aster, white, blue and purple, flaunt myriad blossoms ere the graceful fern turns russet and brown. I like to sit and muse on things amid these herbs or watch the squirrels and chipmunks busy harvesting nuts from hickory and walnut or acorns from the stately oaks. The trees and their idiosyncrasies are known, and before August is done, on red maple a few leaves here and a branch yonder assume a purple tone and tell of fall's approach. As September advances, the signs increase and mid-October sees the wondrous mantle of green replaced with rainbow colors as the Master Artist adds finishing touches to the scene. Later, when the leaves have fallen, there is pleasure in their rustle as the foot kicks them aside. I love the autumn colors, have enjoyed them in many northern lands, but the season is never long enough to drink in all the delights. And when deciduous trees are bare, the conifers become more friendly and one unconsciously lingers beneath their outspread branches.

I like to fill my woods with elfs and fairies, sprites and gnomes, and feel their presence as I sit or walk. To me they are friendly, busy little people sharing in my enjoyment and multiplying the pleasures of my rambles abroad. Soon for a period they will seek rest, but in the autumn they frolic gaily and sing gladsome songs to ears attuned to understanding. Yes, the garden that I love is richly peopled with pleasant folk—trees, shrubs, vines, herbs, birds, beasties, fairies and their ilk, and now and then I am privileged to listen to the wisdom that is theirs and bidden to heed to lessons taught. My garden, your garden, everybody's garden is a treasure trove of pleasant sights, pleasant smells, and pleasant memories. If we would understand, how much tree, shrub, and herb could teach us on how to live in harmony with all men! Joyous of heart, rich in the knowledge of work completed and well done, Goddess Flora anoints the autumn season of the year. So should it be with each of us in the autumn of our lives. If each can say that he has done his best, contentment is his, since more cannot be expected of man or woman.

12

Cotoneasters: Shrubs of Many Virtues

COTONEASTER IS AN Old World group of shrubs which recent plant hunting work in the Orient has greatly enriched. It is a genus in which I am particularly interested and take pardonable pride in the fact that of the thirty-eight species and varieties listed in *Standardized Plant Names* I am responsible for nineteen. Of the more complete list given in Rehder's *Manual of Cultivated Trees and Shrubs*, it has been my good fortune to have introduced into gardens thirty-four of the seventy-seven kinds enumerated.[1]

As a group, cotoneasters possess many virtues of outstanding merit. In point of fact they rank with the indispensables in garden making. And, moreover, their uses are not restricted to any one part of the country for among them are sorts for the northeastern states, for the middle states, for California and the warm south.

[1] During the past forty years, many of Wilson's introductions have been widely propagated. New kinds and improved forms have been added, so that these versatile shrubs are in wide use and greatly prized.

They are closely related to the hawthorns but have entire leaves and no thorns. The flowers are either white or pinkish and borne few or many together in clusters along the branches. Occasionally they are solitary. The plants are in blossom from May to the end of June; in the fall they are heavily burdened with red or black, rarely brown-purple, fruits, either globose, oval, or egg-shape, which in many sorts remain on the bushes with little loss of brilliancy far into the winter. Some of the deciduous species boast fine autumn coloring, while the evergreen kinds are always an attractive green.

Uniformity may in general characterize their flowers and fruit but cotoneasters are remarkably rich in diversity of form and habit of growth, in size, in the arrangement of their branches, and in the tracery of their branchlets. Some like *C. dammeri* are prostrate groundcovers, rooting as they trail over the soil; others like *C. frigida* are trees of moderate size. Some (*C. microphylla, C. adpressa,* and *C. horizontalis*) are especially well suited for the rockery or for planting on or against walls and stonework. A majority, however, are best as specimens on lawn and in border where they have room to display to advantage their graceful habit of growth, their beauty of blossom and fruit. For the cold parts of the country such as *C. lucida* and *C. acutifolia* are excellent for making hedges and in warmer parts, so too, is *C. simonsi.*

The hardiest sorts all lose their leaves in the autumn, but there are a large number of evergreen species much at home in California and other lands blessed with a mild climate. Two of the most popular shrubs in California are *Cotoneaster pannosa* and *C. francheti,* both native of southwestern China. The hardiest of the evergreen species is *C. salicifolia* closely followed by *C. glabrata* which flourish amazingly from Newport, Rhode Island, south to Georgia. All the cotoneasters are handsome in fruit but the red-fruited group is the most attractive. A limited number, of which *C. hupehensis, C. soongorica* and *C. turbinata* may be instanced, are as beautiful in flower as any spiraea. All in all these plants have many claims for places in every garden, large or small.

Related to the crab apples and hawthorns, the cotoneasters are likewise lovers of sun and wind and demand full exposure to the elements. A well-drained situation and a loamy soil are other essentials and if lime be present so much the better. A weak point about the family in general is they do not transplant readily from the open ground, especially the low-growing sorts. Nurserymen now appreciate this fact and are growing them in pots and this is the type of stock which should be sought. Pot-grown dwarf cotoneasters can be transplanted with assured success and at almost any season of the year. If they have been properly grown and transplanted in nurseries to develop a fibrous root system, the larger growing kinds are less particular.

Provided they be planted where they enjoy good air and root drainage, few shrubs give returns in beauty of form and fruit equal to cotoneasters. On poor soil they are quite at home though naturally they relish good food and respond accordingly. In well-drained situations exposed to the heavens and all the winds that blow, the plants are thrifty, keep free of aphis and scale insects, flower and fruit abundantly, and are a never-failing source of pleasure to the lover of shrubs.

Seeds afford a ready means of propagation although the bulk of the seeds may lie a full year in the ground before germinating. Cuttings of half-ripe wood taken in July and of hard wood in the winter will root freely. Formerly the reprehensible practice of grafting cotoneasters on hawthorn and mountain-ash stocks obtained among nurserymen. The results were disastrous to the purchaser and this indefensible method of propagation has met with the contumely it richly merited. Such work today should place a nurseryman beyond the pale.

In spite of the many uses to which cotoneasters are admirably adapted, their all-round good qualities and their suitability in a wide climatic field, they are little appreciated in these United States. However, it is only a question of time and these shrubs of many virtues will be among the most widely planted garden subjects. At the moment not more than half a dozen sorts are properly known among nurserymen and the amateur has had but little chance of getting acquainted with the group at large.

The oldest cultivated among the low-growing sorts is *C. microphylla* to which the applicable name of rockspray has been given. This is an evergreen species scarcely hardy around Boston, Massachusetts, which makes a broad, uneven hummock sometimes a yard high on the level ground but is best planted on top of stone walls or banks and allowed to trail curtainwise. It has small, glossy, dark green leaves, conspicuous axillary white flowers with pink anthers, and red berries in the fall. A variety with smaller leaves is appropriately named *thymifolia*, another is var. *glacialis*; both are first-class plants for the rockery. The most prostrate of all is *C. dammeri* or *C. humifusa* as it is commonly called. This is a trailing plant which roots as it creeps over the ground. It has more or less oval, bright green leaves, white flowers, and scarlet fruits. In central China, from whence I introduced it into gardens a quarter of a century ago, it covers areas of windswept mountain slopes and pheasants—golden, Reeves, and ringneck—are partial to its fruits. Unfortunately we have not been successful with it in the Arnold Arboretum, but a friend on Long Island rejoices in a magnificent carpet of this unique species. For clothing banks, especially those of a gravelly nature, this plant is usually valuable but it must not be allowed to suffer drought. In California and elsewhere, under the name of *C. wheeleri*, a low-growing evergreen, red-fruited cotoneaster is cultivated. The correct name for this is *C. prostrata*. A related trailing species from the Nilghiri Hills in southern India is *C. buxifolia*. The names of the Indian cotoneasters are much confused and the plants themselves are tender in New England.

Deservedly the most popular of red-fruited cotoneasters is the Chinese *C. horizontalis*, characterized by its flat sail-like or frondose branching habit. In climates rather milder than that of New England it is sub-evergreen but it is quite hardy although fully deciduous well north of Boston. In the open border it makes broad, hummocklike, irregular masses a yard high possessed of much character in habit. Planted against a wall—stone for preference— it can with little difficulty be trained to form a close screen. Placed on top of low walls, it grows into an irregular thicket of singular charm. The flowers are abundant, pinkish but not conspicuous; its fruits are about the size of a pea, bright red to scarlet, and brilliantly jewel the branches in the dullest days of winter and far into the spring. In addition of the type there is var. *perpusilla* with smaller leaves and var. *wilsoni* of more even, although loose, habit of growth. Topping a boulder in the rockery or planted in a crevice and allowed to spread itself at will, *C. horizontalis* and its forms rank among the most useful, pleasing, and decorative shrubs gardens possess.

Somewhat similar, but of close-tufted habit, with larger, thinner leaves and fewer fruits, is the pretty *C. adpressa*, also delightful as a rockery plant. Of taller habit and forming neat mounds a yard high with overlapping branches, which are studded with scarlet berries in the fall and winter, is the newer *C. apiculata*, also of Chinese origin. Taller plants best suited for planting in groups or as individual specimens in the open or among rocks are *C. divaricata* and *C. rotundifolia*, both intricately branched, red-fruited shrubs from 5 to 8 feet high and broad. The first-named is the hardiest and has bright red fruits in clusters, usually of three, produced in amazing profusion. In *C. rotundifolia* the fruits are larger, usually solitary and long retained on the branches, which are flattened and sail-like in appearance. All three have pinkish, inconspicuous flowers and are sub-evergreen in mild climates.

A handsome shrub with arching-spreading branches and clus-

Sungari rockspray (*Cotoneaster racemiflora soongorica*), Wilson's favorite among the tall-growing cotoneasters, is a big-scale shrub of uncommon aspect with grayish-green foliage. The small white flower clusters are followed by a profusion of pink berries in the fall. (P. E. GENEREUX)

Specimen plant of a low-growing cotoneaster in its natural form in the garden of Mr. and Mrs. Philip H. Lord, Marblehead Neck, Massachusetts. The plant, set out more than twenty years ago, was allowed to develop, with a minimum of pruning, to cover a large boulder. (GEORGE TALOUMIS)

The spreading cotoneaster (*Cotoneaster divaricata*) is noted for its pink flowers in May, its broad, spreading habit, and its showy red berries in autumn (P. E. GENEREUX)

tered scarlet fruit is *C. dielsiana,* or *C. applanata* as it is also
called. This will grow fully 10 feet tall and as much through with
branches arching to the ground. There is a variety (*major*) with
larger leaves and another (*elegans*) with coral-red fruits and sub-
evergreen foliage. Another good sort is *C. zabeli* which has slender
branches, dull green leaves, and bright red hanging fruits. This is
a broad shrub growing some 6 feet high and its foliage turns
bright yellow in the autumn. More pleasing than the type is var.
miniata with orange-scarlet berries.

The great decorative value of cotoneasters in general is in their
fruit, but there are several whose beauty of blossom rivals that
of the spiraeas. Three of the best of these are *C. soongorica, C.
hupehensis,* and *C. multiflora,* all of which have flattened clusters
of white, hawthornlike flowers borne freely all along the stems.
The first-named has rigid branches arranged to form a broad,
rounded bush from 6 to 10 feet high and more in diameter, gray-
green foliage, owing to the presence of a covering of hairs, and
large coral-pink fruits. If the gray-green leaves do not afford sufficient contrast to show off the flowers to advantage, ample
amends are made in September when the whole plant is necklaced
in coral-pink. The fruit is relatively large and so abundantly produced that the stems appear as ropes of beads. The fruit ripens
early and falls before the winter sets in, but throughout September
and October the bush is conspicuous from afar and of exquisite
loveliness. The other two (*C. hupehensis* and *C. multiflora*) have
dark green leaves and whiplike arching and spreading branches
which form fountainlike masses of white in early summer; in the
autumn they are strewn with brilliant crimson fruits. Both are
very hardy, free-growing shrubs from 8 to 10 feet high and from
10 to 15 feet through. Combining the qualities of abundant blossom and wealth of brilliant fruits, I count *C. soongorica* and *C.
hupehensis* two of the most valuable shrubs it has been my privilege to add to northern gardens. If any doubt their usefulness or

beauty, they have but to visit the Arnold Arboretum and see for themselves.

A graceful shrub with slender branches, pink blossoms, and red fruit is *C. rosea*, native of remote Afghanistan but quite hardy in Massachusetts. Fairly well known are *C. racemiflora*, *C. integerrima*, and *C. tomentosa*, vigorous-growing shrubs with rather large leaves and clustered red fruit. A newcomer from western China is *C. bullata* with its varieties *floribunda* and *macrophylla*. These are shrubs some 10 feet tall with ascending branches and relatively large ovate, pointed, deep green leaves much wrinkled above, and clustered berries that shine like beads of sealing wax.

The largest of all cotoneasters is the Himalayan *C. frigida* which is often a tree some 25 feet tall with a broad rounded crown. It has dull green, deciduous leaves, each from 3 to 5 inches long, more or less oval in shape, flat corymbs of white flowers, and rich red fruits. In the fall and early winter the branches are wreathed in broad clusters of colored berries and the whole tree presents a brilliant spectacle. Unfortunately it is tender, but for California and gardens from Washington, D.C., southward there is no more beautiful berried tree. Other good Himalayan species for warm temperate climates are *C. acuminata* with red fruits and *C. affinis* and *C. bacillaris* with purple-brown fruits, all large shrubs of good habit.

The black-fruited cotoneasters have less garden merit than their brethren with red fruit, but *C. moupinensis* and *C. foveolata* are worthy of a place on account of their orange-to-scarlet autumn-tinted foliage. These are hardy, vigorous shrubs growing from 10 to 12 feet tall and as much in diameter with abundant clusters of black fruits. Slender arching stems, lustrous leaves, and jet-black fruits characterize *C. nitida* and *C. tenuipes*, recent acquisitions from western China.

For the middle states and colder parts of the country in general, *C. melanocarpa*, *C. acutifolia*, and *C. lucida* with clustered black fruits are to be recommended. Also they have much merit as hedge plants being of shapely growth, stand clipping well and of iron constitution. For California and warm temperate regions, the long known *C. simonsi* is not only a good shrub but is admirable for hedges. It has red fruits and is sub-evergreen in mild climates. In New Zealand I often admired the well-kept hedges of this useful shrub. Until the advent of many attractive species from China, it was the most widely grown cotoneaster.

Since the present century dawned, western China has contributed to gardens a host of useful and beautiful shrubs, noteworthy among them being many evergreen, red-fruited cotoneasters. California in particular has cause to be thankful for this contribution. Two of the most prized shrubs grown in the gardens of that favored state today are *Cotoneaster pannosa* and *C. francheti*, natives of Yunnan. Both are free-growing, slender-stemmed shrubs, with arching branches, attaining a height of from 8 to 15 feet and more in diameter with abundance of blossom and fruit. Superior to either with large leathery leaves, dark green and lustrous above and clothed with a gray felt below, and broad clusters of bright red fruits is *C. harroviana*, also from Yunnan. From the same region of China came *C. amoena* with small leaves crowding stiff-spreading branches and rich-red, densely clustered berries. It is a shrub of from 5 to 8 feet high and more in breadth.

The hardiest of the evergreen tall-growing cotoneasters is *C. salicifolia* of which there are narrow (*floccosa*) and broad-leafed (*rugosa*) varieties. These are handsome shrubs with leaves lustrous above, felted with white hairs on the underside, and clusters of conspicuous white flowers which are followed by a wealth of small, bright red fruits. The many arching, ruddy-barked branches sweep the ground and form fountainlike masses of from 12 to 18 feet in height. From Newport, Rhode Island, south, these plants are perfectly hardy and of their class there are no more useful or desirable shrubs. Almost equally hardy is *C. glabrata* with oblong, lance-shaped leaves some 2 to 3 inches long, bright green and wrinkled above, smooth and pale below. It is a handsome vigorous shrub from 12 to 15 feet tall with flowers and fruit like those of *C. salicifolia*. Somewhat similar and equally beautiful is *C. rhytidophylla*, characterized by its strongly wrinkled leaves heavily felted on the under surface. One of the most floriferous of all is *C. turbinata*, a shrub of elegant habit growing 10 feet and more tall, blossoming in July and bearing in autumn clusters of pear-shaped red fruit. I fear that neither this nor the very desirable *C. serotina* and *C. glaucophylla* are in cultivation in this country, but they ought to be speedily added to Californian gardens.

There are other evergreen species, all of them worthy, but my list shall end with *C. henryana*, a tall-growing shrub with pendulous branchlets, large leaves, broad corymbs of white flowers followed by rich crimson fruits. It is of lax habit and rather sparingly branched, and it has the largest leaves of any evergreen cotoneaster. In autumn when its pendent branches are weighted with crimson berries it is seen to best advantage.

13

The Glory of the Autumn

WHEN THE BEAUTY of the aster displaces that of the goldenrod in September; when blue and purple transcend the yellow in field and border; the deep green mantle of foliage draping hill and dale, mountain and ravine, streamside and roadside, commences to show signs of portentous change. The pines, the hemlocks, and their kin look even darker as the contrast with their deciduous-leaved neighbors becomes stronger. In the swamps about the last week of August and at the first whiff of autumn in the air, the red maple begins to assume a purplish tint and. its example is soon followed by other kinds of trees. To all of us the season of the year becomes apparent, warning signs of stern winter's approach increase rapidly and soon the whole country puts on its gayest mantle of color. The peoples of the tropics, where monsoon rains are followed by burning heat and where the young unfolding leaves of many forest trees are brightly colored, never enjoy the wonderful feast of color displayed in the forests and countrysides of this and other northern continental areas. They have other things of which we may envy them but autumn tints are peculiarly our own. The brightly colored codiaeums of the tropics and our hot-houses (where they are erroneously called crotons), beautiful as they are, do not equal the red maple, sugar maple, sassafras, and tulip tree in the fall. No scene in nature is more delightful than the woods of eastern North America in the fullness of their autumn splendor.

It is a weakness of humans to crave most those things beyond their immediate reach, but the wise among us are content to enjoy those which fall within the sphere of everyday life. To revel in the splendid riot of autumn color no long journey has to be undertaken. It is at our very door. From the St. Lawrence Valley and the Canadian Lakes southward to the Allegheny Mountains, there is displayed each autumn a scene of entrancing beauty not surpassed the world over. Central Europe, Japan, China, and other parts of eastern Asia have their own season of autumn color and each area has its individuality, but, if they rival, they cannot surpass the forest scenes of eastern North America.

But wherefore and why all this gay autumnal apparel? Is it the handiwork of the charming fairies and wood nymphs of our childhood beliefs and nursery days? Surely some guiding hand, some beneficent agency, some lover of mankind must have prepared the scene as the final tableau of the seasons! The talent of the Master Artist is unveiled and the picture surpasses the dreams of those who live in less favored areas of the world.

Those skilled in the mysteries of organic chemistry and plant physiology tell us that autumn tints are due to chemical changes associated with the storing away of food material and the discharge of certain waste products. This explanation, though matter of fact and disturbing to our youthful belief in fairies and wood nymphs, opens up a field of inquiry which must tend to enlarge our viewpoint and increase our appreciation of nature's wonderful methods. We find that all is governed by laws which act and react in such manner as to ensure the end and object desired.

Now briefly the autumn metamorphosis is effected as follows:

At the approach of winter, leaves which cannot withstand frost cease their function as food factories; and the various food substances are conveyed from the leaf-blade into the woody branches or subterranean rootstock and there stored, chiefly in the form of starch, until the season of growth re-commences the following spring. The leaves from which everything useful has been transported form nothing more than a framework of cell chambers containing merely waste products, like crystals of calcium oxalate, which are thrown off with the leaves and help to enrich the soil. But while the process of food evacuation is going on other changes take place. In many plants a chemical substance known technically as anthocyanin is produced in the leaves, and often to such an extent as to become plainly visible on the exterior. It appears red in the presence of free acids in the cell sap, blue when no acids are present, and violet when the quantity of acids is small. In a great many leaves the bodies which contain the green coloring matter become changed to yellow granules while the evacuation of food substances is in process. Sometimes these granules are very few and anthocyanin is absent; then the leaf exhibits little outward change except the loss of its freshness before it falls. In others the yellow granules are abundantly developed and if anthocyanin is absent, or nearly so, the whole leaf assumes a clear yellow hue. If there is an abundance of yellow granules together with free acids and anthocyanin, the leaf assumes an orange color. Thus the leaf at the period of autumnal change, by the presence of these substances in a greater or lesser degree, loses its green hue and becomes brown or yellow, crimson or orange, purple or red. The play of color is greater according to the number of species and individuals associated together in a particular spot. But the greatest display of color is seen when the neighborhood is sprinkled with plants having evergreen foliage, when it often happens that a relatively small area of woodland and meadow appears decked in all the colors of the rainbow.

The most casual observer knows that all trees and shrubs do not assume tinted foliage in autumn. Some, like the alder, the locust (robinia), the elder, and most willows, exhibit little or no change save perhaps a number of yellow leaves scattered through the green before they fall. But this group is relatively small and only adds additional contrast to the landscape. Again, plants whose leaves are covered with silky or woolly hairs or with a felted mat of hairs never present any autumn coloring, and in those in which the green color disappears the change is to pale gray and white.

In a rather large group of trees, which includes the walnut, butternut, catalpa, elm, hickory, chestnut, horsechestnut, linden, buttontree, white birch, and others, the tints are a general mixture of rusty green and yellow and under favorable circumstances occasionally pure yellow. In the poplar, tulip tree, honey locust (gleditsia), mulberry, maidenhair tree (ginkgo), beech, and most of the birches, the leaves change to pure yellow of different shades. In none of the above-mentioned groups is purple or red of any shade developed.

In favorable years the American or white ash (*Fraxinus americana*) is unique in its tints, passing through all shades from a dark chocolate to violet, clear brown, and salmon, but it has no reds.

The peach, plum, pear, apple, quince, cherry, mountain-ash (sorbus), hawthorn, silver maple, wild roses, and brambles (rubus) have a predominance of green with a slight or considerable admixture of purple, red, and yellow, and individuals are frequently strikingly brilliant. In another group purple, crimson, and scarlet with only a slight admixture of yellow, if any, obtains. Here belong the tupelo, scarlet oak, white oak, poison ivy, Virginia creeper, sumach, viburnum, sourwood, cornel, blueberries, and many other plants. A final group, to which belong the red, sugar, striped, and mountain maples, smoke tree (cotinus), poison dogwood, sassa-fras, and the shadbush or snowy mespilus, has variegated tints comprising all shades of purple, crimson, scarlet, orange, and yellow on the same or different individuals of the same species. Often the leaves are tinted and sometimes figured like the wings of a butterfly.

Careful observers will note that the gradations of autumn tints in all cases are in order of those of sunrise, from darker to lighter hues, and never the reverse. The brown leaves which long persist on some trees (beech, chestnut, and certain oaks for example), though darker than the yellow or orange from which they often turn, are no exception since these leaves are dead and the brown is only assumed after vitality has vanished.

Some species are perfectly uniform in their colors; others, on the contrary, display a very wide range. For example, the maiden-hair tree, the tulip tree, and birch are invariably yellow; the Vir-ginia creeper, sumach, and white oak chiefly red while maples are of as many colors as if they were of different species. But each individual tree shows nearly the same tints every year, even as an apple tree bears fruit of the same color from year to year.

The red maple (*Acer rubrum*), so abundant in swamp and wood, roadside and on dry hilltop, is the crowning glory of a New England autumn. By the last week of August it commences to assume a purplish tint; sometimes a solitary branch is tinted, frequently the coloring process begins at the top of the tree and the purple crown of autumn is placed on the green brow of summer. Trees growing side by side are seldom alike, and in a group may be seen almost as many shades of color as there are trees. Some are entirely yellow, others scarlet, some crimson, purple, or orange, others variegated with several of these colors. Indeed, on different individuals in the red maple may be seen all the hues that are ever displayed in the autumn woods. The sugar maple (*Acer saccharum*), though more brilliant, has a narrower range of color

Paperbark maple (*Acer griceum*) in the garden of Mrs. R. V. C. Bodley, Newburyport, Massachusetts, obtained as a seedling from E. H. Wilson. Exfoliating bark is a feature of this small, roundheaded tree which is ideally suited to the small garden. (GEORGE TALOUMIS)

and is more uniform in its tints which range from yellow and orange to scarlet.

The common tupelo (*Nyssa sylvatica*) more invariably shows a mass of unmixed crimson than any other New England tree. The foliage first assumes shades of purple which change into crimson or scarlet before it falls.

The oaks, the noblest group of trees in eastern North America, assume their autumn tints very late and are not at their zenith until after the maples have passed. In the scarlet, red, and white oaks the tints are ruddy, varying from reddish purple and crimson to pale red; and when at their best, after the middle of October, these trees are the most beautiful of the forests or pastures. The black and swamp oaks develop imperfect shades of orange to leather-colored tints.

In the white oak, the beech, the chestnut, and the red oak when young, the leaves as they die become russet-brown and remain on the trees until the spring and give a sensation of warmth to the woods and landscape in the coldest days of winter. The period of retention varies greatly in different individuals; often the leaves are retained on the lower branches when the upper parts of the tree are bare.

In England, trees with few exceptions, such as the wild cherries and the beech, assume no autumn tints comparable with those of their North American relatives. Indeed, in England the most varied and brightly colored tints are found not on the native trees but on the brambles (rubus). Long ago European trees were planted in this section of America and some, like the elm, linden, and English oak, have grown to a large or moderately large size. In autumn such trees stand out very clearly with their mantle of green foliage when the native trees present are all tints or have shed their leaves. These colonists preserve their green hues until late into October when finally the leaves become mottled, yellowish or brownish, and fall.

Asiatic trees and shrubs cultivated here assume their wonted tints and so also do those of central Europe. The trees of Japan and China color with us rather later than the native trees and lengthen the season fully two weeks.

Whilst I have dealt primarily with trees as the principal objects of admiration in autumnal scenery, I must not omit mention of the shrubs which clothe the wayside and forest floor, or the climbers which drape both bushes and trees or form tangled thickets of themselves. It is true that there are more of these than there are of trees which do not change color materially but remain green until the fall of the leaves. But a great many do change very materially, and it is interesting to note that reds predominate in the shrubs and yellows in the trees. Reds and purples distinguish the cornels, sumachs, poison ivy, viburnums, Virginia creepers, fox grape and others, and yellow the spicebush. Indeed, there is so small a proportion of yellow in the shrubbery that it is hardly distinguishable in the general mass of scarlet, crimson, and purple which forms so marked a contrast with the unchanged greens of many associate shrubs. In miscellaneous mixed woods, on the contrary, yellow prevails among trees.

In Japan, where an intense love of nature is innate among all classes, there prevails a custom which might well be adopted here. The beauty spots in that land are many and are justly celebrated in poetry and song: august Fuji with its perfect cone and snowy mantle; the pineclad islets of Matsushima; the Inland Sea with its hundreds of islands clad with verdure to the water's edge; the Nikko region with its mountains and lakes, its waterfalls and woods; and hundreds of other places more or less famous, including many noted for their maples. In October, when the woods assume their autumn splendor, children from primary and secondary schools, high schools and colleges, with their teachers and professors, make excursions of three or four days' duration to noted places and revel in the feast of color. The railways issue cheap tickets and from all the large towns and cities children, youths, and maidens journey to the mountain woods. One autumn in the Nikko region I saw thousands of scholars—boys and girls varying from eight to twenty years of age (and a happy, orderly throng they were)—enjoying to the full the scenery, breathing in the freshest mountain air, and building up healthy minds and bodies. Their joyousness was wholesomely infectious and it was good to mingle with them. As I look back on the many pleasant experiences I enjoyed in that pretty land, none gives me greater pleasure than the memories of those throngs of happy scholars in the woods and woodland paths of Nikko, Chuzenji, and Yumoto.

Autumn tints is a subject that belongs more especially to the sphere of the artist than to that of the scientist. The poet can sing their song more easily than a writer of prose can describe their beauty, but on equal plane with all the common folk can enjoy the splendor of the autumn colors. Let us then at autumn time lay aside for a brief moment the cares of daily life, break away from engrossing tasks of every kind, and linger for a while among the trees and shrubs of the roadside and woodland, drink in cool draughts of fresh air, and revel in the galaxy of color that beneficent nature so lavishly displays on every side.

14

Winter Beauty in the Garden

NOT IN THE DARKEST and most dreary of winter days is the garden devoid of beauty. The leaves have fallen from bush and tree, but the plants stand boldly forth and display to full advantage their buds and barks. Indeed, it is in winter when naked that the particular characteristics of their habit and form are most clearly pronounced. A garden of herbs at its best has its charms restricted to three seasons of the year, but a garden of woody plants has no such limitations; its charms are perennial, varying in aspect throughout the four seasons. A fall of snow covers the ground and hides all herbs from view, but to the trees and shrubs it is merely a foil which heightens by contrast the beauty of their architecture.

Throughout the winter, berries red, white, and black jewel the bushes of barberry, cotoneaster, black alder, snowberry, and privet, as do shining scarlet fruits on the hawthorns. The gray winter landscapes can be cheered remarkably by the planting of certain thorns, notably the Washington thorn (*Crataegus cordata*) and Sargent thorn (*C. nitida*).[1] Both have shining, bright scarlet fruits, persistent until April with scarcely any perceptible loss of lustre. The Washington thorn is a small tree with more or less rounded crown made up of slender branches. The other is a flat-topped tree with rigid, wide-spreading branches. In habit these two thorns are complementary, and in beauty they are not surpassed in winter by any tree or shrub hardy in the colder parts of this country.

Throughout the winter the branchlets of the elms, silver and red maples are crowded with clustered flower buds. On the birch and corylus hang in thousands clusters of gray, male catkins, and the stems of the goldenbells, spicebush, leatherwood, Japanese witch-hazel are studded with flower buds. All are ready to burst into bloom at the first blush of spring. Occasionally, in a mild February, some of these incautiously open their flowers only to be nipped by heartless Jack Frost. Nor are flowers altogether lacking, for in normal winters a witch-hazel (*Hamamelis vernalis*), native of the gravelly riverbeds of Missouri and elsewhere, unfolds its yellow, starlike flowers, the petals spreading from a wine-colored chalice.

The winterbuds, with their close-packed scales which protect the tender, growing points, are also full of interest. In the beech, the winterbuds are long and pointed; in the common lilac, stout and rounded; in the horsechestnut, broad-ovoid, sticky, and glistening; whereas in the related buckeyes, though the shape is the same, the buds are dry and gray. And handsome, indeed, are the glistening, jet-black winterbuds of the curious Japanese *Euptelea polyandra*. In the yellow-wood and Asiatic cork tree the winterbuds are set within the circular scar of the fallen leaf, in others they are seated within a crescent-shaped scar. In the walnut there are two or three buds set one above another and covered with

[1] Sargent thorn, *Crataegus nitida*, is now called glossy hawthorn.

Korean stewartia (*Stewartia koreana*), noted for its extraordinary flaking bark, is particularly distinctive in the winter landscape. This specimen, photographed in the garden of Mrs. R. V. C. Bodley, Newburyport, Massachusetts, was obtained from E. H. Wilson at the Arnold Arboretum. (GEORGE TALOUMIS)

Detail of the trunk of the paperbark maple (GEORGE TALOUMIS)

scales; in the curious pterocarya[2] the several buds are similarly arranged but, strange to say, they are naked and quite without the usual covering of scales.

The barks of trees are possessed of much character and rare beauty and are deserving of greater notice than is generally accorded them. Take the smooth, pure white bark of the common birch; the gray-brown papery bark, torn and bunched, of the river birch; the smooth, firm, pale gray bark of the American beech; the dark, deeply fissured, rugged bark of the American white elm, black Walnut, or red oak; the gray, fissured, corky bark of the Asiatic cork tree; the thick-flaking bark of the shagbark hickory; or the black bark, fissured into tiny squares, of the American persimmon. Are these not worthy of favorable recognition and comment? Sure they cannot be passed by. Neither can the striped-back maples with smooth, green bark, plenteously marked with lines of white, nor *Acer griseum*, from the mountains of central China, with loose, shaggy cinnamon-brown bark. Among the humble brambles there is much beauty in flower, fruit, and autumn foliage, and in several the winter stems are attractive. Most strikingly so are the pure white stems of *Rubus biflorus* var. *quinqueflorus* and other species which it was my good fortune to introduce into gardens from the back-blocks of China. Then there are certain cornels[3] of shrubby habit, whose barks are crimson or yellow of startling brilliancy, which illumine the winter landscapes, as do the red stems of the common seashore rose of New England (*Rosa virginiana*).

The cornels are a diversified group of much garden merit deserving of a special chapter. At the moment it is those with richly colored stems that demand our attention. The best of them are *Cornus alba* and *C. stolonifera*. The first-named is a wide-spreading shrub producing a thicket of erect-to-prostrate stems which in the

[2] Pterocarya is known as the Caucasian wing nut.
[3] Cornel is another common name for dogwood.

late winter are rich red in color. The other species is called the red osier cornel and is likewise a vigorous shrub which suckers freely and spreads from underground stems. The bark is dark purplish red. In marked contrast is the variety *flaviramea* with pale yellow stems. These are rampant growers, apt to smother anything less vigorous than themselves growing near. They are, therefore, best adapted for forming an isolated mass on a lawn and on the bank of a pond where their colored stems are remarkably effective all through the winter.

A winter landscape of which I never tire has for its dominant note a large clump of American beech near some arborvitae and a hundred yards or so above a hemlock grove. The parent beech tree is dead, but from its far-spreading roots scores of saplings have sprung up and formed a thicket. Right and left are conifers and beyond in the distance a steep slope where grow oaks, on the skyline of which are three old white pine trees. In this setting the clump of beech with its pale gray bark and myriad of slender, spreading branches suggests from a distance a billowy cloud of morning mists.

The grandeur of the conifers, impressive at all seasons, is especially so in winter, with dark masses of foliage and trunk standing sentinel-like above the carpet of snow. The pines, the firs, and the hemlocks take on a deep rich hue in winter, the green is darker, the gray color brighter and the contrast greater. The wind as it blows through the branches may sing a glee or a dirge, but it is warmer in the shelter of these restful evergreen trees. Viewed from near or far, conifers in winter present one of the finest of pictures: black, green, or gray pyramids and columns reared against the sky above the snow-covered ground, a scene at once restful, inspiring, and grand. A protective, yellow-brown pigment marks the green of the arborvitae during the winter, detracting from their beauty, but not so the purple pigment developed in the lovely *Juniperus horizontalis*, finest of all the low-growing savins.

Of broadleaf evergreen trees none can be grown in New England and the shrubs of this class are very limited in number. The native holly (*Ilex opaca*) survives in a sheltered spot; the inkberry (*I. glabra*) is cheerful enough through all but the most exceptionally severe winters. The andromeda (*Pieris floribunda*), with flower clusters standing above its green leaves all ready to open in the spring, laughs at New England winters. The evergreen rhododendrons hang down their leaves and curl them laterally as if distressingly anxious to protect their vitality to the utmost. In marked contrast is the mountain laurel (*Kalmia latifolia*), holding its leaves outspread as in summertime and glorying in the fact that it is New England's best and worthiest broadleaf evergreen.

15

Trees and the Heart
of Man

"No greater beauty can adorn
The hamlet, than a grove of ancient trees."

TREES HAVE ENTWINED the heart of man since he became a sentient being. They hold a prominent place in the legends and sacred writings of all ages and of all people, particularly in those of the old Hebrew race. In the Bible we are told that in the first garden God planted the "Tree of Knowledge of Good and Evil," and in the Old Norse sagas the oak and ash are frequently mentioned. Priest and poet in every land have sung their praises and down the ages a mighty literature on tree lore has been accumulated. From early times trees have afforded man shelter, food, and clothing, and have exercised a tremendous influence over his daily life. The more simple the people the greater their appreciation, at least so it would seem since as nations became civilized they one and all by fire and axe have destroyed the friendly trees, and of these vandals the white man ranks head and shoulders above all others. From the early stages of his colonizing days down to within a few years of the present, wherever he has gone he has laid waste the tree wealth of the lands in an effort, often vain, to make a blade of corn grow where two trees grew before. A halt has been called to this ruthless waste, and we are at least beginning to appreciate the danger done and cast about for means to amend the damage. Tree planting is now the vogue and ere long, maybe, tree worship will yet again hold man enthralled. All tree lovers could wish that this lofty conception of nature's grandest work could be widely inculcated. There is nothing statelier than a tree and no handiwork of man is one tithe so wonderful. In loftiness of stature, massiveness of trunk, architecture of branch and bark, shapeliness of crown and bud, and in beauty of foliage, no living thing is comparable with a tree.

These United States are singularly blessed in their tree birthright. No other northern land is so richly dowered and no other land boasts such variety of useful and ornamental trees as does this country. From coast to coast and from border to the gulf except in the prairie states, a rich assortment of trees are found. In all more than six hundred different species are recognized and these include the tallest and largest members of the tree world. The mammoth tree[1] of California is mightiest of all living trees. Specimens more than 300 feet tall with trunks 100 feet in girth, clean, and without a branch for half their height, and clothed with bark often 2 feet thick, are numerous on the California Sierras. In the redwood of California we have the tallest of living trees, although Australia with her lofty eucalyptus stiffly challenges us. Redwoods measured at more than 350 feet in height are known; others have been reported as much as 400 feet. These giants with trunks 75 feet in girth, buttressed at the base, form natural groves scattered from the southern border of Oregon south to Monterey County in California. Not only is the redwood the tallest of trees but it furnishes the most valuable timber of all the forests of the Pacific side of this great continent.

[1] Also known as the giant sequoia, *Sequoiadendron giganteum*.

In the fertile bottomlands of the Mississippi Valley and of southern Illinois and Indiana grow pecan and black walnut trees up to a height exceeding 150 feet with trunks 15 or 18 feet in girth. In the alluvial valleys of the Ohio River system and on the high mountains of North Carolina and Tennessee the tulip tree exceeds in height 150 feet with its clean, bold trunk 18 feet in girth. In the south Atlantic and gulf states the bald cypress covers vast areas of the river swamps, attaining as much as 150 feet in height and 30 feet in girth of trunk.

New England, too, has its magnificent trees and none more so than the American white elm, the most familiar wayside tree and commonly planted in front of old homesteads. In rich meadowlands individual trees 120 feet tall with trunks 25 feet in girth, often nobly buttressed at the base, are not infrequent. Oaks, dear to all white men, and among the most familiar of trees, are richer in species in this land than elsewhere in temperate regions, no fewer than one hundred and forty-five kinds being known. The tallest of all is the burr oak, which, in the lowlands of southern Indiana and Illinois, often towers 160 feet above the ground, its noble, broad-spreading head being supported on a trunk 20 feet in girth and unbranched for 70 to 80 feet. In the southeastern states the live oak is famous. A low tree, seldom more than 50 feet high with a comparatively small trunk, not more than 10 or 12 feet in girth but arising from a swollen and buttressed base, it supports a dense, wide-spread, round-topped crown often 150 feet through. In California the valley oak is the noblest representative of its tribe. Trees often 100 feet high with a short trunk 20 feet in girth give off massive, wide-spreading limbs, draped with graceful hanging branches that sweep the ground, the whole forming an umbrageous mass sometimes 20 feet in diameter. No land has a monopoly of tree growth, but these United States in their share are indeed well blessed.

In all countries where trees grow, the noblest specimens ought to be preserved as national monuments since, when all is said and done, no nation can boast anything more magnificent than the forest giants nature gave it. In the preservation of the redwood and mammoth trees of California a beginning has been made, but it should be extended to include specimens of extreme size of no matter what species. These are more priceless than the arts of man and belong not to any person or group of persons but to the country at large; indeed, those who govern lands in which noble products of nature's skill grow lustily ought to consider themselves as trustees of world treasures. Some day a country will awaken to the fact that its magnificent trees are truly national monuments. May this come while there are yet old giants to protect! Why should not the conscience of this great country lead in organizing a tree protective society and ensure the preservation not only of the giant redwood and mammoth trees but the finest specimens of oak and ash, elm and maple, tulip and sweetgum, cypress and cedar, pine and fir, and, indeed, all other varieties of the rich and varied tree growth that North America boasts? It could be easily done in association with a newly awakened conscience in forestry matters. Forestry officers could report the subjects and then a simple law preserving them whether on public or private property would do the rest. No other land in this broad world boasts trees of greater bulk and height, of greater beauty, or greater usefulness, or in so great variety, as these United States, and well would it be if as an example to the world at large we assumed the van in tree protection and preservation.

There is something friendly in a tree, friendly to man, to bird and to beast. From heat and cold alike it spreads a shielding crown of branch and leaf. To note at the approach of spring the melting snow around the base of a tree bole is to realize its warmth, and one has but to step beneath its shadow at midsummer to appreciate its cooling shade. Man everywhere is fully alive to the value of trees and their products in the arts and crafts of human affairs. Would that a tithe of this appreciation could be aroused for the tree's aesthetic charm.

Trees possess both character and personality as anyone may appreciate by contrasting, say, an oak with a birch. Each country and each nation has its favored trees but to the English no tree is so dear, so sacred as the oak. Was it not beneath an ancient oak that the Magna Charta of the English-speaking people was signed at Runnymede? I like to marshal my tree acquaintances into groups and types and to compare them with similar members of the human family. To me the English oak (*Quercus robur*) and the American white oak (*Q. alba*) typify in one instance the squire of old England, and in the other a prosperous plantation owner of this country in days past. As tree-lovers know, these oaks thrive best in rich deep bottomlands and meadows where the soil is mellow and fat and where drought is never known and where good drainage always obtains. Under such conditions their short, massive trunks give forth numerous stout, wide-spreading branches, forming a broad flat-topped, umbrageous crown. Under the shadow of one of these trees a herd of cattle or a flock of sheep can find shelter, and in the branches a thousand birds can rest and gladden the ear with song. They may look smug and self-satisfied but such trees possess a tower of strength and unmoved have withstood storms of centuries. There is an air of prosperity about them, of good living, of contentment, exercising a soothing influence on the spectator. They may be greedy inasmuch as they will suffer no other tree to grow within their shadow; they may insist on enjoying to the full the good things of life but in return they show stability and give an air of prosperity to meadow or pastureland in which they flourish. And so, too, the squire, the country gentleman, the plantation owner, or prosperous farmer, exhibit all the characters enumerated, but who shall say when all is done that for centuries past they have not been the backbone of the country?

Much has been written decrying the old English squire but he has served his country well and so, too, has the lordly oak, whose descendants are today pensioners in many an English park and meadow. The American white oak is worthy of similar recognition.

If the white oak be lord of the pasture, the American elm is lady, and like her human analogue she is at times of masculine proportion and appearance. In rich soils magnificent specimens shaped like a wine glass, clean of bole or sometimes with feathered trunks and pendent branches, grace the countryside. These trees possess all the charm of femininity, and of wayside trees none is more lovely, but not uncommon are types with massive, wide-spreading branches distinctively oaklike in appearance and quite as masculine in character as any white oak. Here in trees, as in the human family, we find types which would usurp their proper sphere and adopt the role of the opposite sex. In the elm, at any rate, this is assumed at the expense of the charm of litheness and graceful beauty which all so much admire in the feminine.

The coconut, with slender trunk and long, plumelike leaves fanning the breeze, is queen of the tropic strand. She rules in equatorial regions. The mud larks of the tropics are nipa palms and mangroves which people the muddy flats and estuaries of rivers, living in black, filthy ooze where malaria and other fevers are rampant. Their counterparts in the north are certain alders and willows which flourish in and about streams and lake shores. We have no envy or even admiration for such that prefer to live in regions so unhealthy and uninviting. A true amphibian is the swamp cypress (*Taxodium distichum*) which like a marine is equally at home on land or on water. In the swamps of Louisiana and everglades of Florida, this striking tree rules. Its trunk, fluted at the base, is a curious sight, especially when seen reflected in the water. Round about it are clustered gnarled, kneelike growths as to the function of which scientists dispute. This tree has a narrow crown clad with pure green, feathery foliage which turns brown in the fall and its branches are usually hung with gray locks of Spanish moss (*Tillandsia usneoides*).

The Monterey cypress and other coastwise trees may be dubbed coast guards, defenders of their rockbound homes. Wind is their great enemy and the feud between them is eternal. From youth to old age the struggle persists, and marvelous is the fight the trees of the shore put up against their unrelenting, death-dealing enemy, wind. The struggle may go on through centuries yet sooner or later victory is with the wind, but nothing in the tree world commands admiration more than the magnificent fight an old pine or cypress puts up.

Forests, especially the coniferous forests of the Northern Hemisphere, boast a sheltered people, gregarious in habit like the denizens of towns and cities, a people fond of the soft things of life, happy enough when everything is going well but unable to bear adversity with impunity. Let wind or storm, axe or fire, isolate trees of the forests and they are doomed; they are as unable to adapt themselves to changing conditions as are the factory or shophands of our cities. So long as their normal life is not interfered with all is well, but if brought face to face with changed conditions and adversities they have no reserve of adaptability and fall by the wayside. I have often noticed a pine tree left on the edge of a clearing or a lake looking forlorn and miserable—a wraith shrieking for lost companions. In the picture of lake and lone pine tree one can almost hear the cries this wind-tossed survivor gives forth in loud appeal for the companionship of lost neighbors.

In deserts and arid regions no trees grow save in the vicinity of wells, as for example, the date palm in the Sahara, but in certain dry regions where rain falls at infrequent intervals trees highly specialized to withstand drought find a home. These like the camel, "ship of the desert," are especially equipped to store and retain water over long periods. Most remarkable of these are the bottle trees (*Brachychiton rupestris*) of Australia, whose flashlike trunks are reservoirs of water which in times of emergency have saved many a traveler's life.

Australia is, indeed, remarkably rich in trees and in her eucalyptus boasts the loftiest types known outside the realm of conifers. The species are very numerous—hundreds of them all told—but queen of all is the karri (*Eucalyptus diversicolor*). This is one of the tallest of the eucalyptus and the polished white and gray trunks stand like marble columns in nature's cathedral. Never shall I forget two glorious days in the wondrous karri forests of western Australia.

In the sequoias western North America is blessed with the giants of the tree world which outstrip in size all other trees. Imagine trees nearly 400 feet high with trunks 100 feet in girth, the stupendous results of growth cell upon cell for two thousand years and more, the crowns, spare of branches, often broken by storms, yet resisting all adverse forces through century upon century—the oldest living thing.

The people of the Orient have a profound veneration for old trees and tree planting has been practiced from time immemorial. The most wonderful deciduous-leaved trees planted by man that I have seen are the Oriental planes (*Platanus orientalis*) in the grounds of the old Mogul palace and temples at Srinagar, Kashmir. Avenues and groves of giants 100 feet high with trunks 20 feet in girth and wide-spreading crowns canopied in broad leaves afford most welcome shade to man and beast. Those who planted these trees knew how and did not stint them room to develop their full characters and they stand today majestic monuments to departed greatness.

In temple and palace grounds and sheltering shrines in southern India I saw a tree which in beauty of architecture ranks without a peer. It is a fig tree named *Ficus benjamina*, a close relative of the famed banyan tree. Benjamin's fig is evergreen with small, lustrous, dark green foliage, a monstrous trunk, short and fluted with a vast number of large ascending stems which give off myriad pendent branchlets that hang down to the ground. The crown is very shapely in form, being more or less rounded and so wide that it covers half an acre of ground. In the Lalbagh at Bangalore there is a tree that could easily shelter a company of soldiers.

In the tropic regions of Africa luxuriates the gigantic baobab, about which old travelers told many fabulous stories. At Mombasa it grows in quantity and in the dry season, when the branches are naked of leaves, there is no more ugly tree in all the world. The height is not great, seldom more than 80 feet, and the crown is of moderate size only, of no particular shape and made up of gnarled branches and stubby branchlets, suggesting a gigantic crow's nest. It is the bulky trunk that is so imposing, being often 100 feet in girth and clothed with a smooth bark. Thick as is the trunk a bullet from a rifle of high velocity will pass right through it, for its tissues are soft and pulpy. The foliage is handsome and so, too, are the large, white, saucer-shaped flowers. The fruit is extraordinary, being as large as an ostrich's egg, pointed at both ends, and clothed with short, yellowish-brown hairs, and hanging from a long stalk. Inside the fruit is a white powder which tastes like cream-of-tartar. On an island immediately above the Victoria Falls of the Zambesi River, the missionary explorer, David Livingstone, carved his name on a baobab tree when he discovered this eighth wonder of the world.

The horsechestnut of village blacksmith fame with its myriad white candles upthrust is a rather ostentatious member of the tree world. The beech is the Adonis of the forest, while the silver birch is Venus of the woodlands. The beech, like Adonis in Shakespeare's comedy, holds aloof, preferring his own company to that of Venus. She, too, strange to say, prefers the role of nurse and protector of the dark-hued pine, spruce, and fir to the companionship of the more vigorous, broad-limbed deciduous denizens of her own kin. Were squirrel and chipmunk consulted, they would vote the walnut, hickory, and chestnut kings of the countryside. Indeed, their grief at the sickness which has overtaken the chestnut cannot be assuaged although they find no reason for discontinuing their work as the greatest planters of nut trees in the northern world. Beavers acclaim the aspen most useful of trees since with it they construct their homes. The gorgeous blossomed flamboyant (*Poinciana regia*) of the tropics is, indeed, a living Prometheus still grasping in his hands and holding aloft the fire of Jove. Resplendent in autumn dress, the red and sugar maples may be termed the huntsmen of the tree world, their brilliant autumnal tints outrivaling the colored jackets of those who follow fox and hound. Grief or love forlorn is well portrayed by the weeping willow, while no cleric is more upright in character than the Lombardy poplar, and white birch and trembling aspen are the nursemaids of our northern forest trees.

This analogy of trees and the human family could be carried to extreme lengths with wholesome lessons to mankind. Indeed in the tree world may be found just as diverse groups, types, and characters as in the human family—the strong, the self-willed, the reliant and masterful, the weak and clinging, those who only have strength when gathered into crowds, the beautiful, the ugly, the useful, the worthless, the fighter, the slacker, and so on *ad infinitum*.

16

China: Treasure Trove

CHINA PROPER AND without its dependencies is a very large country, occupying about twenty degrees of latitude and twenty degrees of longitude, being equal to about two-thirds of the United States. The south is just within the tropics whereas the north enjoys a climate similar to that of New England. The country is well watered and is rich and fertile to an extraordinary degree. It has many fine rivers navigable for very long distances. Rich alluvial valleys, plains and plateaus, and a complex mountain system make up its physical formation. The western boundaries, separating it from Tibet, are a series of high parallel ranges with their major peaks clad with snows eternal. The highest exceeds 25,000 feet in altitude. Except in the treeless areas of the northeast, China enjoys a good rainfall, evenly distributed throughout the year, though in many parts there is a decided leaning toward a summer rainfall.

China is densely populated and the people are essentially agricultural. All suitable land is under crops, and forests (except in inaccessible parts) have been all destroyed. In spite of this the Chinese flora is the richest temperate flora in the world. Fully 20,000 different species are known to grow there and we are far from knowing the full richness of this remarkable land. Enjoying a climate congenial to plant life, every kind of soil, and altitude ranging from sea level to perpetual snows, China is of course highly favored. Moreover, the country was not glaciated during the Tertiary times and though agriculture, practiced as it has been for several thousand years, has wrought the destruction of we know not how many species and genera of plants, the flora as it exists today is really an epitome of that of the whole north temperate region in times before the last glacial epoch. This itself is of great interest, but the fascination to us lies in the fact that it contains such a wealth of different plants preeminently suited to the embellishment of our outdoor gardens.

No other country has given us so many ornamental trees and shrubs, and a majority of the most prized woody plants of hardy gardens are native of China. The woods and forest-remains of China are in the main composed of plants generically the same as those of North America; indeed, there is a very close relationship between the floras. In China we find pine, fir, spruce, larch, juniper, oak, ash, elm, maple, willow, poplar, birch, alder, and so forth, even as in North America and Europe, but the species are different. In short, in aspect the forests are similar though in detail they differ greatly. However, the flora is in general familiar and not wholly alien, like those of Australia and South Africa.

I do not wish these chapters to degenerate into mere lists of plant names, but it is difficult to do any sort of justice to the Celestial Empire's contributions to gardens of the West without enumerating such names by the score. The outstanding feature of Chinese flora is its great richness in plants with showy flowers which blossom at every season of the year except winter in the cold north. Our spring-flowering forsythias and magnolias, summer-flowering roses, buddleias, and lespedezas, and autumn-flowering chrysanthemums are all Chinese in origin. Space is too limited for any proper analysis, but a few words may be given to some of the principal groups which characterize the flora of China.

Broadleaf evergreen trees and shrubs are prominent in the milder parts of China and chief among them are rhododendrons. If we ignore for the moment the section familiarly known as azaleas, the first species of rhododendron proper was discovered in Hongkong in 1849 and was named *R. championae*, after the wife of Colonel Champion, its discoverer. Robert Fortune found on the mountains of Chekiang, in 1855, a second species which was named *R. fortunei*, and this fine plant has been of great value to rhododendron breeders. The next discoveries were made by Père David in western Szechwan, followed by those of Père Delavay in Yunnan and Augustine Henry in Hupeh. In more recent times a couple of hundred other species have been discovered in western China and that region established as the headquarters of the genus.

The rank and file among Chinese rhododendrons are as hardy as the well-known *R. ponticum* but, unfortunately, none are hardy in the colder parts of this country. In England, on the other hand, these Chinese rhododendrons have proved most adaptable and are among the most useful and acceptable gifts China has given to gardens. Different species of rhododendron grow on the mountains in every one of the eighteen provinces of China, but their greatest concentration is found in the extreme west. In height they vary from prostrate or tufted plants a few inches high to forest trees 60 feet and more tall with trunks from 4 to 6 feet in girth, but the majority are wide-spreading bushes from 6 to 15 feet tall. On alpine moors they grow gregariously in the same manner as does the heather in Europe, and phyllodoce and various species of vaccinium in this country. The flowers vary in size from tiny saucers not half an inch in diameter to huge bells from 4 to 6 inches across the mouths. The colors are of every known hue and include some quite good yellows, and the different species are to be found in bloom from the New Year until well into August. The distribution of nearly all the species is quite local; many of them occupy definite altitudinal zones on the mountains and this gives rise to belts of color. To traverse the mountains of western China in the rhododendron season is to enjoy a feast of beauty not excelled the world over. On the mountains not far from Peking and northeastward into Korea and beyond grows the lovely *R. dauricum* var. *mucronulatum*, a deciduous plant whose numerous rose-pink to rose-purple blossoms open the first warm days of spring. For the gardens of New England there is no more satisfactory springflowering shrub.

Azaleas mentioned earlier demand a few words. From the coast to the extreme west, from sea level to about 5,000 feet on the mountain slopes, *Rhododendron simsi*, parent of the modern Belgian or Indian azaleas, luxuriates. This red-flowered azalea is a gregarious plant seldom exceeding 8 feet in height, and in season its mass of blossoms dazzle the eyes with their intensity of red. The fragrant, yellow-flowered *R. molle* is also abundant in the milder parts and well deserves a word of praise. Unfortunately, this plant is not quite hardy in the climate of New England.

A feature of the moist rich woodlands of China are different species of magnolia, several of which open their large flowers before the leaves unfold. Foremost among these must be placed the yulan, well known wherever hardy trees are cultivated in the temperate regions of both hemispheres. This handsome flowering tree, which grows naturally on the mountains of central China, for more than a thousand years has been a favorite tree in Chinese gardens. It was introduced into England in 1789, being the first Asiatic species to reach Europe. In a wild state both white and pink-flowered forms are known, but the latter was introduced into gardens only some twenty-five years ago.

A choice pink-flowered lilac, *Syringa reflexa*, introduced from western China in 1904
(P. E. GENEREUX)

Blooming a little later than the widely known Van Houtte spirea which it closely resembles, Korea spirea (*Spiraea trichocarpa*) is of more upright branching habit. The yellow centers give the large white flower clusters a creamy appearance.
(P. E. GENEREUX)

Wilson introduced half a
dozen species of spirea,
all of which produce
pleasing textural effects
when in flower.
(P. E. GENEREUX)

Wintergreen barberry
(*Berberis julianae*),
a handsome, spiny
evergreen with yellow
flowers and bluish-black
fruits, noted for its
hardiness (P. E. GENEREUX)

The rose family is abundantly represented in China and its trees and shrubs are among the most beautiful flowering plants of the woodlands, mountain slopes, and valleys. In thin woods the pink and white blossoms of various cherries are a conspicuous feature of early spring, as in the open are those of *Prunus tomentosa*. Crab apples, too, in variety there are, but these have a chapter unto themselves. In early summer spiraea in many species adorns low thickets with arching sprays of white and none are more comely than *S. henryi* and *S. veitchi*. The related genus sorbaria favors moist woodlands and the sides of streams where after midsummer is past its members are conspicuous with large, terminal panicles of white flowers standing well above the pinnate leaves each a foot long. The handsomest of the genus is the luch-growing *S. arborea*. A quince, (*Chaenomeles lagenaria*), with white-to-pink and scarlet flowers and large, fragrant fruits is a feature of rocky places. The true Chinese quince, (*C. sinensis*), is a small tree with smooth, flaking bark, and rose-pink blossoms which appear at the time the leaves unfold. It is a favorite of the priests and is commonly seen in temple grounds throughout the Orient.

Conspicuous in the valleys and open mountainslopes everywhere in China are roses, and from that land have come the principal parents of the races of roses we cultivate today and also some of our most prized rose species. Very common in southwest China is *Rosa odorata* var. *gigantea*, prototype of the tea rose, with white and pink fragrant blossoms. In central China, though not common, is found the red-flowered *R. chinensis* var. *spontanea*, parent of the China monthly rose. In the same region and partial to alluvial river-flats *R. multiflora* var. *cathayensis*, parent of the crimson rambler and the polyantha roses, is abundant. The wilding has pink flowers and conspicuous yellow stamens and is more lovely than many of its offspring cultivated under fancy names.

These and other roses have been cultivated for we know not how many centuries by the Chinese, in whose gardens forms in

variety have originated, and it was these that toward the end of
the eighteenth century and early in the nineteenth were introduced
into Europe, some by way of India and some by that of Mauri-
tius, whither they had been carried by early voyagers. These products of Chinese gardens received names, became the accepted
types of species, and by crossing and intercrossing with the roses
long grown in European gardens have given us the modern rose
in all its multifarious forms. The discovery of the wild forms of
these Chinese garden roses is of recent date and all the facts concerning them are far from being fully known.

Abundant everywhere at low altitudes in central China is *R.
laevigata* with its large, pure white flowers. This rose was first
named by Michaux in 1803 from plants growing wild in this country, where it is familiarly known as the Cherokee rose. When and
by what means it first reached America is one of the unsolved
problems of plant introduction. In the heart of China in extraordinary plenty grows the wild banksian rose with fragrant, single,
white flowers arranged in umbels. This rose, by clinging and
scrambling, covers trees from 40 to 50 feet tall, and in the early
summer its festoons of blossoms are among the loveliest pictures
of the countryside. With it grow several species with musk-scented
flowers, of which none is finer than *R. helenae*. To travel through
the mountains of China when the roses are in bloom, and especially
in the cool of the morning or evening when the air is laden with
the fragrance from their myriad flowers, is to taste of paradise.
On the highlands of the extreme west grows *R. moyesi*, of which
no species has flowers of richer shades of red or more brilliantly
colored hips in autumn. The open mountain slopes of north central
China and westward is the home of *R. hugonis*, most exquisite of
all the yellow-flowered hardy roses. There are many other species—
dozens of them—but I cannot attempt to mention all. Everywhere
in China rose species are to be found and as individuals no shrubs
are more plentiful, more floriferous, or more lovely.

In the gardens of the colder parts of eastern North America lilacs hold an undisputed place, for they are satisfactory shrubs and deservedly popular. Most of the familiar sorts grown are derived from *Syringa vulgaris*, considered to be native of the mountains of Bulgaria. In China grow many other species and their beauty is greater than that of the prototype of the common lilac; moreover, their season of blossoming extends over a period of six weeks. Many of them are quite recent introductions and have scarcely been employed by the breeders of new lilacs. All so far introduced, and there are a dozen and more, have proved perfectly hardy in the Arnold Arboretum, where in the early summer of each year they may be seen in flower. An older species is *Syringa viollosa* of neat, rounded habit and erect masses of rosy-pink flowers. Among the newcomers I shall mention only *S. reflexa*, which has the flower trusses hanging after the manner of those of the wisteria.

Different kinds of shrubs and trees bearing ornamental fruits are plentiful in China and many of these have conspicuous flowers and gay autumnal foliage. Bush-honeysuckles, barberries, viburnums, and cotoneasters there are in scores of species, worthy of a place in any garden. The deciduous-leafed cotoneasters are a particularly valuable gift to the gardens of New England, where they have proved themselves most adaptable. Of them all, none is finer than *C. racemiflora* var. *soongorica*, which has a profusion of relatively large, pure white flowers and bright coral-pink fruits. This is a perfectly hardy shrub with rigid, zigzag branches and grows from 5 to 8 feet tall and twice as much in diameter. For clothing banks nothing is better than *C. horizontalis* and its forms. In milder climates such evergreen cotoneasters as *C. pannosa*, *C. salicifolia*, *C. henryana*, and *C. francheti*, either for hedges or as specimens, are valuable plants, having bright red fruit in autumn. In China cotoneasters are a feature of scrub-clad mountain slopes and valleys where they enjoy full exposure to sun and winds and they do best when given the same conditions in gardens.

Earlier it has been mentioned that *Wisteria sinensis* came to us from China, but this plant is less often seen in gardens than its Japanese relative, of which more anon. A group of hardy climbers which our gardens are justly proud of is clematis, and from the Orient came the parents of the familiar large-flowered race of hybrids much grown today. Among climbing plants of recent advent none is more beautiful than *Clematis montana* var. *rubens*, which is native of the margins of the woods and thickets of central China. There are fifty and more other species of clematis native of China, including the handsome *C. tangutica* with grayish-green foliage and top-shaped, rich yellow flowers.

In the matter of herbs China also has been most generous. The chrysanthemum has already been mentioned and so too, has *Primula sinensis*, but the well-known *Primula obconica* and the baby primroses *P. malacoides* and *P. forbesi* are also natives of China; so are *Anemone japonica, Dicentra spectabilis, Incarvillea delavayi, Rehmannia angulata, Lilium browni, L. concolor, L. sargentiae,* and many others, including the magnificent regal lily (*L. regale*), many peonies, aconitums, poppyworts, *Senecio clivorum, Artemisia lactiflora,* and the China aster (*Callistephus chinensis*). The alpine regions of the Chino-Tibetan borderland are gardens of vivid colors in the summer, where gentians and primroses and hosts of other pretty things carpet square mile upon square mile from the tree limit to the edge of perpetual snows. In woodland glades grow many tall herbs and on cliffs and steep mountain slopes lilies in variety luxuriate.

In China many fruits are grown and most of them have during centuries of effort been evolved from native plants. Such is the history of the apple, the pear, the cherry, and the plum grown in China, for they have not common origin with ours which are of Eurasian birth. The apricot, the peach, the orange, the lemon, the pomeloe, including the grapefruit, are natives of China. The walnut and grapevine (*Vitis vinifera*) have been introduced into China from the Caspian and central regions of Asia but her other fruit- and nut-trees are her own. To China we owe of fruits the various citrus and the peach; among economic vegetable products tea, vegetable tallow, and wood oil, and the medicine rhubarb.

There is not a season of the year when flowers are open in the hardy garden but what some jewel from China calls forth admiration, from the first blossoms of the forsythias in early spring to those of the chrysanthemum in the late fall. Whether it be among trees or shrubs, climbers or herbs, whether they be grown for the beauty of their flowers, their fruit or their foliage or for all three, the plants native of China are to be found in the gardens of temperate regions of both hemispheres. They have been won to us by all sorts of agencies and by all sorts and conditions of men. To no part of the world do gardens owe more than to China—the kingdom of flowers.

17

China: Jewels of Her Alpine Meadows

THE FLOWERS OF the alpine regions of the world are justly famed for their brilliant blossoms. On these storm waifs of the mountains Goddess Flora lavishes her brightest pigments and masses them in mile-wide sheets of ravishing color. From the forest limits on the mountains upward to the cradle of eternal snows stretch these alpine gardens strewn with a galaxy of plants. The Rocky Mountains of North America, the Alps of Europe, the Himalayas of northern India, the alps of New Zealand and elsewhere, each and several, have their alpine regions carpeted in loveliness. So, too, has that remote hinterland which separates western China and the Tibetan plateau. This is a region of stupendous mountains far flung, in a series of more or less parallel, snow-capped ranges, from the borders of Assam northward some 2,000 miles. A wild and savage land is this, and little known, for much of it the white man's foot has never trod.

Hidden among these mountain ramparts are thousands of alpine valleys, known only to shepherd tribesmen or nomad cattle herders on their summer visits with sheep and cattle. Above these lonely valleys stretch herb- and scrub-clad slopes of a hundred unnamed and unscaled snowy peaks. Into a few isolated points of these fastnesses the plant hunter has penetrated, to be rewarded by a rich harvest of new plant treasures. But most is virgin territory awaiting the coming of the investigator. Here and there between the frontier towns of Tachien-lu and Sungpang Ting, some 600 miles apart, I have known these flower-clad mountain ranges since 1903, when search of red and yellow poppyworts lead me to them. 'Tis foolish attempt to paint the lily, yet would I strive to give a glimpse of a floral paradise in all its wealth of beauty.

To picture these alpine regions during the short summer that is theirs, one must visualize mile upon mile of color spuming like foam about a storm-tossed shore—seas of yellow, red, orange, blue, violet, and purple. From sun-kissed snows of dazzling whiteness, treacherous glaciers, and hummocked moraines, downward stretch green grassy areas decked with a million flowers of every hue. Herbs, low and tall in stature, but mostly low, predominate, but entangled shrubs in variety struggle until reduced to flat matlike growths. Gray-green juniper, willow, buckthorn, and spiny, pink-blossomed caragana flounder gamely in an ocean of rosepurple and magenta blossom borne by low-growing, fragrant-leafed rhododendrons, which lord the mountain slopes as heather lords fair Scotland's moors. The wetter places herbs claim solely unto themselves and transform them into lakes and seas of vivid color. Carpeted with anemones, primroses, gentians, poppyworts, delphiniums, androsaces, orchids, groundsels, lilies, irises, varicolored pedicularis, and a multitude of other flowers, these rainbow-hued alpine meadows rivet and fascinate attention.

Above an elevation of 10,000 feet around Tachien-lu a cowslip (*Primula sikkimensis*), a most remarkable rhubarb (*Rheum alexandrae*), and a globeflower (*Trollius yunnanensis*) demand a foremost place. The Sikkim cowslip is well known to plant-lovers, but I would that they could see it as it grows there. In moist meadows, and by the sides of streams and ponds, it occurs in thousands and hundreds of thousands, like cowslips in an English meadow. On many a plant may be counted twenty scapes, each with large umbels of flowers filling the air around with soft delicious odor. The rhubarb forms pale pyramidal towers, a yard high, of inflated reflexed bracts that conceal the flowers, and, overlapping one another like tiles, protect them from the wind and rain; a mass of dark green ovate leaves spread on the ground in marked contrast with the yellow transparent bracts. Whilst I am not prepared to grant *Rheum alexandrae* first place amongst the herbs of these alpine regions, its right to a foremost place cannot be denied. I have in mind as I write, a sloping mountainside, somewhat spongy and boggy with boulders jutting out here and there, whereon grew thousands of these plants with their pale yellow pyramidal towers upthrust. *Trollius yunnanensis* is also peculiar to these alps. Imagine *Ranunculus cortusaefolius* with small leaves and slightly larger flowers, and you visualize this trollius. It is essentially a social plant, and to see thousands massed together forming sheets of rich yellow is to remember it.

Pedicularis is the genus *par excellence* of these alpine meadows. About 130 species are recorded from China and of these two-thirds occur in the far west. Many are prostrate plants, some are a few inches high, others, again, grow a foot or more tall. They grow socially in thousands, having a mass of flowers which embrace every color save blue. It is a great pity we cannot cultivate this most charming genus; the difficulty is that all are more or less parasitic on the roots of grasses and other herbs.

Another genus which deserves more than mere passing reference is corydalis. Some fifty-eight species have been recorded from China, of which fully half are found in the alpine districts where the majority favor rocky or healthy places. All the cardinal colors,

save green, are represented in this genus. A lovely species growing from 4 to 8 inches high, with deep blue flowers, is one of the
features of the highland flora around Tachien-lu.

That favorite flower, the gentian, in multitudes forms pools of
blue on every side. Some sorts are tiny tufted plants clustered
with starry blossoms, others carry tubular flowers clustered at the
ends of upright and leaning leafy stalks, but most conspicuous
are those that sprawl over the ground upthrusting large, intense
blue or striped blue and white funnels. On sunny days the alpine meadows are filled to overflowing with gentian blossoms, but
on dull or wet days not one is to be seen. The funnels, tubes,
and stars are all close shut to protect the delicate pollen. Yes,
lovers of fine weather are these bright-hued children of the alps.

Nor must mention of the upland orchids be omitted. They are all
terrestrial sorts with blossoms white and varying shades of red, or
pink, or yellow. They may be only a couple of inches to a foot
tall but what they lack in size they atone for in quality. So abundant are they in the meadows of these regions that one cannot
move without treading down their pretty flowers. Listera and
goodyera, orchis and herminium, platanthera and habenaria, saty-
rium and hemipilia, all are there in many species and numbers
countless; and cypripedium, with large slipperlike flowers—pink,
dark red, and yellow, like guardians stare placidly or nod benignly
over the entire family. Many of these orchids are widespread
through Asia, but greatest wanderer of all is my lady's tresses
(*Spiranthes australis*), who so pertly rears slender spikes crowded
with tiny, fragrant, white and pink-lipped, spirally arranged blossoms. From the borders of eastern Europe to the Pacific, and south
to Ceylon, Java, Australia, and New Zealand this little plant is
found; it has the distinction of being the most widely distributed
member of the whole orchid tribe.

I have mentioned one primula but must enumerate a few others
which are striking constituents of this alpine flora, such as *Primula*

Candelabra primroses are native to the Orient, among them several species which Wilson introduced. He knew and loved the entire genus, named one species for his daughter Muriel (*Primula murielae*), and christened her Muriel Primrose. (P. E. GENEREUX)

involucrata and *P. amethystina.* Acres of moist grassland are carpeted with the pink flowers of the former, and even larger areas of
heathland with the dark blue or purple flowers of the latter. Then
in quantity there is *Primula cockburniana* with unique orange-
scarlet flowers arranged in tiers on slender scapes. Also, tiny little
things like *P. pratti, P. pinnatifida,* and *P. kialensis,* only an inch
or so tall but damsels of the daintiest type clad with laughing
blossoms. And in wet, stony places high up luxuriate several of the
snow-loving primroses, typified by *P. nivalis* and *P. orbicularis,*
with flowers of varying shades of blue, violet, purple, and yellow,
and oblong leaves coated on one or both surfaces with a meal-like,
waxy bloom. Coy and difficult to cultivate in gardens are these
gems of the primrose family.

Alongside streams and on the moors grow several species of
groundsels, some with handsome flowers and foliage. One fluviatile
species (*Senecio nelumbifolius*), with enormous rounded leaves
and large, cymose clusters of small yellow flowers, is particularly
striking. In moist places *Iris chrysographes* rears aloft its handsome,
royal purple streaked with yellow blossoms, and in drier land the
blue-flowered *I. ensata* is found. Higher on the mountains are
other kinds, but iris is less plentiful than many other herbs.

In bog and meadow and among the scrub *Lilium duchartrei*
with turk's cap blossoms, marble-white spotted and splashed with
wine-purple, luxuriates in thousands; and in drier areas the cinna-
bar-red-spotted black flowers of David's lily flaunt their brilliance.
The dwarf *Lilium lophophorum*, with quaint, nodding, top-shaped,
cream-colored flowers abounds and various anemones, with white,
blue, and yellow flowers, many leguminous herbs and sub-shrubs add
to the gaiety of the scene.

Above 12,000 feet an occasional plant of the medicinal rhubarb
(*Rheum officinale*) may be seen. This is a handsome and conspicuous plant, its much-branched inflorescence of white flowers being
often 7 feet high. It occurs as high up as 14,000 feet, the highest

altitude of any tall-growing herb in Szechwan. On dry, heathy ground, several typical Tibetan plants are found, such as stemless saxifragas, the tiny *Ephedra gerardiana* var. *sikkimensis*, and the pretty *Stellera chamaejasme* with terminal globular heads of vari-colored flowers on slender tufted stems a foot high, and very orna-mental. Beneath the gnarled and twisted stems of rhododendrons, *Cassiope selaginoides* occurs aplenty; on bare exposed rocks, *Po-tentilla fruticosa* is redundant. Three forms of the latter are dis-tinguishable with white, lemon, and deep yellow flowers respec-tively; the white form attains the highest altitude.

Around 14,000 feet grow such interesting plants as *Spenceria ramalana, Meconopsis horridula, M. sinuata* var. *pratti, Incarvillea principis, Braya sinensis, Trollius ranunculoides*, species of fritil-laria, cyananthus, oxytropus, various composites, and the curious Himalayan trefoil (*Parochaetus communis*). The meconopsis grow in the niches of bare granite cliffs and have sky-blue flowers; the incarvillea has bright crimson flowers and abounds in grassy places. At 15,000 feet, which is virtually the limit of vegetation here-abouts, is found *Meconopsis horridula, Ranunculus glacialis*, are-narias, drabas, primulas, saxifragas, sedges, some curious compos-ites, and the lovely *Myosotis hookeri*, all small, tufted plants. Hooker's forget-me-not forms cushions a foot or more across of lovely blue and is a most bewitching alpine.

I have stated that the quest of certain poppyworts first took me to the alpine regions of the Chino-Tibetan borderland. On the mountains beyond Tachien-lu, at 11,000 feet above sea level, on July 18, 1903, I came across the first plant of the yellow poppywort (*Meconopsis integrifolia*). It was growing amongst scrub and was past flowering. At 12,000 feet and upwards, miles and miles of the alpine meadows were dotted with this plant, but only a few late flowers remained. Associated with it is found in thousands *Meco-nopsis henrici*, a charming plant with dark violet-purple flowers of medium size borne on scapes 6 inches to a foot high.

I will not attempt to record the feelings which possessed me on first beholding the object of my search in these wild mountains. My journey was for the sole purpose of finding and introducing this, the most gorgeous alpine plant extant. I had traveled some 13,000 miles in five and a half months and to be successful in attaining the first part of my mission in such a short time was a sufficient reward for the difficulties and hardships experienced. The second part of my mission was easily accomplished in due season, and today this plant, with 8-inch broad flowers, blossoms every year in British gardens and is known to all readers of horticultural journals.

Of another highland area in this savage hinterland my diary records: "The flora of the grassy ridge leading to the Pan-lan shan pass is strictly alpine in character, and the wealth of herbs truly amazing. Most of the more vigorous growing had yellow flowers, and this color in consequence predominated. Above 11,500 feet altitude, the gorgeous *Meconopsis integrifolia*, with huge, globular, incurved, clear yellow flowers, emblazon miles of the mountain-side. On stems from 2 to 2½ feet tall myriad flowers of this wonderful poppywort presented a magnificent spectacle. Nowhere else have I beheld this plant in such luxuriant profusion. The deliciously fragrant pale yellow Sikkim cowslip (*Primula sikkimensis*) is rampant in moist places. Various kinds of senecio, trollius, caltha, pedicularis, and corydalis add to the overwhelming display of yellow flowers. On boulders covered with grass and in moderately dry loamy places *Primula veitchi* is a pleasing sight with bright rosy pink flowers. All the moorland areas are covered so thickly with the Tibetan lady-slipper orchid (*Cypripedium tibeticum*) that it was impossible to step without treading on the huge dark red flowers reared on stems only a few inches tall. Yet the most fascinating herb of all was the extraordinary *Primula vincaeflora*, with large, solitary, violet flowers, in shape strikingly resembling those of the common periwinkle (*Vinca major*), produced on stalks 5 to 6 inches tall. This most unprimrose-like primrose is abundant in grassy places. The variety of herbs is indeed legion, and the whole countryside was a feast of color. Silence reigns in these lonely regions, a silence so oppressive as to be almost felt and broken on rare occasions only by the song of some lark soaring skyward."

The search for the red poppywort (*Meconopsis punicea*) took me to the valley which leads to the Kungala Pass beyond Sung-pang Ting in northwest Szechwan. This valley is flanked by high mountains, whose upper parts are bare, barren, and uninviting. The lower parts were clothed with coniferous forests, which here and there reach down to the river's edge. Two species of picea (*P. asperata* and *P. purpurea*) and a juniper (*J. saltuaria*)—all three handsome trees—are the sole constituents of these forests. The tree limit is about 12,000 feet. Near the bed of the river small trees of birch occur. In the distance, to the right, tower a range of vicious-looking peaks, barren and flecked here and there with snow.

Where free of forest, as it mostly is, the valley is covered with a dense, low scrub composed almost entirely of *Potentilla fruticosa*, *Clematis tangutica*, *Daphne tangutica*, *Berberis vernae*, *B. brachypoda*, *B. diaphana*, *Lonicera syringantha*, *L. hispida*, *Hippophae rhamnoides*, *Sibiraea laevigata*, caraganas, astragalus, spiraeas, and willows. The spiraeas form fully fifty percent of the whole scrub.

These moorland heaths merge into grassland, which extends in northwesterly direction for hundreds of miles into the Amdo Country, a region of undulating prairies which support vast flocks of sheep and herds of yak, and are peopled with nomadic Tibetan tribes. The meadows and bog lands around the head of the pass are gay with herbs, blue and yellow being the predominating colors. Species of senecio, *Saxifraga diversifolia*, and other species, hypericums, and various composites furnish the yellow; several gentians, the dwarf *Delphinium souliei*, and others supply the blue—acres upon acres are alternating carpets of blue and yellow.

Other herbs growing there are species of caltha, parnassia, cory-dalis, erigeron, swertia, pedicularis, ranunculus, allium, adeno-phora, sedum, and saussurea, with *Vicia cracca, Epilobium angus-tifolium, Hieracium umbellatum, Polemonium coeruleum, Taraxa-cum officinale, Carduus crispus, Polygonum aviculare,* and various others. In ripe fruit I gathered *Primula tangutica* and *Meconopsis racemosa.* Compared with the alpine meadows around Tachien-lu the wealth in species is limited, but in numbers and intensity of color the flora of the Kungala Pass is no whit less rich and fasci-nating.

At 11,800 feet above sea level on August 31, 1903, amongst scrub and long grass, I stumbled on the first plants of my red pop-pywort (*Meconopsis punicea*). As if to assure me of its identity, a couple of plants were in flower! Now, since I had deliberately traveled from Tachien-lu nearly 600 miles in search of this plant, guided solely by the following scrap of information, culled from a label on a specimen of this plant preserved in the Kew Herbarium: "Potanin, China borealis, Prov. Szechuan septentrionale, '85," I will leave it to the reader to imagine and appreciate my delight. From 12,000 feet to the head of the pass (12,200 feet) this meconopsis was abundant; the capsules were just ripe and a rich harvest of seed rewarded the day's labor. The seeds were transmitted to Eng-land and many plants were successfully raised. It flowered for the first time under Western skies in September, 1905, but did not take kindly to cultivation, and the original stock with its descendants are now lost to gardens. This is to be regretted, for it is beautiful with solitary, dark scarlet flowers, 6 inches in diameter, nodding from stalks 2 feet tall. The flowers are produced in quantity but the petals are rather flimsy in texture. The storm-swept mountains have claimed it back but the memory of its loveliness still glad-dens his heart who first bore it forth on that memorable August day.

18

Japan: Land of the Rising Sun

AND WHAT OF JAPAN, land of the cherry blossom, with whose name every garden-lover is familiar? Japan has drawn freely on the civilization of her ancient neighbor—China. Her written language, art and culture are borrowed and modeled on those of China. The love for flowers is, today, more universal in Japan than in China, yet in all probability it was in emulation of the Chinese that flowers began to enter so largely into the life of the Japanese people. Whether this regard for flowers antedates the coming of Buddhism into Japan I do not know, but in any case this religion has done much toward developing and fostering it. Many flowers and trees—the moutan and ginkgo, for example—were introduced by Buddhist priests. The style of gardening practiced in Japan and the art of dwarfing trees are Chinese, and many of the flowers grown in Japan are natives of China and old favorites with the Chinese people. Bamboo and wisteria are common to both countries but of indigenous plants appreciated by the Japanese there are cherries, maples, azaleas, iris, pine, cryptomeria, *Enkianthus perulatus,* and various arborvitae.

Japan, or the group of islands which form the country, in length is about the same as that of the Atlantic seaboard of this country from Nova Scotia to the Florida Keys. Nowhere is the width considerable but the coastline is much indented and broken. There is a backbone of high mountains, chiefly volcanic, the loftiest of which is sacred Mt. Fuji rising to a height of 12,000 feet above the sea level. In the central part of the main island there are granite peaks well-nigh 10,000 feet high, but limestone is rare. Many of the volcanoes are still active and in a yet greater number the highest parts are bare cones of ashes and volcanic debris. The rivers of Japan are short and swift with broad, rock-strewn mouths where they debouche from the mountain valleys. The land surface of Japan is therefore very broken and rugged; plains of any size are almost wanting except such as have been made by ashes ejected from the major volcanoes. The alluvial flats and valleys are highly cultivated but land suitable for agriculture is insufficient to supply the needs of the people. Over the greater part of Japan the soil is excessively poor and incapable of producing vegetables, root crops, or cereals. The forests of Japan are the country's greatest indigenous wealth and to them and her rugged land surface Japan owes her natural beauty. And Japan is from the scenic viewpoint an extraordinarily pretty country rivaled only in this connection by New Zealand.

The climate of Japan is very similar to that of the Atlantic seaboard of this country. It is strongly influenced by a warm ocean current which flows along its shores to as far north as the latitude of Tokyo, the capital of the empire. South of Tokyo broadleaf evergreen trees, chiefly oaks and laurels with pines and other conifers, are the dominant trees of the forests. North of Tokyo deciduous-leafed trees (oak, maple, birch, beech, alder), with pine, larch, fir, and spruce are the prevailing forest elements; the autumnal

Specimen of chamaecyparis in the garden of Mr. and Mrs. Carl Goddard, Nahant, Massachusetts. This plant was propagated from seed by the late E. H. Wilson and given to his friend Fred Wilson, a noted horticulturist who lived in Nahant. (P. E. GENEREUX)

tints of the deciduous trees are a striking feature everywhere in Japan.

The flora of Japan is, of course, closely related to that of China, though there are very few species common to both lands. There is also a marked affinity with that of eastern North America. The absence of lime in Japan is most favorable to the development of the rhododendron and vaccinium family and this numerically, both in genera and individuals, is the richest group of plants found there. This family of Ericaceae, as it is technically called, boasts no lofty trees and no herbs. It is essentially a family of shrubs, which carpet the ground, form low thickets, or grow from 5 to 12 feet tall and as much in diameter. A few in Japan are small trees and elsewhere in the world are found trees of moderate size. This group possesses many attributes which are pleasing to the garden-lover. The flowers of nearly all are pretty or handsome and produced in very great quantities; the foliage of all is good, and many, very many, are evergreens with lustrous leaves; quite a host of them are ground covers of great beauty. If vaccinium be included, edible fruits of pleasant flavor are another feature but it is to the aesthetic rather than the utilitarian spirit that this family most strongly appeals.

In the forests and far up on the mountainsides in Japan grow two species of broadleaf rhododendron (*R. metternichi* and *R. brachycarpum*), which are handsome in foliage and flower, and most suitable for the gardens of New England and elsewhere, though they are but little known. It is, however, in species of rhododendron with rather small and deciduous leaves and familiarly known as azaleas that Japan is so astonishingly rich. From the extreme south northward far into Hokkaido on mountain slopes, in thickets and on the edge of forests grows the red-flowered *R. obtusum* var. *kaempferi*. This is perfectly hardy as far north in this country as Boston, and is one of the finest plants ever introduced into New England gardens. Though known for over two centuries and everywhere abundant in Japan, it was not introduced into cultivation in the West until 1892, when Professor Sargent sent seeds to the Arnold Arboretum. Why earlier collectors omitted to send seeds home is a mystery.

Another species (*R. japonicum*) with large, flame-colored flowers grows with Kaempfer's azalea in many places, but nowhere in this more common than around Mt. Fuji and in the Nikko region. This is also perfectly hardy in the Arnold Arboretum, where each year it puts forth a wealth of blossoms. On the higher slopes of the mountains in the south of Japan grows a small-flowered azalea, of which the forms *amoena* and *obtusa* have long been familiar in Western gardens. By selection and raising from seeds and vegetative sports during the past hundred years there has been originated in the town of Kurume a race of azaleas so remarkable as to entitle them to a separate chapter.

There are many other species, so many, in fact, that there is a book written about them; all are meritorious and not least *R. quinquefolium*, whose pure white bells illumine the margins of woods and the dark recesses of ravines high up in the Nikko region. In truth, much of the brilliant color of the landscape in Japan during early summer is due to the abundance of azalea bushes which flourish everywhere except in the depths of the forests. One of the very first plants sent to Europe was *Azalea indica*, which reached Holland by way of Batavia before 1680, and was subsequently lost; one of the last was the Kurume azaleas and in no group of plants with handsome flowers has Japan given more freely than of her azaleas—the pride and glory of her scrub-clad mountainsides.

A mayflower (*Epigaea asiatica*) grows on the mountains of north Japan and is just as coy and lovely as her American sister. Several species of the heatherlike phyllodoce clothe the higher mountain slopes where also vacciniums in variety luxuriate. In dry woods in the south the well-known *Pieris* or *Andromeda japonica* is plentiful. There are others, but since this is not an article on the erica family in Japan I will close with reference to enkianthus, a genus whose merits are far from being properly known to garden-lovers. They are shrubs from 5 to 20 feet tall, with many rigid, slender, ascending branches, and small leaves which change to glorious tints of orange, yellow, and crimson before they fall in the autumn. The flowers are borne in clusters or on short racemes in extraordinary profusion; they are either urn- or bell-shaped with prominent anthers; the color is white to red, often salmon or maybe striped with yellow or crimson, and are wonderfully attractive. Of the several species the tall-growing *Enkianthus campanulatus*, of which there are many forms, is perhaps the best. The Japanese favor the low, round-topped *E. perulatus* which has white urns and is planted in almost every garden in Japan. On a dry wind-swept bank in the Arnold Arboretum all the species so far intro-duced from Japan have proved perfectly hardy, and either for their flower in early summer or their tinted foliage in the autumn are worth coming a long distance to see.

By the side of rivers and lakes and to a lesser extent on the margins of woods throughout the length and breadth of Japan grows *Wisteria floribunda*, which with its Chinese relative is the finest hardy climber our gardens possess. The Japanese are properly proud of their wisteria and it is much planted in temple grounds and gardens, usually alongside ponds. Under cultivation varieties with white, pink, and violet-purple flowers have arisen and have been brought into our gardens. So, too, has the long racemed form (var. *macrobotrys*, better known as *W. multijuga*), which in Japan is vastly superior to anything seen in Western lands. In an old garden some miles north of Tokyo I measured racemes 64½ inches in length! The plant was a very old one and bore tens of thousands of such flower clusters.

Among the other valuable plants gardens owe to Japan may be mentioned the Japanese quince (*Chaenomeles japonica*), the witch-hazels (*Hamamelis japonica* and its var. *arborea*), the parent stocks of our garden weigelas, very many maples with colored and curiously incised leaves, the well-known hydrangeas, *H. paniculata*, *H. hortensis*, and the wonderful climbing *H. petiolaris*, and that most indispensable shrub and hedge plant *Berberis thunbergi*. The only substitute for ivy hardy in the gardens of New England, *Euonymus radicans* and its variety *vegeta* are Japanese and so, too, are *Lonicera japonica* and *Vitis coignetiae* with noble, massive foliage brilliantly colored in the fall.

Of herbs we have the Japanese iris of many colors, and among lilies the wondrous *Lilium auratum* and the even more useful *L. speciosum*, both with many forms; also the charming *L. japonicum* and *L. rubellum* to mention no others. From the dependency, Liukiu Islands, came that most indispensable species, *L. longiflorum*.

Many magnificent conifers form forests in Japan and several are established in our gardens. The noble *Abies homolepis* and the red pine (*Pinus densiflora*) are two of the best evergreens for the gardens of New England. The two chamaecyparis (*C. obtusa* and *C. pisifera*) are most useful to us and some of their forms exceptionally so. One of the finest ground covers we possess is the Japanese *Juniperus chinensis* var. *sargenti* whilst the Japanese yew (*Taxus cuspidata*) is the most useful exotic evergreen tree and the most valuable gift Japan has made to the gardens of the colder parts of North America.

19

Korea: Land of the Morning Calm

Korea, Land of the Morning Calm, as the people poetically call it, is overshadowed by its greater and richer neighbors, China and Japan, and until comparatively recently its vegetation was virtually unknown. But since the dawn of the twentieth century attention has been given to it and quite a number of valuable plants have been won to our gardens. The clove-scented *Viburnum carlesi*, which reached us by way of Japan in 1902, is rightly esteemed the aristocrat of its family, and if Korea had given us none other than this lovely plant it would be entitled to our gratitude.

This viburnum is a broad, round-topped shrub from 4 to 6 feet tall and more in diameter. The flower clusters are formed in the autumn and, though naked, with flower buds clearly discernible, pass unscathed through the severest of New England winters. The flowers are rose-colored in the bud, pure white and of waxy texture when fully expanded, and as they do not all open at once the con-

trast is singularly pleasing. Added to these qualities is the delightful fragrance of cloves, which in the early morning and evening
can be detected a hundred yards away.

Many of us have but a limited knowledge of geography and our
ideas of the size and location of distant countries are often vague.
In regard to the Orient we are prone to forget that they are lands
other than those of Japan and China and, moreover, that these
lands are not only peopled by indigenous races but also possess
their own peculiar flora. Those who are fond of gardens may add
much to their knowledge of geography in both interesting and
profitable ways by inquiring into the origin of the flowers they
tend so lovingly. I am minded of this by Carles' viburnum, for it is
one of the plants whose home writers persist in referring to either
Japan or China, or, to both countries, where, as a matter of fact,
it is quite unknown. Let me state it most emphatically, *Viburnum
carlesi* is native of Korea only, is there confined to a few islands
and to the coast, and is a purely littoral shrub. It has been my
privilege to travel extensively in Korea and to gather this shrub
wild on the sea-cliffs in several localities, and I would like to see
honor given where honor is due. This is perhaps in itself but a small
matter; yet, it is a fact, and it is facts that we should treasure, for
real knowledge is but an accumulation of truths small and great.

Korea, or Chosen as it is designated by the Japanese, is a peninsula bounded on the east by the Japan Sea, on the south and west
by the Yellow Sea, and on the north by Manchuria and the Primorsk
province of eastern Siberia, from which it is separated by the Yalu
River, Paiktu mountains, and Tumen River. Until quite recently it
was styled the "hermit kingdom" by peoples of Western lands and
it had little or no intercourse with the outside world. The whole
peninsula (including adjacent islands) is confined within lat. 33°
12' and 43° 2' N and long. 124° 13' and 130°54' E, and has a total
area of 84,173 square miles.

Geologically speaking nearly four-fifths of Korea is of granites and highly metamorphosed rocks of Precambrian age. In the central parts between lat. 38° and 40° N and stretching almost from sea to sea is an area of paleozoic rocks, chiefly mud shales, slates, and a little limestone; in the southeast is an area of mesozoic limestones with intrusive porphyritic rocks, and isolated outcroppings of this combination of rocks obtrude in other parts of Korea. Basalt underlies much of the peninsula and in the volcanic areas—Paiktu mountains, highlands south of Gensan, the islands of Quelpaert (Sai-shu-tō), and Dagelet (Ooryongtō)—it has been forced to the surface and is surmounted by trachyte lavas. Each of these geological formations has certain plants peculiar to it. For example, larch (*Larix dahurica* var. *principis-rupprechti*) grows only on the recent volcanic soils of the Paiktu region and there forms vast forests; a birch (*Betula schmidti*), one of the most valuable of Korean hardwood trees, is confined to the granites and metamorphic rocks; a lilac (*Syringa dilatata*) is found only on the paleozoic rocks of north-central Korea.

The climate is the best in the Far East and the country is destined to become the health resort of the Orient. It is essentially continental in character but in the extreme south and east-south-east, near the coast it is moderated by the influence of the Japan current—a warm ocean stream similar to our Gulf Stream. On Quelpaert, the camphor and orange trees grow at sea level and the temperature there seldom falls below the freezing point; in the extreme north in the valleys of the Yalu and Tumen rivers it falls as low as twenty below zero Fahrenheit—that is 52° F. of frost; round Keijo or Seoul, the capital of Korea, the rivers freeze solid or nearly so, and in winter all vehicular traffic crosses on the ice where bridges are not available.

Korea is a very mountainous country; there are no plateaus nor plains worthy of the name and the only flat land is confined to narrow valleys and river estuaries. The mean height of the broken country is from 900 to 3,000 feet and that of the mountains from

1,800 feet to 5,500 feet; the highest peak is Paiktu-san, 8,300 feet, but there are many above 6,000 feet high. Agriculture is the staple industry of the people and the whole of the fertile soils in the most accessible and climatically best parts of the country have been brought under cultivation.

Since the winters are very cold much fuel is necessary and unfortunately coal is found in one or two places only, so the people are almost entirely dependent upon wood for fuel. These facts, and especially the absence of coal, have been mainly responsible for the disappearance of the forests from the greater part of the peninsula. It is true that in the extreme north, which is very difficult of access and the population sparse, magnificent forests of great extent remain; on mountains, like the Diamond Mountains, where Buddhist monks have managed to maintain their influence, and around the royal tombs, the vegetation has been very little disturbed. But over fully two-thirds of the whole country the forests have been destroyed, and where no cultivation is today attempted coarse grasses, shrubs, and scrub pine are all that remain. These constitute the chief fuel supply of the country. The scrub pine is *Pinus densiflora* and has been extensively planted, both under the old Korean regime and by the present Japanese government, and to the casual observer appears to be almost the only tree in the country. It is hacked and maimed annually to supply fuel, yet it manages to maintain itself under the most adverse conditions in the poorest of soils and on the barest of rocks; where left alone it develops into handsome trees. From the railway, which traverses the country from southeast to northwest, the impression left on the minds of nearly all travelers is of treeless, scrub- and grass-clad hills, bare rocks, low scrub pine scattered over mountain slopes with patches of cultivation in the valleys. In winter when the crops are harvested and the grass is shorn and brown, the whole countryside looks cold, drab, and cheerless. However, a more intimate acquaintance, a closer study will show that, in spite of the naked appearance in winter and the marked absence of trees from accessible areas and routes, Korea can really boast a fairly extensive flora comparatively rich in trees, shrubs, and herbs having conspicuous and beautiful flowers.

Compared with that of its neighbors, China and Japan, the flora of Korea is much less rich and varied, yet in individuals of striking merit it has many claims, and these none the less strong for remaining virtually unknown until quite recently. For, although small collections have been made from time to time since 1854, when Baron Alexander Schlippenbach gathered the first plants in Korea, no real investigation of the flora had been undertaken before the country's annexation by Japan in 1910. Since that date the Government-General has systematically undertaken an investigation of the natural resources of Korea placing the botanical work in the hands of Dr. T. Nakai. So far 2,822 species, varieties, and forms, belonging to 780 genera, representing 151 families, have been recorded, but the work is by no means completed. About one-fourth of these are woody. Most of the families which occur in Japan, north China, and northeast Asia are present but often much reduced in number of representatives. For example, the magnolia family is represented by two genera (magnolia and schisandra) with three species. The most prominent family that is missing is that of the witch-hazel (*Hamamelidaceae*). A genus that one might expect to be present, and which is not, is cercidiphyllum.

Now whilst the seas are natural phytogeographical barriers, the political boundaries of Korea—that is, the Yalu and Tumen rivers and the Paiktu mountains—are not, and the flora is essentially part of that of the great region of northeast Asia, including Manchuria and the northernmost parts of China proper as far west as Mt. Wutai in Shansi. Of woody plants at least two genera (pentactina and abeliophyllum) and a limited number of species (*Abies koreana, Thuja koraiensis, Viburnum carlesi, Cornus officinalis, Forsythia ovata*, and others) are endemic, quite a number, such as *Abies holophylla, Rhododendron schlippenbachi,* do not cross the Yalu watershed to the plains of Manchuria, but the majority are widespread on the continent of northeast Asia and many cross to Hokkaido and to northern Hondo in Japan proper. Of the latter, mention may be made of *Alnus japonica, Rhododendron brachycarpum,* and *Styrax obassia.* Further, a few species, including five (*Quercus acutissima, Q. aliena, Q. dentata, Q. serrata, Q. variabilis*) of the six species of deciduous-leafed oaks, are widely distributed in China and Japan.

The two volcanic islands, Quelpaert off the extreme south and Dagelet off the east coast in the Japan Sea, are peculiar. The first-named, with its peak, Hallai-san, 5,875 feet high, has largely a Japanese flora and is marked by the presence of broadleaf evergreens in variety. A few species, for example, *Maackia fauriei,* are possibly endemic and pure woods of hornbeam (*Carpinus laxiflora* and *C. tschonoski*) with *Daphniphyllum macropodum* and *Taxus cuspidata* as conspicuous undergrowths, are a characteristic feature between 3,000 feet and 4,000 feet. Such woods are unique in the Orient. The trifoliolate orange (*Poncirus trifoliata*) is indigenous, growing in the beds of torrents or among boulders; nowhere else in my travels have I seen this plant truly wild. No species of spiraea, deutzia, or philadelphus grows on Quelpaert, yet they are common shrubs on the mainland. On the other hand, *Hydrangea petiolaris, Schizophragma hydrangeoides,* and *Ostrya japonica,* unknown on the mainland, are common on this island. Two other common plants are *Rhododendron weyrichi* and *R. poukhanense;* the first-named does not grow elsewhere in Korea, whereas the latter is widespread through the peninsula. Such typical Japanese trees as *Pinus thunbergi, Torreya nucifera, Myrica rubra, Machilus thunbergi* and *Magnolia kobus* are indigenous in Quelpaert but grow nowhere else in Korea. The fir on the island is *Abies koreana,* which is similar in habit to *Abies veitchi,* has cones like *A. sachalinensis,* but less resinous, and bark like that of *A. nephrolepis.* It just crosses to the mainland and finds its northern range on Chiri-san. This range is interesting phytogeographically, since it is the southern limit of such characteristic Korean plants as *Rhododen-dron schlippenbachi, Pinus koraiensis, Abies holophylla, A. nephro-lepis,* and the widely spread *Picea jezoensis* and *Alnus hirsuta* var. *sibirica*; also it is the only region in Korea where grows *Rhododen-dron tschonoski,* a typical Japanese plant.

The flora of Dagelet Island is most singular, being much more closely related to that of Japan than to that of Korea. The Japanese *Pinus parviflora* and hemlock (*Tsuga sieboldi*) find their western limits on the island, and woods of an endemic beech (*Fagus mul-tinervis*) are a feature of the forests high up on the mountains. No beech grows on the mainland of eastern Asia east of the province of Chekiang in China. Among other endemic species worthy of mention are *Acer okamotoi, Abelia coreana, Sambucus pendula,* and *Cotoneaster wilsoni.* The keaki, *Zelkova serrata,* common to Japan and Korea, is also indigenous on Dagelet Island and so, too, is *Pinus densiflora.* The Chinese juniper (*Juniperus chinensis*) is wild on the sea-cliffs and has a huge short trunk though the trees are not tall. The lovely *Viburnum carlesi* is also indigenous, but so far has not been found on the adjacent east coast of Korea although it grows in one or two localities on the west coast and on Quel-paert. These two insular outposts of the Japanese flora are the more remarkable when it is remembered that, although both are volcanic, their basalt and trachyte lavas prove they belong to the Korean and not to the Japanese system of volcanoes.

The whole flora of the Korean peninsula is essentially boreal in character and its outstanding feature is the almost complete absence of broadleaf evergreens. Of these, fourteen species— *Zanthoxylum alatum* var. *planispinum, Ilex cornuta, Euonymus radicans, Buxus microphylla* var. *koreana, Rhododendron brachy-carpum, R. micranthum, R. chrysanthum, R. parvifolium, R. re-dowskianum, Ledum palustre, Vaccinium vitis-idaea, Phyllodoce coerulea, Empetrum nigrum,* and *Sasa spiculosa* only are found there. The first six are confined to central and southern Korea; the sasa, although widespread, is nowhere very abundant; the others are alpine plants and grow only in central and northern Korea. Except the social, alpine plants and the sasa these broadleaf evergreens are local in their distribution, few in numbers, and nowhere a conspicuous feature of Korean vegetation. Mistletoe with both greenish white and reddish fruit is a pest everywhere.

The deciduous broadleaf trees which compose the woods and forests belong to familiar northern genera and include several species each of willow, alder, birch, poplar, hornbeam, elm, oak, maple, cornel, hackberry, and one or two each of cherry, bird cherry, crab apple, wild pear, ash, walnut, sweet chestnut, spiny elm, honey locust, linden, apricot, sophora, koelreuteria, phellodendron, and keaki. The woods and forests of these trees are left on steep, rocky mountains unsuited to agriculture and where the soil is poor, so they are not large when compared with trees of America, Europe, or Japan. Occasionally, when for religious or sentimental reasons groups of trees or individuals have been allowed to remain in valleys and by roadsides, good specimens may be seen, but in general Korean broadleaf trees are small and their timber of less value than that of the same species in Manchuria or Hokkaido.

The largest of Korean trees is *Populus maximowiczi,* which in the sparsely peopled north is often 100 feet tall with a trunk 20 feet in girth. A black ash (*Fraxinus mandshurica*) ranks next, but I have seen in Hokkaido far larger trees of this species, and logs rafted down the Yalu from its Manchurian tributary show that in Manchuria it is also a larger tree. The Mongolian oak (*Quercus mongolica*) probably ranks third in size, but on a part of the Diamond Mountains only did I see any really noteworthy examples of this oak. The most widely distributed trees are *Quercus mongolica, Betula ermani,* and *Prunus serrulata* var. *pubescens,* which are common from Quelpaert to the Manchurian border and northward. Almost as common are *Alnus hirsuta* var. *sibirica, Populus tremula* var. *davidiana, Betula davurica, B. japonica, Quercus dentata, Phellodendron amurense, Ulmus japonica, Acer pictum, Salix koreinsis,* and *Maackia amurensis.* Trees with the least distribution are *Cornus officinalis* and *Sophora japonica,* which are spontaneous on a mountain slope about thirty miles northeast from Keijyo and nowhere else in Korea.

The genus salix is richest in species and some, like *S. nobilis, S. cardiophylla,* and *S. koreinsis,* are large and handsome trees; betula and acer with nine species each come next, followed by quercus and cornus, each with six species, and ulmus with five. The birches, except the shrubby *Betula fruticosa* and *B. chinensis,* which is always a small tree, are handsome and grow to large size. The most remarkable is *B. schmidti,* which has hard, close-grained wood, heavier than water, and much exported to Manchuria and China for making axletrees and felloes for carts. This species grows on steep, rocky slopes and the trees though not tall have a short, stout trunk, clothed with thick, dark bark which flakes off, and a broad crown of no particular shape made up of massive branches. Curiously, the wood and bark of the very different *B. chinensis* is almost identical with that of *B. schmidti,* but the tree is always small and is found in lower altitudes and on any kind of soil. On the Diamond Mountains I saw the best examples of *B. chinensis.* Of true maples only *Acer pictum* grows to any great size and this calls for no special comment. Another (*A. pseudo-sieboldianum*) makes a poor-looking tree of medium size but is abundant, and in autumn its foliage assumes wonderful tints of orange, scarlet, and crimson and is responsible for much of the autumn beauty of the forest.

In open country and especially by riversides and in swamps, *A. ginnala* is abundant as bushes or low, shapeless trees. Its leaves have considerable economic value; they are gathered in late sum-

White flowers of the Korean stewartia (*Stewartia koreana*), a worthwhile summer-flower tree with exfoliating bark well suited to the small garden (P. E. GENEREUX)

Hedge of Korean boxwood (*Buxus microphylla koreana*) planted more than twenty years ago which has been maintained at its present low height of 15 inches by annual trimming (P. E. GENEREUX)

mer and after drying in the sun are packed in bales and exported to China, where blue, black, and khaki-colored dyes are prepared from them. Of the eight maples two are negundos, both handsome trees. The oldest known of the two is *A. mandshuricum*, which grows 80 feet tall, has a shapely crown and a straight trunk clothed with firm, pale gray, slightly fissured bark. The other, *A. triflorum*, is of about the same size, has thicker branches and a thin, papery, gray-brown bark which shreds off. The autumn tints of both are yellow, orange, and salmon and singularly beautiful.

Of the oaks *Quercus mongolica* is the best and most valuable, and where the soil is good, as on Nemonrei in the Diamond Mountains, it is a fine tree, in habit and size resembling the white oak (*Q. alba*) of eastern North America. As usually seen in Korea, however, the Mongolian oak is not attractive, being of moderate size and frequently stagheaded. The less abundant *Q. serrata* is usually a better-looking tree, and in the autumn its ruddy tinted foliage makes it conspicuous. Of the cornels, besides the well-known *Cornus kousa* and *C. controversa*, both strikingly beautiful in summer when in full flower, the less known *C. coreana* deserves mention, if only on account of its bark which, on adult trees, is almost black and deeply fissured into tiny squares like that of *Diospyros virginiana*. The Korean cornel grows 60 feet high and has a trunk from 4 to 5 feet in girth; the leaves are opposite, but the flowers and fruit are similar to those of *C. controversa*. It is interesting to note that the old *C. officinalis*, long known as a cultivated tree in Japan, is endemic in Korea, where it is often 35 feet tall with a trunk from 4 to 5 feet in girth clothed with thin, pale gray bark which scales off in loose, papery sheets. The common elm is *Ulmus japonica* but nowhere did I see large trees of this species such as are common in Hokkaido; indeed, the largest elm in Korea is *U. pumila*, which in the valleys of the north is often 80 feet tall with a trunk as much as 12 feet in girth.

Trees with conspicuous flowers, striking objects in the landscape, are *Prunus mandschurica*, distinguished among apricots by its large size and by its thick, corky, black bark which is red beneath, a cherry (*Prunus serrulata* var. *pubescens*); wild pear (*Pyrus ussuriensis*), crab apple (*Malus baccata* var. *mandshurica*), tree lilac (*Syringa amurensis*), *Maackia amurensis* and *Aralia chinensis*, *Acanthopanax ricinifolius*, and two lindens, *Tilia amurensis* and *T. mandshurica*. These trees all grow in plenty and when in flower their effect on the landscape can be imagined. The pear in particular is noteworthy as the most cold-resisting of Asiatic species and as growing to a larger size than any other—trees from 60 to 70 feet with crowns as much in diameter and trunks from 10 to 14 feet in girth are not uncommon. It is widespread in Korea and is frequently found in the forest depths, though more usually by the side of streams and on the edge of woodlands. The fruit, which is depressed-globose and from one-third to one-half an inch in diameter, may be ruddy or green and with or without the remains of the calyx; the leaves, which vary in shape and serration, assume rich bronze and purple tints in autumn. Cultivated forms of this species are grown in gardens in Korea, Manchuria, and north China and yield palatable fruit of good size. The crab apple is a tree of moderate size and its wealth of white blossoms in spring is followed by an abundance of small, greenish-red to scarlet fruits. It loves a cool soil and is particularly happy in thickets on the banks of mountain streams.

As in other boreal floras conifers are abundant. Besides the red pine (*Pinus densiflora*), whose prominence has already been alluded to, the Korean nut pine (*P. koraiensis*) is a very common tree on the mountains, and the creeping pine (*P. pumila*) clothes the upper slopes and summits of most of the higher peaks from Kangaku-san; about lat. 38° 30′ N, northward, except that of Paiktu-san itself from which it is entirely absent. Two firs (*Abies holophylla* and *A. nephrolepis*) are both plentiful, the first-named being indigenous and confined to the low levels and the other a mountain species. A third species restricted to Quelpaert and Chiri-san has been referred to already. A flat-leaf spruce (*Picea jezoensis*) and another with four-angled leaves (*P. Koyamai*) grow in Korea. The latter is confined to the north and more especially the northeast but the flat-leaf species grows as far south as Chiri-san. A species of thuja (*T. koriensis*) is common on high non-volcanic land from the Diamond Mountains northward; in the forest it is a sturdy shrub or small tree, often 30 feet tall, but on high treeless slopes it is an undergrowth to *Pinus pumila*. One juniper (*Juniperus rigida*) is very common, more especially in open country and thin woods of red pine or oak; another (*J. communis* var. *montana*) grows only in the north, whilst a third (*J. chinensis* var. *sargenti*) is confined to rocky places high up on the mountains, but is distributed from the extreme north to Quelpaert, where it grows on Hallai-san at 4,800 feet upwards. To complete the list of conifers indigenous on the peninsula it remains to mention a larch (*Larix dahurica* var. *principis-rupprechti*), which covers much of the volcanic area of the north and is not found elsewhere. This larch with the two spruces, the nut pine and the mountain fir, either grow together or form more or less pure forests and the wood of one and all is of good quality. The other fir (*Abies holophylla*) is of little value as a timber tree but for garden purposes it ranks with the Japanese *A. homolepis* as the best of the east Asiatic species. The branches are moderately stout, spreading or ascending-spreading, and crowded with dark green leaves. Trees 100 feet tall with trunks 12 feet in girth are not uncommon in fairly open country where the soil is rich and moist.

Of Taxaceae only *Cephalotaxus drupacea* and *Taxus cuspidata* grow on the mainland of Korea. The cephalotaxus as a small shrub of no particular shape is scattered here and there from the vicinity of Seoul, the capital, southward; the yew is much more widely spread, growing as far north as the upper waters of the Yalu River. It is not a common tree, though on the Nemonrei in the

Diamond Mountains it is more plentiful and of greater size than I have seen it anywhere else in the Japanese Empire.

At this point it seems opportune to say a little about the natural rotation of forests, or the succession of forest growth as it may be termed—a subject little understood but clearly demonstrated in and by the virgin forests of north Korea. To appreciate this succession and to properly understand what follows, it is necessary to state that in the temperate regions of northeast Asia (and probably everywhere in the world) there are aggressive northern and southern types that are ever extending their geographical range at the expense of (a) types already in occupation of intervening regions, (b) those that flourish under peculiar conditions only, (c) themselves finally. Of these aggressive northern types in Korea may be mentioned aspen (*Populus tremula* var. *davidiana*), alder (*Alnus hirsuta*), birches (*Betula davurica*, *B. ermani*, and *B. japonica*), creeping pine (*Pinus pumila*), fir (*Abies nephrolepis*), spruces (*Picea jezoensis* and *P. koyamai*). Of southern aggressive trees red pine (*Pinus densiflora*), oaks (*Quercus mongolica*, *Q. dentata*, and *Q. serrata*), hornbeam (*Carpinus laxiflora* and *C. cordata*), ash (*Fraxinus rhynchophylla* and *F. mandshurica*) may be instanced; of types in possession, that is, species endemic or nearly so, fir (*Abies holophylla*), nut pine (*Pinus koraiensis*), birch (*Betula Schmidti*), maple (*Acer pseudo-sieboldianum*), box-elder (*Acer triflorum and A. mandshuricum*), wild pear (*Pyrus ussuriensis*), and apricot (*Prunus mandshurica*) may serve as examples.

After forest fires or deforestation by man, birch, usually *Betula davurica* or *B. ermani*, less commonly *B. japonica*, is the first tree to appear in almost any part of Korea. In the south and at low altitudes and to a less degree in central Korea, the birch may be forestalled by coarse grasses (miscanthus and relatives) and natural reafforestation long retarded, but normally, birch is soon joined by other broad-leafed deciduous trees and frequently by red pine and fir (*Abies holophylla*) and in the course of time develops into pure broadleaf forest, mixed forest, or pure pine forest, according to the type which becomes dominant. On the east side of the Diamond Mountains, where man has much thinned the former pure forest of red pine, broadleaf trees are rapidly changing the whole character of the forest. On the west side of the same mountains, especially around the monastery of Choanji, the broadleaf forests are being displaced by nut pine and fir. In central Korea and northward, coarse grasses are less aggressive and birch is associated with aspen in increasing quantity, until the volcanic areas of the Paiktu-san region are reached where larch becomes a prominent companion of the birch and aspen.

It is in this Paiktu-san region that the succession of forest types is most clearly shown. The cycle is roughly as follows: In the course of time after volcanic activity in that region had ceased, as after forest fires at the present time, seedlings of birch, aspen, and larch sprang up from seeds transported from the north by wind. Then, as now, the three kinds of trees grew well together for a few years, the birch and aspen the faster at the commencement, but the larch, though it needs when young a certain amount of shade, just such as the twiggy branches of birch and aspen afford, is a light-demanding tree and after twenty or thirty years it outstrips its fellows in pace of growth, finally kills them, and pure forests of larch remain. Such forests are thin, open and parklike in aspect, and the trees almost of the same age, for no larch seedlings will vegetate in such forests except by the side of well-tramped paths, or on fallen, rotting trunks, but where fire breaks through they thrive exceedingly. As the larch trees increase in size, so the forest floor beneath becomes more and more shady and invites the presence of shade-loving trees, such as fir and spruce. When the larch is from 60 to 100 years old, seedlings of fir and spruce establish themselves, in the course of time grow into trees and, finally, kill out the larch and form pure forests of themselves. Like the larch the trees are of about the same age, for in such forests seedlings do not vegetate under the dense shade of the parent trees either because the shade is too great, because there is too much humic acid in the soil from the constant accumulation of rotting vegetation, or because of both. On the edges of these forests, in glades or on fallen rotting trunks only are young seedlings of spruce and fir to be found.

Larch, with its deciduous leaves and trunks clear of branches for a considerable distance from the ground, is in much less danger from fire than evergreen fir and spruce, which keep their branches from near the ground upward and, moreover, have very resinous bark and leaves. However, sooner or later, either from electrical storms or through human agency, fire sweeps through the forests and the cycle is repeated.

The larch forests being of open character are easy to traverse and have quite a rich undergrowth of shrubs, among which birch (*Betula fruticosa*), blueberry (*Vaccinium uliginosum*), and *Ledum palustre* in many forms are prominent. The fir and spruce forests are less rich in woody undergrowth and those of pure red pine have none at all. The broadleaf forests on the other hand are rich in shrubs and climbers of an ornamental character, although these reach their greatest exuberance where trees are fewest. Most abundant are azaleas, roses, magnolias, honeysuckles, lilacs, mock-orange, deutzia, forsythia, spiraea, indigofera, symplocos, viburnum, berberis, and the climbers actinidia, celastrus, pueraria, smilax, and vitis, whilst in central and south Korea on boulders, cliffs, walls, ramparts and trunks of forests trees the familiar *Ampelopsis tricuspidata veitchi* luxuriates. In the rocky beds of summer torrents and on the banks of streams the gray willow (*Salix gracilistyla*) is superabundant.

The tops of the higher mountains in north Korea are clothed with such alpine shrubs as creeping pine (*Pinus pumila*), dwarf junipers (*Juniperus chinensis* var. *sargenti* and *J. communis* var. *montana*), *Thuja koriensis*, dwarf willows in variety, cowberry and other vacciniums, the red-fruited variety of arctous (*Arctous alpinus* var. *ruber*), crowberry, dryas, *Rhododendron chrysanthum, R. parvifolium* and other species. On the barest and most rocky hills and mountain slopes a few woody plants may be found. In spring, late May and early June, according to latitude, the whole countryside is gaily decked with myriad flowers. Wild pears, crab apples, cherries, plums, apricots, and other flowering trees which enliven the glades, edge of the forest, river bank, and open country must not be forgotten in this attempt to visualize Korea in spring, nor the young unfolding leaves of the forest trees, from the pure green of the larch, through the grays of some oaks to the ruddy tints of other species of oak and maple. The undergrowth in the woods and the shrubberies when the trees have been destroyed are splashed with masses of white, yellow, pink, rose and purple. Not even in the richest parts of China or Japan have I seen such extensive displays of pure pink and white as on the Diamond Mountains, where *Rhododendron schlippenbachi* and *Magnolia parviflora* dominate the undergrowth for miles and bloom to perfection.

On the bare hillsides and mountain slopes of central Korea forsythia is plentiful and its yellow bells in spring are conspicuous. On mud shales and limestone a little to the northwest of Keijo grows a lilac (*Syringa dilatata*), which opens panicles of fragrant, pale, lilac-tinted flowers early in spring. It is of good habit, often 12 feet high and nearly as much broad, with dark green, leathery foliage which colors finely in autumn. Bushes 2 feet high bear flowers. In the woods and thickets grow two other lilacs, *S. velutina* and *S. wolfi*, and these produce their nearly white to ruddy purple flowers in early summer; the fragrance of *Syringa velutina* is delightful. In early summer, too, a lovely weigela (*Diervilla florida* var. *venusta*) and the rose indigofera (*Indigofera kirilowi*) bear a wealth of attractive flowers, and since the plants are plentiful the display is conspicuous. Very abundant in open country and thin woods is that harbinger of spring, *Rhododendron mucronulatum*, and so, too, is the less well-known *R. poukhanense* which, with its compact, twiggy growth and wealth of fragrant, rosy-mauve flowers, is a feature of the countryside in late April and May from Quelpaert northward to the latitude of Pingyang. On rocky, grass-clad slopes it covers areas which on the foothills of Chiri-san are acres in extent; on Quelpaert it grows in great plenty from sea level to the summit of Hallai-san. The white-flowered rambler rose (*Rosa multiflora*) and its northern and handsome relative, *R. maximowiczi*, are also features of the early summer flora of Korea.

Since pine and fir are the dominant trees in the landscape over much of Korea, the flowering shrubs and trees are well provided with a setting which enhances their beauty, whether it be the flowers in spring and summer or the tinted foliage in autumn. Often in thin woods of red pine the undergrowth is almost entirely of pink, rose, or rosy-mauve azaleas and rose-colored indigofera; such places are perfect gardens.

In species of climbing plants Korea is poor and it boasts no wisteria nor anything approximating in beauty. However, climbing plants are plentiful if not varied, and in autumn the tints of Veitch's ampelopsis and of the amur grape (*Vitis amurensis*) are not exceeded in brilliancy anywhere. In early summer two actinidias (*Actinidia kolomikta* and *A. polygama*) with fragrant, white flowers in clusters hidden beneath the leaves, a great many of which are pure white or half white and half green, are striking objects on the mountain slopes. The white leaves change to pink and rose as the flowering period passes. In summer the most noteworthy climber is *Tripterygium regeli*, with bright brown, lenticellate branches, large panicles of pure white flowers which are followed by white changing to pink, bladderlike fruits. It is abundant, sprawling over shrubs and trees.

Korea from early times has been the highway over which many

Chinese plants of economic value and of ornamental character have traveled to Japan. For example: Chinese persimmon (*Diospyros kaki*), sand pear (*Pyrus serotina* var. *culta*), Korean apple (*Malus asiatica*), Japanese plum (*Prunus salicina*), bush cherry (*P. tomentosa*), varnish tree (*Rhus verniciflua*), moutan peony (*Paeonia suffruticosa*), the paulownia (*Paulownia tomentosa*), and others, all indigenous in China, reached Japan by way of Korea. Likewise certain Korean plants were long ago introduced to Japan and reached Europe and America from there at a later date. Among older examples may be instanced *Pinus koriensis, Cornus officinalis*, and *Diervilla florida*; in more recent times *Rhododendron schlippenbachi* and *Viburnum carlesi.*

By roundabout ways plants from China have found their way to western lands from the sixteenth century if not earlier, and from Japan since the seventeenth century, though in each case often with long breaks in the periods. Yet the twentieth century had almost dawned before any seeds or living plants direct from Korea reached the Occident. In 1897, a Russian Botanist, Vladimir L. Komarov, made a trip through northern Korea, collected herbarium material and probably some seeds, for in the "Gardener's Chronicle" ser. 3, XLIV, 210 (1908) there is a figure and note about *Rodgersia tabularis*, a typical Korean herbaceous plant, flowering in Kew Gardens from seeds received from the Imperial Botanic Garden, Petrograd, in 1905. In December, 1904, the Arnold Arboretum received, through the Imperial Botanic Gardens, Tokyo, some seeds collected in Korea by T. Uchiyama, which resulted in the introduction of *Abies holophylla* and *Hemiptelea davidi.* In 1905, J. G. Jack, of the Arnold Arboretum staff, was in the Orient and visited Korea. The Russo-Japanese war was in progress and it was impossible to travel freely in Korea. Mr. Jack's main purpose was not plant collecting, nevertheless he sent back living material of quite a number of plants which have proved to be of exceptional interest and value. To him we owe such Korean plants of merit and hardiness as *Rhododendron poukhanense, Diervilla florida* var. *venusta, Tripterygium regeli, Malus baccata* var. *jacki, Rosa jacki, Evodia danielli,* an oak (*Quercus aliena*), and the plants in the Arnold Arboretum of the lovely *Indigofera kirilowi.*

20

Formosa: Pearl of the Orient

"WELL, IF THEY TAKE a fancy for my head during the night I do not see what is to prevent them from taking it." With this lugubrious soliloquy, I rolled myself in a blanket and prepared for sleep beneath the shelter of a fallen tree. A recent storm had blown down one of the giants of the forest and there was plenty of room for a dozen people in the cavern beneath its base. Some pieces of old tent canvas strung across the front shielded us from without and the clayey earth adhering to the roots of the tree formed a roof. Gathered around several fires were two score half-naked ex-head-hunters, armed with bows and arrows, long knives and guns, who had struggled all day up the mountain slope carrying our belongings. It was a weird scene in the heart of the mountains of Formosa. The night was fine but dark with a darkness that could almost be felt. The savages had finished their frugal meal washed down with the crude Chinese wine of which they are fond. Some were smoking and sharpening their knives, others were pleasantly crooning songs of the chase. As I lay on the ground this scene of savages grouped around campfires, in the light of whose flames their faces showed clearly through rents in the canvas, the gloom and mystery of the forest immediately beyond, brought forth my soliloquy and became indelibly written on my memory. It had been a hard day's tramp and soon my Japanese companions and self were sound asleep.

Formosa or Taiwan is an island about 100 miles off the east coast of China and is lapped by the waters of the Pacific Ocean. South are the Philippines, and the tribesfolk of these islands are closely akin. The savages of Formosa are divided into several tribes and many clans and are in constant enmity. They dwell in small villages among the mountains and are hunters all. Many of their quarrels have to do with game rights and are relentlessly pursued. Headhunting is still the pastime of many tribes in the mountain fastnesses and the skulls of strangers and enemies are tangible proofs of the prowess of young braves, giving them favor in the eyes of maidens and of the clan. Agriculture, such as it is, is the business of the women and children, who burn off a patch of the mountainside and there grow millet and a few vegetables. In a few years the area ceases to be fertile and another clearing in the forest is made. But untutored as these savages are they are not unobservant. Some time in the distant past they learned that on their abandoned and exhausted clearing an alder tree (*Alnus formosana*) was first to spring up and lo! in a few years, the land was again fertile. They now plant this tree for the avowed purpose of restoring the fertility of their millet patches. In recent years scientists have discovered that on the roots of the alder among other trees a nitrifying mycorrhiza is found, which has the power of fixing free nitrogen and combining it with oxygen to form the nitrates so necessary for raising crops. The intimate processes of this remarkable action are scarcely known, but without any knowledge of science the Formosan savage appreciates the fact and makes good use of it. To him his native alder is a miracle among tree growth and a blessing above other trees.

Rich in many minerals, in camphor, rice-paper and useful timber, this magnificently forested island is the Pearl of the Orient. Nominally a Chinese possession for many centuries it has had a chequered history, and its aboriginals have waged constant warfare against Chinese and others far back into history. Camphor obtained by distillation from the wood of the camphor tree (*Cinnamomum camphora*) has for centuries been the lodestone of the Chinese invaders. In quest of this product they pushed their way deeper and deeper into the mountains and waged perpetual warfare against the savages. The tribes resenting their intrusion were ever on the alert, and how many thousands of heads they have taken in their forays there is no telling.

The Dutch founded settlements and named the island Formosa, in 1624, and maintained themselves at Fort Zeelandia until 1662, when they were driven out by Chinese. The Dutch farmed the island to the advantage of themselves and attempted to Christianize the aboriginals, but there is nothing to prove that their rule brought any blessings to the savages. The Japanese, more thorough than previous conquerors, have striven hard and with measurable success to bring the savages under control. At first they pursued a rather ruthless method of conquest and extermination, in which they were not very successful, but in more recent years other and more peaceful methods have been adopted. Roads have been built, blockhouses installed, and a large police patrol placed in charge. The more irreconcilable tribes are segregated and surrounded by wire fences charged with a heavy electric voltage. Trading, allowed only through barter at police offices, has been installed, much to the benefit of the savages. This more peaceful penetration has brought better results and in a few decades headhunting in Formosa will cease to exist save as an occasional criminal outburst.

Except in the north there are few good harbors in Formosa and boarding and landing from ships is exciting. At Koshun in the south a tub lashed on a bamboo raft served to convey me to a vessel. On reaching the ship's side one had to be agile to get safely from this raft to the Jacob's ladder and clamber aboard. Landing through the surf, as we did at Pinan on the east coast, is a wet and thrilling experience. Here the full force of the Pacific breaks on the shore and steamers anchor well off. Half-breeds of Chinese and savages work the boats ashore, yelling as loudly as possible all the time. They maneuvered the boat so as to get it carried stern first on the crest of the wave well to the shore. As the wave recedes one jumps ashore and races to safety.

To carry produce from the valleys among the foothills a splendid system of push trolley lines has been inaugurated. These trollies, operated by manual labor, of course, are an invaluable aid to the traveler in Formosa. The lines are roughly laid and frequently out of repair, but many a pleasant day have I spent aboard these trollies. Up-grade is slow work and one usually walks, but down hill is quite exhilarating. The savages love operating these vehicles but they are reckless in their exuberance of spirits. Accidents are frequent though they are rarely fatal. We were one day coasting down a long but fairly easy grade and the trolley jumped the rail. Gathering myself up from the ground I found that the whole crew had come to grief. We suffered none but minor cuts and abrasions, but our police guard quickly had a doctor on the scene solicitous for my welfare.

Though little known to the world at large, Formosa is rich in interest. It boasts the loftiest peaks between the Californian Sierras and mountains of extreme western China, the highest sea-cliffs in the world, and in its forests are found the tallest and the biggest cone-bearing trees in the Old World—giants related to and comparable with the sequoias and yellow cedars of western North America. It was the spring and autumn of 1918 that I was in Formosa to investigate the forests in general and in particular to secure seeds or living plants of these remarkable trees. The Japanese Government, ever solicitous to advance science, had granted me full facilities of travel and detailed as guides two of the best informed forestry officials, Messrs. Kanehira and Sasaki. From the town of Kagi on the west coast a railway, built for the purpose of carrying down lumber, and a marvelous piece of engineering withal, had brought me to Arisan, 7,000 feet up the ranges which form the backbone of the island. At Arisan our caravan had been gotten together and the quest began in earnest.

Like many other unsophisticated people, the Formosan savage is not partial to manual labor; neither is money an overweening incentive to work. A bribe of Chinese wine is much more potent but even this is not always sufficient. Being a born hunter of game as well as human heads, the savage dearly loves a gun and to be allowed to carry a rifle with a nice shining barrel, to aim it, pull back the breech, and kill as his imagination wills is irresistible. So pleasing his fancy in this matter, but allowing him dummy cartridges only, and adding a goodly number of kerosene tins filled with Chinese wine, we had little difficulty in securing some two-score savages as porters. A squad of armed Japanese police, my faithful and most efficient Japanese boy, Morita, with Messrs. Kanehira, Sasaki, and myself, completed the party. We had tents but the overhanging base of a fallen tree was a simpler lodging for the first night out. The famous trees were easily found once we got well into the forests, but fruiting examples of the taiwania were extraordinarily rare. Months later a fine specimen was discovered full of cones and felled. Some bushels of fruit were gathered but not one seed germinated. However, a few young plants were secured and safely transported to the Arnold Arboretum. These have been successfully propagated by cuttings and distributed throughout the five continents.

The taiwania, named for the island, is the loftiest tree in the forests, rearing its small, moplike crown well above all its neighbors.

(ABOVE) Wilson surrounded by headhunters and Japanese policemen in Formosa

(BELOW) An excellent specimen of Formosa andromeda (*Pieris taiwanensis*), similar in many ways to Japanese andromeda, but with longer flower clusters (P. E. GENEREUX)

The average height of this tree is from 150 to 180 feet but specimens exceeding 200 feet are known. The trunk is sometimes as much as 30 feet in girth, quite straight and bare of branches for 100 to 150 feet. It is a strikingly distinct tree, singularly like a gigantic club moss or lycopod. In the dense forests the crown is small, dome-shaped or flattened, the branches few and short, and one wonders how so little leafage can support so large a tree. When the top is broken by storms, the lateral branches assume an erect position. In the more open forest the branches are massive, widespreading, and the crown oval or flattened, and on small trees the branchlets are often pendent. When young it is singularly beautiful in habit of growth.

The big tree of Formosa is a white cedar, technically named *Chamaecyparis formosensis*, and is found throughout the middle forest zone but most plentifully between the altitudes of 6,000 and 8,000 feet. Its maximum height is about 180 feet and the girth of the largest known tree is 64 feet; the average height is from 120 to 150 feet and the girth from 30 to 40 feet. One old felled specimen showed 2,700 rings of growth, so if this be any guide the age of the trees must be from 2,500 to 3,000 years, and very few trees of a younger generation are to be found. The trunks of many of the trees are hollow, some mere shells, but very few dead trees occur, either standing or on the ground. Some 50 feet or so above the base the trunks divide into three or several erect stems. The lateral branches are slender, short, and spreading, the crown thin and tapering, and much of the foliage is usually brownish. These old trees are far from handsome but the bulk of their enormous trunks is most impressive. At one time the taiwania and white cedar probably formed pure forests but, unable to withstand the competition of aggressive broadleaf trees ascending from below, they have lost supremacy. Neither beneath their own shade nor in the dense forests are seedlings or young plants of these trees to be found, but in glades, where landslides have taken place, and on the Arisan, where clearings have been made to accommodate a railroad, young seedling plants of the white cedar in particular are quite common.

Formosa is only some 244 miles long and of varying width, from 7 to 75 miles. Its backbone is a range of mountains averaging nearly 10,000 feet in height, the highest peak being Mt. Morrison or Niitakayama, athwart the Tropic of Cancer. At the time of my visit less than half a dozen white men had stood on the peak of this remarkable mountain, so the temptation to ascend it was very great.

But I had a more definite object than that of personal vanity. To ascend to the summit was to traverse all the forest zones of the island and gain much needed information on the altitudinal distribution of the principal components of the forests. Much knowledge must result from such a trip and so it was undertaken and accomplished. The savages led the way and blazed the trail but the climb was four days of physical fatigue and exhaustion such that only enthusiasm can overcome and that with every ounce expended. We did it, but I can't tell how, and we got back safely to Arisan, but I do not think I could be tempted to repeat the journey.

For three days the weather was glorious and I garnered a rich harvest of botanical specimens, took many photographs of trees, and my notebook fairly bulged. Down from 12,500 feet elevation through a forest of balsam and juniper we plunged 1,500 feet into a ravine—the final chasm separating us from the peak of our goal. There beneath overhanging cliffs we camped in high spirits for the morrow. Scarcely had night fallen when rain began to fall and for three long days it never ceased. We were held prisoners, later to learn that a typhoon had lashed the whole island from south to north with a welter of wind and rain, causing much damage along the coasts. The fourth morning opened dull and threatening but we sallied forth, to encounter a light fall of sleet driven by a strong and bitter cold wind. In the teeth of this gale we struggled onward and upward along the crumbling ridge and finally gained the summit.

The peak of Mt. Morrison or Niitakayama, 13,072 feet above the sea, is reached from the ridge above the ravine by a dangerous path, but the climb is not difficult above the trees. It is bare, save for a few herbs, among which an adelweiss is prominent, occasional low bushes of the evergreen *Rhododendron pseudochrysanthum*, the tiny *Gaultheria borneensis* with snow-white bells, prostrate mats of juniper, and an alpine willow. From the summit a wonderful view, embracing the Pacific Ocean on the east, the Formosan Channel on the west and much of the island to the north and south, is to be had. This is clear weather. We could not see more than fifty feet in any direction and the strong gale and sleet storm made almost inaudible the cheers with which my Japanese companions and police announced our conquest of the highest mountain in the Japanese empire and the loftiest peak between the Californian Sierra Nevada and the snow-clad peaks of the Chino-Tibetan borderland. I had brought along a pint bottle of champagne with which to celebrate our conquest, but so cold were we that I dared not risk opening the bottle until we had gained the shelter of some junipers a thousand feet below the summit.

Success in scaling Mt. Morrison and the fascination of the island determined me to attempt to cross the famous sea-cliffs of northeastern Formosa, heretofore untraversed by any white man. These cliffs stretch northward from near the town of Karenko on the shores of the Pacific. They are of hard crystalline schistose rock and as seen from the sea appear to be vertical walls of rock fully 8,000 feet tall. Arriving at Karenko in 1918, a few days after the armistice had been declared, I found the Japanese authorities in excellent spirits and with a little tact and adroitness obtained permission to carry out my object. Equipped with an armed guard and sufficient savages as porters, it took me five days to make this pioneer trip over the sea-cliffs. The road is exceedingly difficult, not to say dangerous, and the weather was far from favorable, but a rich harvest of specimens of interesting plants well repaid me for the fatigue and hardships. From the sea only can a proper estimate of the height and grandeur of these cliffs be obtained, but only by struggling over them can the forest wealth which clothes all but the most vertical walls be realized. Nearly all the trees are evergreen; oaks and laurels predominate and their canopy of green almost shuts out the heavens. Camphor trees are also plentiful, *Calamus margaritae, Mucuna ferruginea, Bauhina championi*, and other huge lianas cling about the tallest trees and with ropelike stems bind them together. The forest floor is choked with a dense growth of ferns in great variety from mosslike carpets on wet rocks to trees 15 feet tall. *Alocasia macrorrhiza* with huge dark green leaves is plentiful and the rice-paper plant (*Tetrapanax papyrifera*), with huge panicles of snow-white flowers, was conspicuous in the dim, subdued light of the forest depths. Everything was dank and luxuriant, and the tense silence was broken only by the dull roar of the waves of the Pacific Ocean dashing themselves against the cliffs thousands of feet below. Occasionally a bird flitted across the path or a monkey was seen in the treetops, but these were rare events. The armed Japanese police and the savages who carried our baggage were all silent as we trudged slowly through the wondrous primeval forests which clothe the upper parts of the world-famous sea-cliffs of northeast Formosa.

21

Nature's Luxurious Extravagance

PEOPLE WHOSE LIVES are spent in the cool temperate regions of the world have in general exaggerated ideas of the tropics. The great heat of which they hear or imagine impresses them unpleasantly, and visions of noxious wild animals and deadly diseases arise until the picture becomes a nightmare. A visit to the hothouses of botanic gardens or those of private estates, filled with strange plants bearing noble and handsomely marked foliage or brilliantly colored blossoms, gives another aspect to the tropics; yet such a scene is apt to warp our ideas just as much as the thoughts of excessive heat, wild animals, and diseases. It is doubtful if any article or book no matter how truthfully written can give any real idea of the tropics.

As a matter of fact, compared with temperate regions where such kaleidoscopic changes are wrought by the change of the seasons, the tropics are deadly monotonous. Perpetual summer reigns and the only change of season is that of wet and dry and this is not always fixed and recognizable as such. Trees, shrubs, and herbs flower and fruit throughout the year and leaves are shed at any time. Where wet and dry seasons prevail, drought induces a periodic fall of the leaf. Young, unfolding leaves are often delicately and beautifully colored, but the tropics boast nothing comparable with the wondrous autumnal tints of the north.

To the embellishment of our hothouses all parts of the tropics have contributed, but for the proper appreciation of our subject it is necessary to distinguish between the equatorial regions of the Old and New Worlds. It is only the lesser plants of the tropics that can be successfully accommodated in our stoves and palm-houses, be these ever so vast. The climbers and major trees of the tropics are almost unknown to dwellers of the North, since they need greater room than even such giant glass structures as the palm-house at Kew affords. In many parts of the tropics, to which steamers regularly ply, there have been established fine botanic gardens and parks. One so fortunate as to visit these will get a liberal education into the luxuriant vegetation of the tropics. If the visit be extended to several of these gardens, no matter in which hemisphere, the same trees and climbers will be seen planted over and over again. Among climbers the traveler will never be out of sight of the bougainvillea with its intensely colored bracts, of rich magenta or brick red according to the species. Of palms the coconut and royal are omnipresent. These and others are of the New World and have been carried everywhere, the coconut by ocean currents, others by the hand of man. Many other American plants now universally planted in the tropics shall receive their full recognition in due course but first let us survey the tropical plants of the Old World.

One of the trees most widely planted in the tropics for ornamental purposes is *Poinciana regia*, the flamboyant tree, a native of Madagascar. The farthest north I have seen this tree in flower is Port Said, at the entrance to the Suez Canal. The flamboyant is a member of a branch of the familiar pea family which, by the way, is within the tropics the family richest in tree forms. This poinciana is a flat-topped, deciduous leafed tree usually from 40 to 50 feet tall with a short trunk and wide-spreading crown of thick branches. Its leaves, which are finely divided and mimosa-like, are shed at any time in the year. So precocious is this species that I have seen three trees side by side one naked and laden with old fruits, one in full flower, and the third crowded with green foliage. The flowers are borne in large clusters usually at the end of naked shoots, occasionally with the unfolding leaves, and have large, intense scarlet petals flushed with yellow at their base. In full flower this tree is a blaze of scarlet so intense as to dazzle and even hurt the eyes. When bare of flowers and foliage and with only its black-brown flattened woody pods, each well over a foot long, the tree is ugly, but in blossom it is among the most gorgeous members of the tree world. It is one of the most familiar sights in the tropics and one which every traveler admires.

Much more beautiful but more rarely seen is *Colvillea racemosa*, another Madagascan tree also belonging to the pea family. I first saw a large tree in full flower in the Brisbane Botanic Gardens and was captivated immediately by its beauty. It has leaves like the flamboyant tree, similar in size but with rather smaller pinnae, and terminal compound panicles 2 feet and more high and more than 1 foot broad of wondrous orange-yellow flowers. A flat-topped tree, not more than 50 feet tall but more through the crown, this colvillea is in flower a marvelous spectacle of loveliness.

Another tree much planted in the tropics is *Spathodea campanulata*, native of Africa. This is a relative of the indian bean tree (*Catalpa speciosa*) and has pinnate leaves and panicles of large, scarlet suffused and edged with yellow flowers. The African Baobab is among the wonders of the vegetable world. In bulk of trunk it probably exceeds all other trees. In height it is seldom more than 100 feet but the trunk is enormous, yet so soft and full of pith that a rifle bullet easily passes through the largest specimen. When leafless the baobab is perhaps the ugliest of all trees but when clad with leaves and flowers is a noble example of vegetable growth. The huge, egg-shape, pointed fruits are full of a powdery mass which tastes like cream-of-tartar and this name is often applied to the tree.

But gorgeous and wonderful as they are these and other tropical trees of similar character have no value to the greenhouses of northern lands. Here they may serve to give a glimpse of tropical tree growth before we discourse on those of lesser size but to us of greater value.

Palms are a feature of the tropics and are so associated in the minds of all folk. A few species are found in the warm temperate regions but the family is essentially equatorial. The indispensable *Kentia belmoreana* and *K. fosteriana* hail from Lord Howe Island off the east Australian coast. The exquisite *Phoenix roebelini* comes from southeastern Asia, the older *P. reclinata* is African, and *P. rupicola* is indigenous on the foot hills of the eastern Himalayas; the familiar fan-leaved *Livistona chinensis* or *L. borbonica* hails from the Liukiu and Bonin Islands. There are many hundreds of species, the majority of them local in their distribution but some, like the coconut, which fringes the ocean-girt lands of all the tropics, are widespread. All are beautiful and possessed of characters by which the veriest tyro recognizes a palm immediately, never mistaking it for some other plant. Many are of great economic importance yielding fibers, oils, edible fruits, starch, and sugar, and, to the peoples of the tropics palms are the most important of all the families of the vegetable kingdom. Their uses are indeed legion. The Tamil people of India have a song which enumerates eight hundred and one uses of the palmyra palm (*Borassus flabellifer*). Perhaps the chief use of this palm, however, is the production of palm wine or toddy, which is obtained by tapping the sap flowing to the inflorescence and fermenting it. For this purpose the palmyra is cultivated in enormous quantities in India and elsewhere.

The talipot palm (*Corypha umbraculifera*), native of Indo-Malaya and Ceylon, grows 100 feet tall and has the distinction of bearing the largest inflorescence known in the whole vegetable kingdom. This gigantic, much-branched, panicled mass of tiny white flowers terminates the life of the tree and is often as much as 10 feet high and broad. The sago palms (*Metroxylon rumphi* and *M. laeve*) have an inflorescence fully 6 feet broad and die after flowering, but from an underground shoot other stems are produced so that the clump of palms does not cease to exist. Sago is obtained by cutting down the trees as the inflorescence appears, splitting the trunks and crushing and washing the pith.

Voyagers of the Middle Ages told many wondrous tales of the marvels of the tropics, but none more fabulous than that of the coco-de-mer or double coconut (*Lodoicea sechellarum*). The fruit is bilobed, is the largest known among palms, and takes fifteen years to ripen. It grows naturally only on the Seychelles, a small group of islands in the Indian Ocean. Long before its habitat was known the fruit was found floating in the Indian Ocean and was supposed to be the product of some submarine tree. On account of their mysterious origin and remarkable shape these fruits were for centuries regarded with awe and wonder, considered of enormous value, and esteemed a universal antidote against all ills, finding a place of honor in temples and churches, especially in the Spanish colonies of South America. The discovery of the habitat of this palm, combined with the over-enterprise of a certain sea captain who loaded his ship with them, caused the bottom to fall out of the market. Today these fruits are only objects of curiosity. The tree itself grows 100 feet tall and has enormous, fan-shaped leaves; it is one of the noblest of all palms.

A feature of the tidal, muddy shores of the tropics, where they form thickets and help to reclaim land, are various species of

Beauty-bush (*Kolkwitzia amabilis*), a handsome shrub (GEORGE TALOUMIS)

mangroves. In the Old World some twenty-two species occur, in America four. These plants present a great similarity in habit and other characteristics though they belong to several families. They are in general much-branched bushes or low trees with a great development of aerial roots, both buttressing roots from the main stem and supporting pillar roots from the branches. Some, like bruguiera, avicennia, and sonneratia, have in quantity erect, colorless, aerating roots rising out of the mud, suggesting a mass of stout bristles of weird aspect. The seeds of many mangroves germinate in the fruit whilst still attached to the tree and develop long primary roots which hang down often a foot in length. In due season the seedling falls and the root sticks in the soft, oozing mud and escapes the danger of being carried away by the tide. Mangrove swamps, though of great interest, are the most unhealthy places in the tropics.

The coming of the white man with his boundless energy and enterprise, his plantations of tea, coffee, cocoa, rubber, cinchona, and other plants of great economic value is fast changing the face of the tropics, even as his settling has caused wholesale changes in colder climes. The forests which with few unimportant exceptions once formed a broad equatorial belt thousands of miles wide are fast disappearing, destroyed by fire and axe to make way for crops of more immediate commercial value. Those of us who have been privileged to drink in the solitude and grandeur of forest depths whether in the tropics or in temperate lands may well be envied, for to generations of a not very distant future such experiences will be impossible, since the forests will have vanished. Cultivated crops of trees, be they for timber, rubber, or whatnot, are not more interesting than those of wheat or potatoes.

Sometimes friends have said, "You must have endured much hardship wandering in out of the way corners of the earth." I have. But such count for nothing, since I have lived in nature's boundless

halls and drank deeply of her pleasures. To wander through a
tropical or temperate forest with tree trunks more stately than
gothic columns, beneath a canopy of foliage more lovely in its
varied forms than the roof of any building fashioned by man, the
welcome cool, the music of the babbling brook, the smell of mother
earth, and the mixed odors of a myriad of flowers—where does
hardship figure when the reward is such?

The tropical jungle is impassable and aggravating in the extreme
but the virgin forest of the tropics is sublime. A typical tropical
forest is mixed in character with broadleaf, chiefly evergreen trees
placed widely apart, their tall trunks mostly clothed with smooth
barks, and often buttressed at the base or above and below the
main limbs, bearing aloft a broad mass of branches interlocking
with those of their neighbors and crowded with epiphytic plants
in wondrous variety. Vast climbers with ropelike stems hundreds
of feet long hang looped in serpentine coils, their leafy shoots
sprawling over the treetops, binding all into an interminable tangle.
Looking down on such forests from some favorable eminence
flowers may be seen, but to what they belong it is often impossible
to tell. From the forest floor little but a tangled mass of stems and
foliage is discernible even with the aid of strong field glasses. Palms
are the common understorey in these forests and with them are
tree-ferns, bananas and other shade-loving things with broad
sombre green and curiously mottled leaves. Herbaceous plants—
save ferns, mosses, and selaginellas—are rare in tropical forests;
shade-loving, low shrubs with pretty but rarely conspicuous flowers may be there aplenty, but much of the floor in most of the forest depths is completely bare of vegetation and is massed with decaying leaves, twigs, fallen flowers, and fruits.

In the tropics the sun is vertical overhead, or nearly so, the
whole year round and the complete absence of shadows at noon
strikes the traveler from the North as strange. Dawn breaks about
half past five and in a quarter of an hour it seems full daylight.

Suddenly the rim of the sun appears above the horizon and all nature is waked into activity—birds chirp and scream, monkeys clatter, butterflies flutter lazily around, and every creeping, crawling thing moves along; the air is cool and refreshing and it feels good to be alive. The sun rises rapidly, the heat manifests itself, and in a few hours drowsiness pervades the whole forest; about noon every voice is hushed and the forest stillness can be felt. More often than not a thunderstorm of short duration occurs in the afternoon and disappears as suddenly as it came, but leaving the forest greatly refreshed; and toward evening life revives again, sound and music thrill the forest scene. About six o'clock the sun sets and within half an hour darkness is complete; silence reigns, save for the croaking of some frog or noise of an occasional nocturnal animal. Next day the same phenomena repeat themselves. There is perfect equilibrium and monotony in the march of nature under the equator.

22

Tropics of the New World

In the tropics of the New World the land area is much less than that of the Old World but the climatic conditions are virtually the same. The vast valley of the mighty Amazon and those of other only slightly less South American rivers are regions of magnificent forests. The insular areas are much less than those of Malaysia but are nonetheless equally rich in luxuriant vegetation.

The wonderful forests of the Amazon Valley and those of other parts of the American tropics have been ofttimes described in books and he who will may read the story. The major trees have the usual gigantic trunks often buttressed at the base and bear aloft wide-spreading crowns. Huge climbers interlace them into one vast canopy and the branches are laden with a multitudinous variety of epiphytic growths. From the trees dangle the ropelike stems of huge climbers; there is an understory of palms, tree ferns and other shade-loving plants, and the forest floor is similar to that of the forests of the Old World tropics. In general character and

luxuriance the vegetable growth of the tropics of the two hemispheres are singularly alike. The aspect of the forests and the forest scenery presents no striking contrasts although the forests elements are specifically distinct and, as a rule, the genera also are
different.

Of plants of economic importance the tropics of the New World
have given a goodly quota to the world. They include that indispensable drug quinine, obtained from the bark of certain species
of cinchona; the Para rubber (*Hevea brasiliensis*) now abundantly
planted in Malaysia and elsewhere and the rubber-producing tree
above all others; the avocado pear (*Persea gratissima*); the Brazil-
nut (*Bertholletia excelsa*), most familiar of tropical nuts; the pineapple (*Ananas sativa*); cassava (*Manihot utilissima*) from which
is obtained, by special preparation, tapioca, the well-known food-
stuff; and also the potato, sweet potato, and maize.

Though the land area is so much less, the American tropics have
contributed largely to our hothouses and to the parks and botanic
gardens of the tropics in general. One American tree, *Jacaranda
mimosifolia*, has been planted in great plenty throughout the
warmer parts of the world. It is a rather small tree with finely
divided mimosa-like leaves and terminal panicles of violet-blue,
foxglove-like flowers. In South Africa and Australia it is much
used as a street tree and is entitled to rank in the forefront among
the world's most lovely trees.

The coconut palm (*Cocos nucifera*), universally found grac-
ing tropic strands, is considered to be of American origin, having
spread over the world through its fruit being floated by ocean
currents. Among all the great palm family there is none so useful to
mankind or more beautiful than the sea-loving coconut—king of
palms. Moreover, it is the only palm whose edible fruit is known
to the multitudes who live in temperate lands. Another American
palm (*Oreodoxa regia*), the royal palm, is everywhere to be seen
planted in the tropics. This noble, rapidly growing palm with

stout, smooth, gray trunks and long, dark green, plumelike leaves
is a wonderful avenue tree and is much used for this purpose in
many lands. One of the finest avenues I have seen of this palm is
in the Botanic Gardens, Calcutta. The coquito palm of Chili
(*Jubaea spectabilis*), which will grow in quite cool lands, is also
much planted. This palm has a massive trunk and a fine crown of
pinnate leaves. Though the American tropics are rich in palms of
great variety, very few are familiar tenants of our greenhouses.
One, however (*Cocos wedelliana*), with slender stem and finely
pinnate leaves, is a popular favorite, though less so today than
formerly.

Of climbing plants the American tropics have been generous to
our greenhouses. The most common and widely cultivated are
Bougainvillea glabra, *B. lateritia*, and *B. spectabilis* though the
last two are seldom seen flowering in northern gardens. The first-
named, of which there are several forms, is, in spite of its harsh-
colored bracts, a popular plant with our florists and their custom-
ers. Allamanda with its gaudy yellow flowers is much planted
all over the world, especially varieties of *A. cathartica*. These
handsome plants are found in greenhouses under such names as
A. schotti, *A. hendersoni*, and *A. williamsi*. Less frequently seen is
A. violacea, well distinguished by its reddish-purple flowers. Another favorite climber is *Solanum wendlandi* with dark green, pinnate leaves and large clusters of blue flowers. This plant is native
of Costa Rica and was introduced into cultivation in 1882. A very
pleasing, yellow-flowered climber is *Stigmaphyllum heterophyl-
lum*, native of Brazil, and sent to Europe from Buenos Aires in
1841. The foliage is bronzy green and the genus derives its name
from a curious green appendage to the stigma.

Planted almost everywhere in the tropics is the lovely *Bignonia
venusta*, whose wealth of orange-colored flowers presents a never-
to-be-forgotten sight. It is fairly vigorous-growing and loves to ramble over fences, buildings and old trees, draping them with green

foliage, and in season, with gorgeous trumpet-shaped blossoms. At it thrives in Honolulu, Hongkong, and elsewhere, there is no more gorgeous climbing plant. It is native of Brazil and has been known in gardens since 1815. Very pretty and pleasing is *Antigonum leptopus* with festoons of pink or white blossoms wreathing buildings or fences. This is also a favorite plant in tropical gardens where it is often known as the Honolulu creeper. Wayward in habit under our northern skies it is the princess of its family, that of the lowly polygonum and rumex.

Old favorites in our stoves and whose successful culture is looked upon as a test of the gardener's skill are the various species of dipladenia which hail from Brazil, Bolivia, and other parts of South America. One of the finest species is the white suffused with pink flowered *D. splendens*, introduced in 1841. Others are *D. acuminata* with large, deep rose-colored flowers; *D. boliviensis* with white, yellow-throated flowers; *D. atropurpurea*; and the salmon to purple flowered *D. urophylla*. The curious genus aristolochia is widespread in both hemispheres and includes many tropical species with large and remarkable flowers. The most extraordinary is *A. gigas* var. *sturtevanti*, native of Guatemala, with enormous, uterus-shaped flowers, white without, cream-color splashed and mottled with velvety maroon purple within, and a long caudex hanging from the lip. The flowers are pendent on long stalks and are from 1½ to 2 feet wide, from 2 to 2½ feet long with the tail over a yard in length. They emit a strong fetid odor and are fertilized by flies and other carrion-loving insects.

From Peru, in 1847, came *Cantua dependens*, a greenhouse climber, with long, drooping, orange-colored flowers of great beauty and known to the Peruvian Indians as the magic tree. There are other species of cantua and many other climbers of great merit, but the above will serve to illustrate clearly our indebtedness to American tropics for greenhouse-climbing plants.

To the great family of aroids our hothouses owe many of the

finest foliage plants they possess and not a few with striking flowers. Among them no genus has contributed more splendidly than anthurium, which is wholly American. Of the many handsome species in cultivation *A. veitchi,* native of Colombia, has the noblest foliage. The leaves are of extraordinary appearance, often attaining a length of 5 feet with a breadth of over 1 foot; the principal veins are sunk and the waved appearance thus caused is further enhanced by a deep glossy green color and a brilliant metallic lustre. Very beautiful, too, is *A. warocqueanum,* another Colombian species with leaves each from 2½ to 3 feet long, deep green with prominent, almost white veins. Another splendid species with round, heart-shaped, dark green leaves and white veins is *A. magnificum.* A striking inhabitant of our stoves is *A. scherzerianum,* the flamingo plant, with its brilliant scarlet bract and twisted, protruded spadix and relatively narrow, dull dark green leaves. It is very floriferous, lasts in bloom a long time, and always excites admiration. Very similar is *A. andreanum* with paler, lustrous green, rather longer leaves, larger bract, and a straight orange-yellow spadix.

These among other tropical aroids are epiphytes and some of them begin life as climbers, sending down into the humid air of the forest whiplike aerial roots which on reaching the ground develop a branching root system, become streched taut, and resemble hempen strands. A fine example of climbing aroid is *Philodendron andreanum,* native of Colombia. This species has leaves resembling those of *Anthurium veitchi* which are often from 4 to 5 feet long and are deflected vertically from a stout, erect foot stalk. When young the leaves are scarlet tinged with brown, when older bronzy red-brown finally changing to velvety green; the midrib and primary veins are whitish through all the stages of leaf development. In this species the leaves are simple and entire, in others they are pinnated or curiously incised and often full of round holes. Most remarkable in this connection is the related *Monstera deliciosa,* the fruit of which is edible. When very young the leaves of this plant are entire, but as it develops some of the tissue between the veins ceases to grow, becomes dry and tears away, this leaving holes between the ribs.

With smaller, thinner foliage than the anthurium we have many species of dieffenbachia with bright or dull green leaves mottled and striped with white or yellowish color. Among those most frequently seen in cultivation are *D. bowmani* and *D. picta* from Brazil, *D. jenmani* from British Guiana, and *D. pearcei* from Ecuador. The stems of these plants contain a very acrid principle and one species (*D. seguine*) is known as the dumb cane of the West Indies, since it renders speechless anyone chewing a piece of the stem. It was formerly used in torturing slaves.

No species of banana is native of America but there are very many members of closely related families with handsome foliage. Such, for example, are calathea and maranta which have simple leaves, purple on the underside, dark green, mottled or blotched with dark brown and paler green on the upper side. One of the finest species is *Calathea veitchiana* with leaf-blades 14 inches long and 9 inches broad on erect petioles 1½ feet tall. From the thickened rootstock of *Maranta arundinacea* West Indian arrowroot is obtained by grinding and washing to free the starch. But from a garden standpoint the most important American genus of this group is canna, from the various species of which have been derived the wonderful race of cannas our gardens boast today. The wild types are very ordinary looking plants with red or yellow flowers, and it is difficult to realize that they could have produced by hybridization and selection the brilliantly colored plants we know as cannas. The common *C. indica*, now naturalized in many parts of the tropics of both hemispheres, is familiarly known as Indian-shot from its hard, small, round seeds.

One of the most gorgeous flowering plants of our gardens is the poinsettia (*Euphorbia pulcherrima*), a gift of Mexico. The so-called

Allamanda, a tropical
vine bearing immense
yellow blooms,
is native to Brazil
(GEORGE TALOUMIS)

Bougainvillea, a familiar,
free-flowering,
crimson-colored
vine grown in Florida
and West Coast gardens.
It is cultivated in
greenhouses in the
Northeast.
(GEORGE TALOUMIS)

flower of this plant is really an inflorescence of many flowers and the showy part is the surrounding whorl of scarlet bracts. Familiar as we are with this plant in our greenhouses and florist shops its real size and brilliancy is best seen in tropical lands. Quite naturally such an exceptionally showy plant is abundantly planted throughout hot countries. It is often used as a hedge plant though more usually it is accommodated in beds and borders. The finest I have seen grew in the Botanic Gardens, Brisbane, the capital city of Queensland.

A pretty flowering plant is *Amasonia punicea*, native of British Guiana, in which each shoot terminates in a raceme of many white tubular flowers each 1 inch long and subtended by a bright red bract which persists for a couple of months after the flowers have fallen. Very pleasing, too, are the various species of alphelandra, native of Brazil, Peru, and elsewhere. Among the best are *A. nitens* with dark, lustrous green leaves and terminal spikes of orange-scarlet flowers and *A. variegata* whose large orange-yellow bracts, from which bright yellow flowers protrude, are closely imbricated and form a stout spike resembling a fir cone. Closely related is the genus sanchezia from Ecuador, of which one of the best known is *S. nobilis*, introduced into gardens in 1863. This has clear yellow flowers in dense terminal racemes with bright red bracts. The form *variegata* with the midrib and primary veins of the leaf colored yellow is more generally cultivated than the type. Even finer is *S. longiflora* with rich, vinous purple, tubular flowers in drooping panicles.

A useful greenhouse plant is *Streptosolen jamesoni* from the mountains of northern Peru and Colombia, where it was discovered by William Lobb in 1846. It has orange-colored flowers and may be grown either as a bushy plant in pots or as a climber. Very handsome, too, are the various species of tibouchina with their broad dark blue to violet-purple blossoms, of which *T. semidecandra* is perhaps the most widely grown.

The familiar nasturtium or Indian cress of our gardens (*Tropaeolum majus* and *T. minus*) are natives of South America. They are much used as annuals wherever gardening is practiced and in places their buds and young fruits are employed as a condiment instead of capers. There are several other species, of which mention may be made of *T. umbellatum* with clustered not solitary flowers and *T. violaeflorum* with blue flowers and tuberous roots. Another species (*T. tuberosum*) furnishes a farina from the tubers which mixed with molasses is made into a jelly and eaten by Peruvian Indians. The gem of the genus is *T. speciosum* which is native of Chile.

Our greenhouses fuchsias are largely the progeny of *F. speciosa*, which is supposed to be a hybrid between *F. magellanica* and *F. fulgens*. The first-named is native of Peru and southward and is said to have been introduced to Kew Gardens in 1788 by a Captain Firth. *F. fulgens* is Mexican and reached England about 1838. There are several other species of fuchsia in the New World, some of them in the more temperate parts, and one or two outlying species occur in New Zealand.

The waters of the Amazon and Orinoco rivers have given us the *Victoria regia*, which has the largest leaves and flowers of any aquatic plant. The floating leaves of this plant are round, from 5 to 6 feet in diameter, and the edge is turned up to a height of from 4 to 6 inches; on the lower side the ribs project very far and are armed with formidable spines. The fragrant flower is like that of a water lily but 15 inches across, white with a pink center and lasts for a day only. This noble member of the vegetable kingdom was discovered in 1801 but was not introduced until 1846, when Thomas Bridges successfully brought home seeds in wet clay.

Though perhaps less interesting than the Old World family of nepenthes, that of the bromeliads is worthy of notice and is peculiarly American. The bulk of the species are tropical but one (*Tillandsia usneoides*), the old-man's-beard, is abundant in Florida and Louisiana, hanging from the trees in long gray festoons. Though many are epiphytes of the forests, especially those of the Amazon Valley, quite a few are terrestrial plants growing among rocks, often in dry situations. The best-known member of the whole family is the pineapple, now universally cultivated in tropical countries. Most of the species have a short stem bearing a rosette of leaves, often fleshy and channeled on the upper surface, their bases fitting closely together so that the whole plant forms a sort of funnel which is usually full of water. The leaves may or may not be armed along their margins, are often pleasingly mottled and barred with different hues, and in some the upper leaves are brilliantly colored. The inflorescence usually rises out of the center of the funnel and is furnished with closely imbricated bracts, often brightly colored, which add to the conspicuousness of the flowers. Among the more common members of this family in hothouses are species of bromelia, billbergia, aechmea, tillandsia, and ananas. The pineapple (*Ananas sativa*) is among the finest of tropical fruits, and other members of the family are valuable fiber-yielding plants.

23

Butterflies of the Vegetable Kingdom

ORCHIDS ARE THE BUTTERFLIES of the vegetable world, the aristocrats of the greenhouse and the most envied of tropical plants. Their cult has waxed enormously during the past three-quarters of a century and they have their ardent devotees in every land. A collection of tropical orchids and their hybrids is largely a hobby of the rich man, since their wants and maintenance are costly. Many of them are so rare as to be almost priceless, and in a manner these are in the same category as masterpieces of painting, porcelain, and other art objects.

The cultural requirements of many orchids are exacting and the study of orchid growing has brought into being a race of garden specialists devoted to them alone. Little by little their proper requirements have come to be understood; and this knowledge, together with the well-found modern glass-house structure, has made comparatively easy the successful growing of these remarkable plants. Hybridists in great numbers have worked on the family and today orchid hybrids in cultivation are more numerous than the species. Moreover, many of these hybrids have better constitutions and finer flowers than their parents, and in consequence are more permanent plants in collections. But my theme is the wildings, and beyond paying tribute of hearty praise to the orchid breeders of every land have nothing to do with the results of their skill.

The orchid family is one of the most natural and also one of the largest in the vegetable kingdom. Linnaeus, in 1753, knew only about a dozen exotic orchids; whereas, today, fully 5,000 species and more than 400 genera are known! They are most abundant in the tropics but the family is universally distributed; one species, the little *Calypso borealis*, being found as far north as 68° latitude.

In the temperate regions of this country are found many terrestrial species, including such lovely plants as *Cypripedium acaule*, *C. spectabilis*, *C. candidum*, and *C. pubescens*. In Europe and northern Asia, too, grow many interesting orchids, among them being *Cypripedium calceolus*, *C. macranthum*, *C. japonicum*, and *C. tibeticum*, all with large and showy flowers. Many species are native of the temperate parts of Australia; and not a few belong to South Africa where, on dripping rocks on Table Mountain, is found the wondrous *Disa grandiflora*, perhaps the most showy of all terrestrial orchids.

In the cool regions of both the Northern and Southern Hemispheres nearly all the orchid species grow in the ground after the manner of ordinary plants, but in the tropics, where the great concentration of species occurs, nearly all grow epiphytically upon trees; though not a few are found among humus on rocks and mountain tops. Comparatively few terrestrial species are cultivated, and, strange to say, when attempted their cultivation has been found more difficult than that of their epiphytic tropical relatives. A few, of which the bird's-nest orchid (*Neottia nidus-avis*) of Europe and northern Asia is a well-known example, are

Cymbidiums, at the height of their beauty on a summer terrace. These orchids are superb, long-lasting cut flowers, usually grown in cool greenhouses. (GEORGE TALOUMIS)

saprophytes, have no leaves and live on decaying vegetable matter. A few are climbers but it is doubtful if any are true parasites.

Orchids are especially remarkable for the curiously varied shapes and colors of their flowers, which resemble all sorts of dissimilar objects such as a bee, fly, beetle, slipper, helmet, small monkey, moth, miniature swan, dove, cradle, and so forth, and the relative sizes are extraordinarily different. Some like liparis, the twayblades, have flowers so small as to require close searching to detect, while others, like the cattleyas, have flowers 6 inches and more across. The flowers are of every hue from inconspicuous green through all the colors of the spectrum and of every conceivable shade. Nearly all emit an odor and very many are extremely fragrant. The variability in the form of the flowers is considered an adaptation to ensure cross-pollination by insects and honey-loving birds.

The flower is irregular in shape with six, usually petal-like segments inserted above the ovary. The three outer ones, called sepals, and two of the inner ones, called petals, are often nearly alike; but the third inner segment, called the lip or labellum, differs from the others in form and in direction. Properly the lip should be at the top of the flower as it is in *Disa grandiflora*; but usually it is at the bottom, being brought into this position by the twisting of the ovary. Opposite the lip and overhanging it in the axis of the flower is what is called the column, which consists of one, rarely two, stamens combined with the pistil, the one- to four-celled anther of anthers being variously situated on the style itself. The pollen is rarely granular and free, being almost invariably glutinous or agglomerated into two, four or eight masses, termed pollinia, which are fixed either directly or by means of a tiny stalk (claudicle) to a viscous gland below the anther. The style is produced at the top into a prominence or fleshy beak termed a rostellum. The seeds are minute, multitudinous, and easily dispersed by wind. So much for the structure of an orchid flower.

Now a word or two about the plant in general. A feature of most orchids is the storage tissues for reserves of water and foodstuffs. In many terrestrial species, like orchis itself, this warehouse is represented by two or more small tubers at the base of the stem and below the ground; in epiphytes, like cattleyas, dendrobiums, and others, the aerial stems are thickened to serve the purpose and are known as pseudobulbs. In phalaenopsis and other genera the leaves are thick and leathery and serve as storehouses.

Again the roots of epiphytic orchids are of three kinds, each fulfilling a separate function. In the first place, to fasten the plant to its support there are clinging roots which are insensitive to gravity. Secondly, the niche between the plant and its support, and the network formed by the clinging roots, acts as a reservoir for humus; into this absorbing or feeding roots project. Finally there are true aerial roots which hang down in long festoons. The skin of these is colorless and perforated and acts as a sponge to absorb water trickling down over the roots. Their internal tissue is green as may be seen on wetting a root. Orchids have a host of peculiarities, some of which will be mentioned later but the above may serve as a sort of introduction to the family in general.

Since our subject is a large one, it is convenient to divide it and deal separately with the orchids of the Old and the New Worlds. Moreover, as the genera are so numerous, I content myself with brief mention of those most commonly seen in greenhouses.

24

Orchids of the Old World Tropics

In the forests of Malaysia, epiphytic orchids are extraordinarily abundant and they extend southward to northern Australia and northward through the Philippines to Formosa. On the mainland they abound in Indo-Malaya and northward to southern China. On the other hand, the Indian peninsula and Africa are poor in epiphytic orchids. The species mostly have a very limited range, being often confined to a single small island or to a particular mountain. They grow clustered together often in large numbers and the branches of the major trees of the steamy forests of Malaysia and Indo-Malaya are laden with orchids of many kinds. Although there is a peculiarity of habit that enables one soon to detect an orchidaceous plant even when not in flower, yet they vary greatly in size and appearance. Some of the small creeping species are no larger than mosses, while the grammatophyllum of Borneo, which grows in the forks of trees, forms a mass of leafy thickened stems 10 feet long and the whole plant weighs many hundreds of pounds. Owing to the great monetary value of certain orchids and the vigor and enthusiasm with which their cultivation has been prosecuted, the world has been ransacked for these plants. Much human energy has been expended and many lives given in their quest and a halo of romance surrounds the whole topic. More has been made of the subject than of any other branch of plant introduction.

As a matter of fact orchids, at least the epiphytic ones, are easily transported from their homes to our conservatories. With their pseudobulbs and thickened leaves they are capable of withstanding a considerable amount of dessication, though careful and expert handling is needed to properly establish them on arrival at their destination.

Owing largely to the fact that they require great heat, an extensive group, of which vanda may serve as an example, is known as East Indian orchids. Another large group of Old World orchids flourishes best under moderate heat. Of these many coelogynes, dendrobiums, and cypripediums are familiar examples.

The first epiphytic orchids I saw wild in any quantity were *Dendrobium chrysanthum* and *D. chrysotoxum* in the forest of Yunnan, and I may as well begin with this particular genus. It is a large and popular one in gardens and its members are found in great plenty from north Australia throughout the Malay Archipelago and north to Japan; on the mainland it abounds in Indo-Burma, Assam, and south China. The most northern species is the pleasing little *D. moniliforme*, which is abundant on the mighty cryptomerias, planted as an avenue to the shrines at Nikko. One of the most popular of all is *D. nobile*, which is common and widespread in western China south to Burma and for centuries has been a favorite medicine among the Chinese. From Burma came the splendid *D. thyrsiflorum* with large, broad racemes of flowers with rich yellow lip and white sepals and petals. *D. formosum* with its broad, pure white flowers, the lip blotched with yellow, hails from Indo-Burma, and *D. phalaenopsis*, with racemose spikes of finely colored phalaenopsis-like flowers, from north Australia. The fine *D. dalhouseanum* with its tinted gray sepals and petals and velvety, crimson-fringed lip is Indian; and *D. brymerianum* with scented, deep yellow flowers and remarkably fringed lip is a native of Burma. One of the best Australian species is *D. superbiens*, and another good one is *D. bigibbum*, both from the region of Torres Straits. A number of handsome species are natives of New Guinea, one of the best being *D. atroviolaceum* with primrose-yellow, spotted with dusky brown sepals and petals and the lip deep violet-purple with a few paler radiating lines near the margin; on the outside the lip is green with a large, dark violet, irregular blotch on either side. The flora of New Guinea is very little known and we may expect it to yield, some day, many fine orchids and other plants.

More than 300 species of dendrobiums are known. The pseudobulb exhibits much variation, being only slightly swollen and sticklike, relatively stout, cylindrical, or even swollen at the joints and tubercled in appearance.

One of the most popular classes is that of the cypripediums, the lady-slipper orchids, characterized by their united lateral sepals and pouchlike lip. Under this name are grouped in the popular mind species found in the cool temperate region of America, Europe, and Asia, in tropical Indo-Malaya and south China, and in tropical America. But there are sufficient technical differences to divide this composite group into four genera.

Strictly speaking, the true cypripediums are confined to the temperate regions mentioned; the tropical American species are referred to the genera phragmopedilum and selenipedium; and those of the eastern tropics to that of paphiopedilum. This explanation is necessary but for the purpose of this chapter we may adhere to the old accustomed usage of the generic name cypripedium.

Some of the temperate species were mentioned in the introductory paragraphs and space forbids any further reference. There are, however, in south China and Indo-Malaya a whole host of species many of which are among the most popular and best known orchids. Prominent among these is the familiar *Cypripedium insigne*, native of the eastern Himalayas, one of the most easily grown of orchids and one that revels under cool conditions. The flowers are erect, of varying shades of polished yellow, brown, white, and green delightfully blended. There are very many named forms of this, differing in the color of the flowers and all very lovely. Another favorite Burma species is *C. villosum*, which has been so largely used by the hybridist. The mountains of Bhutan and adjacent Sikkim are the home of the pretty *C. fairieanum* with decurved, ciliated lateral petals. It was first introduced in 1857, and flowered and was figured in the "Botanical Magazine" (t. 5024) of the same year and subsequently lost. For fifty years its habitat remained unknown and a large reward was offered for its rediscovery but all efforts failed until 1904. It became famous as the "lost orchid" but its reintroduction was bungled and very little monetary reward fell to those who succeeded in winning anew this plant into gardens.

Those just named and others with scapose flowers have green leaves, but there is another and more tropical section having leaves beautifully marbled with white and dark green. Among them may be mentioned the handsome *C. callosum*, of which there are many named and winsomely colored forms—also *C. curtisi* of Sumatra and *C. lawrenceanum* of Borneo. The latter has a dark red-brown pouch and a broad white, striped with red-brown standard. The limestone-loving Burmese *C. bellatulum* and its yellow-flowered confrère *C. concolor*, have marbled leaves and are found as far north as south China. Another species of the same group is the delightful *C. niveum*, which is native of the Malayan Islands and first introduced in 1868. Another group with large flowers in racemes and long green leaves is represented by a number of species, of which *C. rothschildianum*, *C. stonei*, *C. superbiens*, *C. barbatum*, *C. parishi*, and *C. argus* are fine representatives. These have long, often arching and usually bearded lateral petals, frequently marked with eyelike dots; the flowers are more or less dark colored. Most of them are Malaysian but several grow in the Philippines.

I shall long remember the pleasure I felt on first beholding in a wild state the well-known *Coelogyne cristata*. It was in the forests of Sikkim above the Teesta River where hungry leeches swarmed on all sides. The plants grew on moss-clad rocks and at an elevation where snow lies during the winter months. Greater heat is required for *C. massangeana* and *C. dayana* with their pendent racemes of orchreous yellow and brown flowers. These are natives of Borneo, whilst *C. veitchi*, a related species, with flowers of the purest white, is from New Guinea.

Closely related to coelogyne, and by some authors united with it, is the genus pleione, often called Himalayan crocus. These are curious tufted plants with flattened disclike pseudobulbs and grow among moss on humus-clad rocks or tree trunks. They are deciduous and most of them flower before the leaves appear. The best known are *P. lagenaria*, *P. maculata*, and *P. humilis*. The genus extends northward and eastward into China, where one species (*P. pogonioides*) is common in Hupeh province, growing on rocks in the forest and covered with snow in winter.

A genus of orchids which in quite recent years has been enormously developed by the hybridist is cymbidium. The genus is widely distributed in the eastern tropics with members extended into the temperate regions of China and Japan. Some of the species are truly terrestrial, some grow in the tops of rocks, and others are true epiphytes, growing usually in the forks of trees. One of the oldest and best known species is the Himalayan *C. grandiflorum*

The Yellow Lady's-slipper, *Cypripedium Calceolus,* is one of the handsomest orchids native to eastern North America (GEORGE TALOUMIS)

with long, spreading racemes of flowers splashed and barred with rufous brown, the lip yellow and crimson. Quite different in appearance are *C. eburneum* and *C. sanderae* with their ascending, almost upright flower stems and few flowers, white in the former, spotted and barred with rose-red in the latter. These have proved of great service to the hybridist who, by crossing them with some of the older sorts which have spreading, many-flowered racemes, has evolved a race of useful plants of wondrous beauty whose flowers last for a month or six weeks. Perhaps the most inconspicuous member of the genus is *C. ensifolium*, a terrestrial species common in many parts of China. This the Chinese regard as the king of flowers, its modest appearance and the delicate odor of its blossoms being considered to represent the very essence of refinement.

A common terrestrial orchid in China is *Bletilla hyacinthina*, occasionally cultivated in our greenhouses and interesting as the plant in which Robert Brown discovered the cell nucleus. Another and more widely known terrestrial orchid is *Phaius grandiflorus*, which grows in moist and boggy places from Hongkong southward through Malaysia to northern Australia and presents much variation in the color of its flowers. In Yunnan and southward to Burma grows *Thunia marshalliana* and, in the neighborhood of Rangoon, *T. bensoniae* with amethyst-purple flowers and frilled lip.

The genus calanthe is widely dispersed in the Orient and quite a number of species grow in the forests of China and Japan, but the species most generally cultivated are from Burma. From the neighborhood of Moulmien came *Calanthe vestita* in 1848 and *C. rosea* in 1850 which, hybridized by John Dominy in 1856, resulted in *C. veitchi*, the most popular calanthe of our gardens. This genus calanthe is of exceptional interest since by crossing *C. falcata* and *C. masuca* was raised the first hybrid orchid to flower. The work was done by John Dominy for Messrs. Veitch of Exeter. The plant flowered in 1856 and was named *C. domini* by Lindley who commented that such work would drive the botanists mad.

Very similar in appearance and quite closely related are bulbophyllum and cirrhopetalum, to which belong several hundred species, found from China south to Australia. They are epiphytes but frequently grow on humus-clad rocks where their dwarf habit suggests an incrustation of lichen or small pebbles. The leaves are often mere scales and their functions are performed by the tuberlike pseudobulbs. In an Australian species (*B. minutissimum*) the pseudobulb is hollow and has breathing pores (stomata) on the inner surface. The flowers are not showy but those of species like *B. barbatum* are fascinatingly curious. This has a small, dull-colored flower with a relatively large fringed and ciliated lip so delicately poised that it moves up and down at the slightest air disturbance. Another and similar species is *B. mandibulare,* native of north Borneo. Some of the Cirrhopetalums have attractive small flowers arranged umbellately in a circle at the top of a short stalk and have a protruded straight lip suggesting the beak of a pelican.

No group of orchids is more beautiful in blossom than the phalaenopsis or moth orchids, of which some thirty-five species are known. One of the best known is the white-flowered *P. aphrodite*, native of the Philippines and south Formosa. Very lovely, too, is *P. schilleriana* with rose-pink blossoms. The oldest known is *P. amabilis* which grows in Java, Borneo, and other islands and has large handsome flowers. This species was known to Rumphius as early as 1750, and is figured by him in his "Herbarium Amboinense." A common Philippine species is *P. rosea*, which grows in the hot valleys in the neighborhood of Manila and has been much used by the hybridist. Less frequently seen in collections are the Sumatran *P. violacea* and *P. sumatrana.* All the phalaenopsis have lovely flowers and in many species the strap-shaped leaves are reddish below and prettily mottled on the upper side.

Another fine genus is vanda, with conspicuous fragrant flowers of many hues. Perhaps the most exquisite of all is *V. coerulea*, with large flowers of soft, light blue tessellated with azure. This is one of the gems of the orchid world and captivates all who see it. It was discovered by William Griffith in 1837 on the Khasia Hills, but all attempts to introduce failed until 1850, when Thomas Lobb sent living plants to Messrs. Veitch of Exeter. A related species with pale lilac-blue flowers is *V. coerulescens*, native of upper Burma.

The well-known *V. suavis* and *V. tricolor*, natives of Java, were introduced into cultivation by Thomas Lobb in 1846. Both have axillary racemes of thick fleshy flowers with a strong spicy odor. In *V. suavis* the flowers are white spotted with red-purple and the basal half of the lip is deep purple. The flowers of *V. tricolor* are similarly spotted on a yellow ground. From the Moluccas came *V. insignis* with tawny yellow flowers spotted with dark brown and bright rose-purple lip. A Philippine species is *V. sanderiana* with handsome flattened flowers, white flushed with buff-yellow and reticulated with dull crimson. Very distinct in habit are *V. teres* and *V. hookeriana*, both rambling plants with round cylindric leaves as thick as an ordinary pencil. These have red, white, and purple flowers in racemes but rarely appear in flower under northern skies. In botanic gardens of the eastern tropics they are seen to advantage, but the finest I have ever seen were growing in tubs and pots in the garden of Raffles Hotel in Singapore —scores of large plants receiving little or no care but bearing hundreds of racemes of their brightly colored flowers.

Another plant I saw thriving to perfection in the same garden was *Renanthera coccinea*. The Javan *R. matutina*, with reddish and crimson flowers toned with yellow and changing with age to orange-yellow, has long been known in gardens though it is not common; while *R. imschootiana*, a newcomer, is more generally known today.

Closely related to vanda is arachnanthe, of which *A. cathcarti* from the shady valleys of the eastern Himalayas and *A. lowi* from Borneo are in cultivation. The last-named has a comparatively small cluster of leaves and flower stems which hang down like cords to a length of from 6 to 8 feet and are covered with numbers of star-shaped, crimson-spotted flowers of two kinds.

The giant among orchids of the eastern tropics is *Grammatophyllum speciosum* with leafy stems from 6 to 10 feet long and racemes of many flowers, clear yellow spotted with deep red-purple, each flower 6 inches across, and occasionally as many as one hundred on a raceme. It first flowered in England with Messrs. Loddiges at Hackney in 1852.

Very pleasing are the different species of aerides with their many flowered, often cylindric racemes. One of the best known is *A. multiflorum*, native of Burma, of which there are many forms, including one named *Veitchi* with rose-purple lip and white dotted with rose petals and sepals. To *A. fieldingi*, also of Burma, the name of foxbrush aerides has been given in allusion to the shape of the inflorescence. Very similar to aerides is saccolabium of which the Javan *S. blumei* with waxy, fragrant, rose-pink flowers is well known. The lip resembles the keel of a ship and the flowers are densely crowded in cylindric racemes. Other species are *S. huttoni*, *S. giganteum*, and *S. bigibbum*, the latter with yellowish flowers each with triangular, fringed white lip.

Africa is remarkably poor in epiphytic orchids and there are very few with showy flowers known from that vast continent. There are a number of terrestrial species, especially in the extreme south, and the most remarkable of all, *Disa grandiflora*, has been mentioned as peculiar to Table Mountain.

Of showy epiphytic species the finest hail from Madagascar. Two species of eulophiella (*E. elisabethae* and *E. peetersiana*) are worthy of special mention. The first named has many flowers in a raceme, each flower 1½ inches across, the lip white with golden disk and white sepals and petals, the former marked with rose-color on the outside. In *E. peetersiana* the racemes are more dense and the flowers, each about 3 inches across, are rose-purple with a golden blotch on the lip. Several species of the spur-flowered angraecum are indigenous in different parts of Africa. The pretty little *A. kotschyi* grows in Zanzibar and on the adjacent mainland. On Reunion Island is found *A. fragrans*, the faham, whose leaves, known as Bourbon tea, taste of bitter almonds and were at one time used medicinally to stimulate digestion and in pulmonary consumption. *A. hyaloides*, with small white, semitransparent flowers, and the better-known *A. citratum* are of Madagascar. So, too, is the handsome *A. sesquipedale*, the aristocrat of the genus and one of the most wonderful of orchids. This species has strap-shaped, distichously arranged leaves and in habit resembles certain species of vanda. The flowers, two to several on a raceme, are star-shaped, each from 6 to 9 inches across, waxy in texture and pure white; the base of the labellum is projected into an enormous hollow spur from 12 to 14 inches in length, at the bottom of which honey is secreted. Indigenous in the same island is a moth with a tongue sufficiently long to suck the nectar from the bottom of this spur, and it is the only insect that can remove the pollinia and effect the fertilization of the flowers. This is a marvelous example of mutual adaptation of flower and insect for their common benefit.

25

Orchids of the New World Tropics

FROM THE TROPICS of the New World gardens have received some of the showiest and most popular orchids known. The cattleyas, laelias, oncidiums, odontoglossums, miltonias, masdevallias, and many other favorite genera are all natives of the American continent. The first exotic orchid introduced into Great Britain was *Bletia verecunda* from the Bahamas in 1731, and the species still finds a place in the collection at Kew Gardens. It is a comparatively insignificant thing with erect, racemose, purple flowers, but of great historical interest.

The only orchid of real economic importance is *Vanilla planifolia*, a climbing plant native of Mexico but now much cultivated in the tropics of the Old World. It is a member of a small genus mostly South American. The well-known spice or flavoring agent (vanilla) is obtained from the fruit, which is a long fleshy capsule slightly yellow when ripe; before the pods are ready for market they are subjected to a curing process during which the characteristic odor is developed. The aroma and flavor are chiefly due to the presence of a substance known as vanillin, contained in a balsamic oil which gradually permeates the whole fruit and slowly accumulates as crystals on the outside of the cured pods. The plant has a round green stem, fleshy elliptic leaves, and insignificant flowers and is an inhabitant of hot, swampy regions.

The giants of the American orchid world are the sobralias, which are found on mountains from Mexico to Peru. They have slender canelike stems from 6 to 12 feet tall, well furnished with rather thin, dark green, lance-shaped leaves, which terminate in large cattleya-like flowers. One of the best-known species is *S. macrantha* with rich, red-purple to crimson flowers. The Costa Rican *S. leucoxantha* has white sepals and petals and a yellow flushed with orange lip.

King of the orchid world is cattleya, a small genus of probably less than fifty species, mostly natives of Central America to Brazil. All have large and brightly colored flowers, the lip of which possesses much character, being often fringed and intensely colored. The lip encloses the column but is not united to it and from its base a nectary runs down into the ovary. The familiar *C. labiata* is one of the finest of all species and very amenable under cultivation. Native of Brazil, it produces flowers in October and November. It and its numerous forms are among the most common orchids grown and need neither description nor praise. The variety *warneri* with its rich crimson, fringed lip is also Brazilian; the variety *gaskelliana*, which flowers in the early autumn, is sweet-scented; and the variety *percivaliana*, which flowers in January and February, are natives of Venezuela. The favorite *C. mossiae* with foot-long, furrowed pseudobulbs hails from La Guayra and is in flower from March to August. Of *C. labiata* and indeed of all the species, there are many fine forms which have received distinctive names.

The winter-blooming, pink-flowered *C. trianae* hails from Colombia and is represented by many named varieties and forms. One of the best is the var. *mendeli* with richly colored magenta lip. From Colombia also comes *C. gigas* with short, one-leafed pseudobulbs and large flowers, the sepals and petals of which are pink, the lip large and broad, rich purple or violet with a large yellow eyelike blotch on either side of the throat. Another grand species is *C. warscewiczi*, whose large flowers with white flushed with purple sepals and petals and rich crimson lip are produced during the winter months.

The Costa Rican *C. dowiana* is recognized as one of the very finest of all cattleyas. It has foot-long, furrowed, club-shaped, one-leafed pseudobulbs and bears a spike of five to six flowers. The sepals and petals are bright buff-color suffused with crimson and the lip dark velvety crimson streaked with golden-yellow. The variety *aurea* has primrose-yellow sepals and petals and is native of Colombia. Very distinct in appearance from any of the above is the Brazilian *C. aclandiae* with olive-green flowers heavily barred and blotched with dark purple, the lip magenta-purple.

Orchid enthusiasts will recall dozens of others but this sketch of cattleya must end with mention of the remarkable *C. citrina* from southern Mexico. This has bright yellow, fragrant flowers produced from between a pair of gray-colored leaves which top the small, egg-shaped pseudobulb. The leaves and flowers both hang down, contrary to the usual manner of plant growth.

The mention of cattleya immediately conjures up the closely related genus laelia, which differs in having eight pollen masses instead of four. Laelia is a smaller genus than cattleya and the species are mainly from the hotter parts of Mexico, Guatemala, and Brazil. The first that demands notice is the Brazilian *L. purpurata*, whose magnificent flowers are among the finest of all American orchids. The pseudobulbs are 2 feet and more long, furrowed, more or less spindle-shaped, with a pair of oblong leaves notched at the apex, and bear a truss of from three to seven flowers. The sepals are recurved and spreading and with the broader petals are pure white; the lip is rich crimson, sometimes tipped with white, passing to rose-color at the base and yellow within the throat. It flowers during the early summer. From the same country hails *L. harpophylla* with slender, round, one-leafed pseudobulb and racemes of from six to eight flowers with lance-shaped, orange-vermilion sepals and petals, the lip of the same color edged with white.

Very different in habit is the Mexican *L. anceps* with clusters of from three to six flowers at the end of a long slender but rigid stem. The flower is about 4 inches across with purple to rosy lilac sepals and petals and a crimson lip marked with yellow toward the base. It blossoms in December and January. As is the case with other species, there are lovely pale-colored and albino forms of this charming orchid. Somewhat similar, but a dwarfer plant with recurving petals and sepals and broader lip, is *L. autumnalis*, also from Mexico.

A truly superb orchid is *L. superbiens*, a vigorous species with a flower scape from 3 to 9 feet long, produced in winter and bearing sometimes as many as twenty flowers. The sepals and petals are deep rose-color paler toward the base, the lip crimson in front, yellowish on the sides. This is a Mexican plant and so, too, is the dwarf *L. majalis*, whose flowers are from 7 to 8 inches across with rosy lilac sepals and petals, and three-lobed, purplish marked with white lip. It flowers from the young growths during the summer months. The whole plant is only a few inches high and the size of its flowers is in consequence most surprising. There are other fine species of laelia and the crossing of this genus with that of cattleya has produced the bigeneric laelio-cattleyas in all their astonishing variety and beauty.

On the Organ Mountains in Brazil grow some half-a-dozen species of sophronitis, a genus of diminutive plants with large flowers that have been of immense service to the orchid breeders.

Crossed with cattleya and laelia it has given rise to some glorious hybrids. The finest species is *S. grandiflora* with one-leafed pseudobulbs and flowers each 2 inches across. The sepals and petals vary from cinnabar to dark scarlet and the lip, which has pointed and incurved sides, is yellow streaked with bright red. It flowers in November and December. A related species with violet-colored flowers is *S. violacea*.

Another genus which has been crossed with the above three genera, much to the advantage of the orchid lover, is brassavola. One of the handsomest and most used species is *B. digbyana* from Honduras. This has cattleya-like flowers with the edge of the lip broken up into long, hairlike fringes which character has been transmitted to its hybrid progeny. The sepals and petals are greenish-white tinted with purple and the lip cream-colored stained with purple at the tip. The gray-colored *B. glauca* from Mexico differs chiefly in its white lip which is not fringed.

The genus epidendrum, of which over 400 species are known, has also been united with cattleya and the other genera by the hybridist. An old but very beautiful species is *E. vitellinum* with erect racemes of orange-vermilion flowers with segments, the lip especially sharp-pointed, and the column yellow. The form called *majus* is superior to the type. This orchid is Mexican but also grows in Guatemala.

Very different in habit are *E. evectum* and *E. radicans*, which have tall, slender, leafy branching stems and which terminate in racemose clusters of flowers, magenta-purple in the first named, orange-scarlet in *E. radicans*. The flower is small with a deeply lobed and toothed lip, but lasts for a long time and the plants themselves are in flower well-nigh the year round. These and others are natives of Mexico and other parts of Central America.

From the mountains of Colombia came *E. wallisi*, another leafy, thin-stemmed species that grows 2 feet tall and has flowers 2 inches across, yellow spotted with purple, the lip flattened, whitish, prominently streaked with purple. This again is in flower for most of the year and is a very attractive species. The West Indian *E. fragrans* with rather small, cream-colored flowers, the tip streaked with crimson, deserves mention on account of its delightful fragrance.

Of the many others I have only space to name *E. prismato-carpum*, a striking species of vigorous habit and foot-long leaves crowning stout pseudobulbs. The flowers are racemose, creamy yellow, the sepals and petals marked with dark purple blotches and the free part of the lip rose-colored margined with pale yellow. It is native of Central America and blossoms in June and July.

Very closely related to the epidendrums is the handsome *Diacrium bicornutum*, native of Trinidad and Demerara. It is distinguished by the lip being free at the base and spreading, with two hollow horns between its lateral lobes. The pseudobulbs are fusiform about a foot high; the flowers are pure white each about 3 inches across with a few crimson spots in the middle of the lip and produced from six to twelve in a raceme. A lover of strong heat and abundant moisture, it is seldom seen to perfection under cultivation.

The oncidiums are a very large group comprising about 300 species, found from Mexico and the West Indies southward to Brazil. Many have beautifully colored flowers produced, in some species, many hundreds together in large, much-branched, paniculate inflorescences. Such a species is the Guatamalan *O. leucochilum*, whose flower stems are sometimes as much as 10 feet long and bear a multitude of greenish yellow barred and blotched with dark brown flowers each with a lobed white lip. The Brazilian *O. flexuosum* with its showy yellow, spotted with brown flowers produced in abundance is a favorite orchid with many folk.

Lovely, too, is *O. varicosum* and its variety *rogersi* with rich clear yellow lip, 2½ inches across, insignificant sepals and petals; the inflorescence is much branched and bears a hundred and more flowers in the late autumn. Yet another with flower stems of similar character is *O. tigrinum* from Mexico and adjacent lands, with yellow lip 2 inches across and greenish yellow marked with shining, chestnut-brown sepals and petals. The flowers have the odor of violets and open in late autumn and winter. The very similar *O. splendidum*, native of the same countries, flowers in spring and early summer. Very different in appearance is *O. macranthum* with large sepals and petals, each with a distinct claw and a very small, pointed lip. The color is varied and attractive; the upper sepal is olive brown suffused with gold, the two lateral ones orange-yellow, the petals bright yellow and the lip white marked with brown on the sides. The blossoms are from 3½ to 5 inches across and are borne on twining, branching, many-flowered stems several feet long.

From the Organ Mountains, Brazil, came *O. crispum* with its large and remarkably handsome flowers borne some fifty or so together in a panicle. The blossom is from 2 to 3 inches across, greenish brown to reddish brown with yellow stripes, and the parts are beautifully crisped. This orchid seems to have no set period of flowering and is in bloom at different times through the year.

There are scores of other species worthy of description but *O. papilio*, the butterfly orchid, must not be forgotten in the briefest of lists. This species with its singularly attractive flowers is native of Trinidad and Venezuela and has dark-colored, flattened pseudo-bulbs each capped by a single, purple-brown, leathery leaf. The flower scapes which arise from the base of the plant are slender, erect, about 2½ feet tall, and continue to bear through a long season flower after flower, though seldom is more than one open at the same time. The back sepal and the two petals are each about 3 inches long, linear and erect, dark green without, purple within; the lateral sepals are oblong, tapering, wavy and arched downward, bright yellow with transverse bands of orange-red; the lip is roundish, about 1½ inches across, yellow mottled all over with brown and waved along the edge. Its common name well describes the appearance of the flower.

Some oncidiums like *O. varicosum* have ordinary-looking pseudobulbs; in others like *O. papilio* they are flattened and make humus-collecting niches against the support; in others like *O. cavendishianum* they are absent and their function is served by thick, fleshy, erect leaves.

A favorite genus is odontoglossum with curiously blotched flowers, of which about 100 species are known from the high mountains of Mexico south to those of Peru. They require cool conditions and are not easy to grow at sea level under our hot summer sun but in England they thrive amazingly. The hybridist has been very successful with this genus and the outcome of his work is seen in hundreds of named sorts, many of which have flowers of extraordinary coloring.

Queen of the genus and one of the most useful of all orchids is the Colombian *O. crispum*, of which there are many named forms. The flowers are fragrant and are borne in arching racemes which are sometimes panicled and vary from white to yellow and pink; some of the forms are wondrously spotted and marked with chocolate-brown, purple, and yellow. It has been introduced in vast quantities and no orchid has been more diligently searched for by collectors. It blossoms at various seasons of the year but most freely from February to April.

Native of the same country is a sister species, *O. pescatorei*, also a great favorite. Likewise *O. harryanum* whose flowers are very different in appearance with their petals curving sharply downward. The sepals and petals are chestnut-brown, barred and edged with yellow; the lip is white and yellow, heavily feathered with bluish purple. A very showy species is the Guatemalan *O. grande*, an old denizen of orchid houses. This has gaily colored yellow barred with chestnut-brown flowers, each from 5 to

7 inches across with rounded lip, white with a few concentric bands of chestnut-red.

Very sweetly scented are the golden yellow, blotched with red-brown flowers of the Colombian *O. odoratum*. The Mexican *O. rossi* is a pretty and well-known species with white and purple flowers freely produced during the winter season.

First cousin to odontoglossum is cochlioda of the Peruvian Andes, of which four or five species only are known. The best known is perhaps *C. vulcanica* with erect racemes of bright rose-colored, waxy flowers each 2 inches across; *C. sanguinea* is similar but has drooping racemes. In *C. rosea* the flowers are less brightly colored but in *C. noezliana* they are a wonderful orange-scarlet with a violet-purple column in marked contrast. These cochliodas crossed with odontoglossums have given rise to the hybrid genus odontioda, whose remarkable reddish flowers are among the choicest and most highly prized products of the orchid breeders' skill.

Miltonias with their relatively huge, flat flowers with bilobed lip are greatly appreciated wherever orchids are grown. The genus is a small one of about a dozen species, found from Costa Rica south to Brazil. One of the very finest is *M. vexillaria* from Colombia with pink flowers, of which half a dozen or so are borne on a slender raceme; there are many forms, some with white others deep rose-colored blossoms. The Brazilian *M. spectabilis* has white flowers with a finely colored lip, deep violet-purple at the base, rosy crimson in the center. Beautiful are the flowers of *M. Phalaenopsis* with their fiddle-shaped lip, blotched and striped with crimson; whilst those of *M. roezli* are delightfully fragrant.

Very useful plants are the lycastes, and *L. skinneri* and its forms rank among the finest ornaments of orchid houses. The pink to white flowers are from 6 to 7 inches across, the lip is three-lobed and variously spotted with rose-red or crimson. It flowers in the winter months and is native of Guatemala.

Panama is the home of *Peristeria elata*, the dove orchid, from the resemblance of the column of the flower to a dove hovering with expanded wings, somewhat like the conventional dove seen in artistic representations of the Holy Ghost. The flower stems are erect, from 3 to 5 feet tall, and bear racemosely many white, waxy almost globose blossoms from July to September.

Very curious is catasetum with hoodlike flowers of three different forms which sometimes appear on the same plant. For a long time these forms were regarded as belonging to different genera, but it is now known that they represent merely the male, female, and hermaphrodite forms of one genus. The lip is uppermost in the flower and the column is provided with a pair of horns or antennae which in many species cross one another diagonally. When one of these antennae is touched the pollinia are ejected with great violence. Among the best-known species are *C. macrocarpum, C. tridentatum, C. bungerothi,* and *C. saccatum.*

Even more remarkable are the flowers of the related genus stanhopea, which are borne on pendent racemes or solitary and hanging. The flowers are massive in texture, beautifully barred and spotted with color, and strongly fragrant. Perhaps the handsomest of all is *S. tigrina* with flowers 8 inches across. The lip and the column form a cage, narrowing toward the mouth and as smooth and slippery as glass. The base of the lip is like a bucket and is covered with juicy hairs. Other fine species are *S. wardi* and *S. gibbosa,* the latter with flowers 6 inches across, yellow barred and spotted with crimson.

Another close relative is cycnoches, the swan orchid, of which *C. pentadactylon* may serve as an example. The flowers are racemose, of two sexes, resembling those of catasetum, greenish yellow, sometimes white, barred and blotched with chocolate-brown, and the lip in parts white spotted with red. The species was introduced in 1841, from Rio de Janeiro into England, by William Lobb.

But the most extraordinary of all of this group is coryanthes, the helmet orchid, a tropical South American genus of four or five species. The flowers are pendulous and wonderful in appearance, not easy to describe clearly without figures. The sepals are fairly large and bent backward, the petals are small; the lip is of a most complex shape; projecting horizontally from the base of the column is a bar bearing a dome on the end from which is suspended a bucketlike organ; the mouth of the bucket faces upwards and the edges are incurved; there is also an overflow pipe projecting towards the sepals and closely covered in by the bent end of the column with the stigma and anther. From the base of the column project two horns which secrete a thin watery fluid that drips into the bucket keeping it full to the overflow pipe. The dome above the bucket is composed of succulent tissue very attractive to bees, who fight for places on it whence to drill the tissue; every now and then one of them gets pushed off and falls into the bucket. It can neither fly nor climb out and has to squeeze through the overflow pipe. In so doing the bee passes the stigma, fertilizing it if it carries any pollen and then passing the anther is loaded with new pollinia to be transferred to other flowers.

One of the best-known species is *C. macrantha* from Caracas, whose flowers are rich yellow dotted with red; the hood and part of the bucket are brownish red. Another is the Venezuelan *C. maculata* with dull yellow flowers, the bucket blotched with dull red within.

The winter-blooming genus zygopetalum, of which some twenty species are known, has handsome flowers often with a good deal of blue in their coloring. Such a species is *Z. mackayi* with erect racemes from 1½ to 2 feet tall which bear from six to ten flowers, each with purplish-brown sepals and petals and a flattened rounded lip, white heavily striated with blue. This species is a native of Brazil and so, too, is *Z. crinitum* with its bearded lip; *Z.*

gautieri, whose lip varies in color from rose to blue-purple; and several others, including the well-known *Z. maxillare*.

The Mexican *Chysis bractescens* with nodding racemes of thick, fleshy white marked with yellow flowers must not be omitted. Its yellow-flowered sister *C. aurea* is Venezuelan.

A noteworthy orchid is *Schomburgkia tibicinis* with horn-shaped pseudobulbs each 1½ feet long and a terminal mass of flowers on a stem 5 feet in length. The blossom is about 3 inches across with many pink, spotted with chocolate sepals and petals, and lip white spotted with rose on the lobes which are erect. There are several other species and all are fond of sun and strong heat.

The masdevallias are a large and varied group though very few have conspicuous flowers. A characteristic feature of the genus is the drawn-out apex of the three sepals which is often decidedly tail-like; the petals and lip are usually small. The flowers vary greatly in form and many of them are grotesque in appearance. Such species as *M. coccinea* and its variety *harryana*, *M. lindeni*, *M. ignea*, *M. tovarensis*, and *M. veitchiana*, have erect scapes from 8 to 15 inches tall bearing one, rarely two, pleasing flowers. These species are very free-blooming and deservedly popular. Another section, to which belong *M. chimaera*, *M. bella*, and *M. nycterina*, has singular flowers with extraordinarily long tails to the sepals; in color the flowers are more or less yellow heavily blotched with purple-brown.

The tropical American cypripediums are now referred to the genera phragmipedium and selenipedium, but here it is convenient to mention them under their old and more familiar name. Many of the species have remarkable flowers but none more so than the noble *C. caudatum* of Peru. This has tufted leaves and from the center of the plant, after the leaf growth is finished, arise flower stems each from 1 to 1½ feet tall. The lateral petals are narrow, tail-like from 2 to 2½ feet long and pendent, giving the flower an extraordinary appearance. The color is yellowish marked with brown. With this wonderful orchid we may contrast *C. schlimi* with its racemose, bright rose-colored flowers, each 2 inches across with a globose pouched lip.

The sins of omission here are many, as the orchid enthusiast will be quick to note, but no attempt at finality is intended. These discursive sketches of a few of the prominent types of a wonderfully polymorphic family will have served their purpose if they impress upon the minds of readers the debt we owe to the tropics of both Old and New Worlds for the wonderful plants we know as orchids.

26

Plants that Kill and Eat

With the exception of orchids most of the Old World tropical plants grown in our hothouses are cultivated for the sake of their handsome foliage; but the members of one not unimportant genus (nepenthes or pitcher-plants) are grown for the remarkable leaf-appendages known as pitchers. Few if any vegetable productions more excited the minds of early voyagers to the eastern tropics than the nepenthes, and many were the curious speculations indulged in respecting the purpose of the pitchers. The name nepenthes was given by Linnaeus and in itself is interesting and most applicable. The word "nepenthes" is of Greek origin and occurs in Homer's "Odyssey" (Book IV, line 221) where it signifies a freeing from and causing an oblivion of grief. Translated the passage reads: "She (Helen) threw a drug into the wine, from which they drank that which frees men from grief and from anger, and causes an oblivion of all ills." Linnaeus, alluding to the pitchers, writes: "If this is not Helen's nepenthes it certainly will be for all botanists. What botanist would not be filled with admiration if, after a long journey, he should find this wonderful plant. In his astonishment past ills would be forgotten when beholding this admirable work of the Creator." The truth of this prophecy is from the pen of F. W. Burbidge, who introduced several fine species. He writes in his "Gardens of the Sun" (p. 100): "All thoughts of fatigue and discomfort vanished as we gazed on these living wonders of the Bornean Andes. To see these plants (nepenthes) in all their health and vigor was a sensation I shall never forget."

The genus is preeminently Malayan with headquarters on the mountains of Borneo, where grow species like *N. rajah, N. edwardsiana, N. lowi, N. northianae*, and others which have the largest and most handsome pitchers. One species (*N. phyllamphora*) is found as far north as the neighborhood of Canton in southern China and several occur in the Philippines; one species (*N. khasiana*) grows in Assam, one (*N. distillatoria*) in Ceylon, another (*N. pervillei*) on the Seychelles Islands. The most eastern species is *N. viellardi*, peculiar to New Caledonia, and in north Australia grows *N. kennedyana*. Most extraordinary of all in the point of distribution is the fact that one species (*N. madagascariensis*) is indigenous on the island of Madagascar. This was the first species discovered, being found in 1661 by P. Commerson, the first European traveler in Madagascar. To this the name of "Amramatica" was given by Flacourt. This Madagascar species was lost sight of by botanists until 1797, when Poiret published its name in Lamarck's famous "Encyclopedia" but it was not introduced into cultivation until 1879, when Messrs. Veitch of Chelsea received it from their collector, Charles Curtis. It was upon the Ceylon species that Linnaeus based the genus.

The story of *N. northianae* is worth recording. This fine species was revealed to science through a painting made by Miss Marianne North, whose life was largely spent traveling over the world with paintbox, brush, and canvas. The results of her skill are many hundreds of accurate pictures of flowers painted in every land and which, bequeathed to the nation, are one of Kew's proudest possessions.

The sketch made in Sarawak was shown in 1880 to Mr. Henry Veitch, who at once recognized it as representing a new species of nepenthes. Miss North said the specimens had been brought to her by an employee of the North Borneo Company "who traversed pathless forests amid snakes and leeches to find and bring them down to her." Charles Curtis was about to start on a collecting trip in Malaysia for Messrs. Veitch and he received special orders to try and introduce this nepenthes into England. Curtis experienced much difficulty in finding the plant. After searching vainly for several days he decided to give up the task in the belief that Miss North had been wrongly informed as to the locality in which it grew. When on the point of leaving it occurred to him to look over a steep escarpment, which he accomplished by lying prostrate on the ground, and to his great joy he discovered the plant growing at some distance below him. On reaching the plants he found ripe fruit capsules and lost no time in transmitting the seeds to Messrs. Veitch, with whom they soon germinated. Later the species was named for the estimable lady who first brought it to our knowledge. It has proved to be one of the most tractable under cultivation, and it is one of the handsomest of the genus.

Some nepenthes are low sub-shrubs, others climbers with stems 30 feet and more long; they grow in humus-filled niches on the face of cliffs or on the top of rocks, or, epiphytically in the forks of trees. The flowers are insignificant and are pollinated by the wind, but the pitchers, so striking in their shape, color, and size, are the most reliable organs with which to discriminate between the species.

These pitchers on different species may be tubular, cylindric, urn- or flask-shape, and are close-capped by a lid when young.

The pigmy of the genus is *N. phyllamphora* with pitchers no larger than a man's thumb; the giant is *N. rajah* whose pitchers hold as much as two quarts of water. Between these extremes are found every gradation. In color the pitchers are usually some shade of red without and darker, often purple, within; many are mottled and striped and blotched in a striking manner; a few are green without. The ridged rim of the pitcher, which always curves inward, is variable in width and the channeling is often very remarkable. These pitchers at their entrance secrete honey which acts as a decoy to entrap insects and small animals whose bodies are decomposed by a fluid secreted from the walls of the pitchers and supply the plant, in part at least, with its nitrogenous food. In other words these extraordinary plants, by the aid of their pitchers, capture and eat insects and small animals.

On Mt. Kina Balu, in 1851, Sir Hugh Low discovered *N. rajah* and other noble species, but the bulk have been introduced by the house of Messrs. Veitch, to whom we owe most of the handsome hybrid nepenthes which, on the whole, are more easily cultivated than their wild parents.

27

Wilson's Plant Treasures

As a COLLECTOR and introducer of plants, Wilson's concept of his work was enormously far-reaching. While his primary interest was focused on hardy woody plants—trees, shrubs, and vines for garden use—he did not neglect the herbaceous and bulbous plants that he saw on his expeditions. As a consequence, the sum total of his achievements rests in the introduction of more than a thousand species, a greater number than any other plant collector had succeeded in gathering. Some had been previously discovered and described, but they had not been introduced into cultivation.

Another aspect of his accomplishments is represented in the 16,-000 herbarium specimens which he collected, prepared, and shipped home together with many duplicates. In addition to the written record contained in *Plantae Wilsonianae*, the great herbariums of the world contain a representative number of his plants. Because he collected in a climate similar to that of the great gardening regions of the world, the impact of his work has been

by no means limited to the temperate and subtropical sections of
America alone, but also extends to the British Isles, Europe, and
Australia. Add to these statistics the extraordinary collection of
photographs, totaling several thousand, and the result can only
be described as encyclopedic.

The following list of descriptions is but a sampling of the extensive variety and range of Oriental plants which Wilson brought
to the garden world. It represents, largely, those readily available
in the nursery trade, or those that can be obtained from specialists.

Beauty-bush   *Kolkwitzia amabilis*

Nearly twenty years after it was introduced, the beauty-bush
caught on with the gardening public, primarily through extensive
advertising. Had the flowers of this exotic shrub been bright red instead of a delicate pink, popular acceptance would have been immediate. Wilson was justly proud of this "Chinaman of surpassing
merit, closely related to the weigelas but more elegant in habit."
It is a big-scale plant, making fountainlike growth, highly ornamental in flower and in fruit. The small, pink, tubular flowers
which appear in late May or early June, borne in clusters, are a
pleasing shade of light pink, fading to white as they mature. Of
equal eye appeal are the fascinating fruits, clothed in shining
white pubescence, suggesting somewhat the hazy effect of the
smokebush.

Exfoliating bark gives beauty-bush added winter interest. Where
space permits, it makes a tall, widespreading, billowy hedge, to
8 feet, usually extending its branches somewhat wider than it is
high. It is, however, no shrub for a small garden unless one is willing to use the pruning shears drastically and skillfully to keep it
within bounds. Combined with other flowering shrubs or used as a
specimen, it is noticeably ornamental. The clean, soft, fuzzy

foliage holds up well throughout the year, turning reddish in autumn. Young specimens obtained from nurseries are often ungainly and need hard pruning. Plants cut to the ground, have, within two years, produced a showy mound of bloom. Average garden soil and full sun are its simple requirements. There is hardly a nursery that does not offer beauty-bush.

Butterfly Bush   *Buddleia davidi*

A favorite summer-flowering shrub is the butterfly bush, *Buddleia davidi*, which Wilson preferred to call summer lilac. It grows with ease, flowering on the wood of the current season, but often dies back to the ground where winters are severe. For the most part, it is root hardy but, in any event, it is so easily propagated as to be comparatively inexpensive to replace. The tail-like spikes of bloom are typically purple, but red, pink, lavender, and white forms are now offered by nurserymen. Several of these bear flowers with a distinct orange eye. Père Armand David, a French missionary to China, had discovered this species some years earlier, but it was only after E. H. Wilson had introduced several distinct varieties to cultivation that it became widely known. He found also the tender species *B. asiatica*, with its graceful, drooping clusters of white bloom, a favorite greenhouse plant in the North, but hardy in the South and on the West Coast. Delicious fragrance is a prime asset of these summer-flowering shrubs, which thrive in full sun. However, the foliage is coarse and the dead flowers which turn brown need to be removed frequently. The better the soil, the more luxuriant the growth. The most shapely plants are those which are cut back almost to the ground each spring. Their usual height is 4 to 6 feet, but butterfly bushes often spread much wider, providing an abundance of bloom from early summer until late fall.

Chinese Actinidia   *Actinidia chinensis*

This vine of tropical aspect, considered the handsomest of all the actinidias, was discovered by Robert Fortune in 1849 and introduced by Wilson a half century later. The young leaves are reddish as they unfold and develop to a rich dark green with a silvery undersurface, each measuring 3 to 6 inches in diameter.

The creamy-white, fragrant, cup-shaped flowers, 2 inches in diameter, borne singly or in clusters in the leaf axils, change to buff yellow as they mature. Roundish, hairy berries appear on the female specimens; plants of both sexes are needed for fruiting. The edible fruits, which resemble those of the gooseberry in flavor, came to be known as "Wilson's gooseberries" in western China where the plant hunter introduced them to the foreign residents. Growth is rapid and luxurious in areas where it is hardy, south of Washington and on the West Coast. It thrives in rich garden soil on the moist side and is at its best away from wind since the leaves are torn easily.

Chinese Dogwood   *Cornus kousa chinensis*

Native from central China northeastward through Korea and much of Japan, the kousa dogwood is a truly notable small tree. It was the Chinese form *C. kousa chinensis* which Wilson found. He championed this species because its flower buds proved to be much hardier in severe winters than those of our native dogwood, *C. florida*. Also, it blooms a month later than *C. florida*, extending the season of these highly ornamental flowering trees. The showy, creamy-white bracts, commonly referred to as flowers appear when the leaves have unfolded and last 3 to 4 weeks, turning somewhat pink as they fade. In early autumn, red strawberry-like, edible fruits appear, but they are soon discovered by the birds. At this season, the foliage assumes reddish-purple tints. To the Chinese it is known as strawberry tree.

Unless pruned vigorously, it may assume the aspect of a big-scale shrub. A well-grown specimen with a single trunk is stately and vaselike in habit. Wilson described the Chinese form as having larger and broader bracts than the type which sometimes overlap. "Some experts," he wrote, "acclaim this the finest gift of china to Western gardens. Certainly, it ranks high in the realm of beauty among hardy flowering trees and its fortunate introducer is proud of the opinion its merits have won for it." Then he added, "In the not distant future, this Chinese dogwood will be in great demand." Despite its attributes, it remains much less well known than it deserves to be. Yet, all who see it admire the Chinese dogwood. It requires time to develop the fullness of its beauty, since young plants bloom sparsely, but it is worth waiting for. In the eastern United States, 15 to 20 feet seems to be its typical height.

Cotoneaster   *Cotoneaster species*

Few groups of shrubs are more ornamental and adaptable to a greater number of uses in gardens than the various cotoneasters. These denizens of China have for the most part loomed on the horizon since the beginning of the twentieth century. E. H. Wilson introduced nearly half of the species now in cultivation, and it was largely through his urging that nurserymen undertook their propagation nearly forty years ago. Since he has described them in detail in chapter 12, there is no need to describe the various species here. Their picturesque habit of growth, their refined texture, and the lacy effects created by their branches are the prime attributes of cotoneasters together with the fruits and the rather showy flower clusters of certain kinds. Contrary to popular notions, these shrubs thrive in comparatively poor soil and usually flower and fruit more abundantly under these conditions. They are ideal for hot, dry situations and windy sites. The surest way to ruin the natural beauty of these handsome ornamentals is to subject them to formal pruning. To reduce plants in height or over-all size, remove branches at the base. A certain few are adaptable for hedges, but for the most part cotoneasters need ample space to develop the fullness of their natural beauty. Their chief drawback is based on several diseases which sometimes afflict them.

Dove Tree   *Davidia involucrata*

This tree and the regal lily are the two Chinese plant treasures best known to gardeners as linked with the name of "Chinese" Wilson. Yet, comparatively few people have ever seen the dove tree in bloom since it does not produce flowers freely, from year to year, on every site where it grows in cultivation. Obviously, the flower buds are sensitive to low winter temperatures and are easily damaged. Since it has been described in detail in chapter 1, it requires no further comment here except to add that gardeners in the Northwest have nicknamed it the "laundry tree" because of its conspicuous white bracts which wave in the breeze.

Early Forsythia   *Forsythia ovata*

Best described as the earliest to bloom and the hardiest, *Forsythia ovata* is by no means the most spectacular of the forsythias. Yet its ironclad hardiness with relation to its flower buds in extreme winters is a strong feature in its favor. The leaves are more rounded in form than other species. It may yet prove of further use and interest to hybridizers. Fifty years is a short span in which to judge the true value of some plants.

Evergreen or Armand Clematis   *Clematis armandi*

An evergreen species with showy panicles of fragrant, white flowers, this is a spring bloomer for warm climates. South of Washington and on the West Coast where it flourishes, it rates high as a decorative vine. The long plumy seed heads appear in late summer adding new luster to its appearance. When in flower it has been compared to a white cloud scrambling over fence tops, on pergolas, and up the sides of houses and gables. It is slow to start when young, but grows rapidly as it climbs by its twisting peticles. The glossy foliage is notable for its eye appeal throughout the year. Since it produces flowers on the growth of the previous year, pruning is done after flowering. To admire this handsome vine in foliage, flower, and fruit is, at the same time, to marvel at the diversity of the plant material which E. H. Wilson introduced. There is also a pink-flowered variety known as appleblossom. The cultural requirements are the same for the pink anemone clematis, discussed below.

Formosa Andromeda   *Pieris taiwanensis*

Because it is easily propagated and grows rapidly, the Japanese andromeda has been planted extensively in city and suburban gardens during the past few decades. When thoughtfully placed, it is one of the handsomest of all broad-leaved evergreens, especially when contrasted with yews, ilexes, azaleas, and the like. Ernest Wilson introduced the Formosa andromeda, *P. tai-*

wanensis, which flowers a little later than *P. japonica*, carrying somewhat longer flower clusters. It is not yet as widely grown as it deserves to be; perhaps because it is believed to be less hardy in the Northeast than *P. japonica*. Our native species *P. floribunda* of lower and broader habit is equally decorative and useful.

Fragrant Sarcococca   *Sarcococca ruscifolia*

Sarcococca is something of a mouthful and when a species name like *hookeriana* or *ruscifolia* is linked with it along with a variety designation of two or three syllables, the result is a tongue twister. Consequently, a goodly number of plants burdened with awkward or inept names are not nearly as well known or as widely grown as they deserve to be. (Another case in point is enkianthus, an excellent Oriental shrub to which Wilson added a worthwhile species.) The generic name sarcococca, derived from the Greek, means fleshy berry, referring to the fruit.

This is a broad-leaved evergreen, belonging to the box family, notable for its excellent foliage and its adaptability to shade. In England it is known as sweet box. Discriminating gardeners who know and grow it are enthusiastic about its excellent textures and glossy sheen. Wilson introduced *S. hookeriana humilis*, a valuable groundcover sort, 12 to 15 inches tall, which spreads by underground runners. Another of his finds from the sacred mountain of Wa-Shan was *S. ruscifolia*, known as fragrant sarcococca, with conspicuous red fruits borne in autumn. It may grow to 6 feet but usually is lower.

Helen Rose   *Rosa helenae*

Wilson's concept of a garden, even a home garden, encompassed a sizable plot of ground, much larger than the average home grounds of the present. As a result, a number of the plants which he introduced are unknown or little planted today, except in arboretums, because of the space they require. True, with careful pruning, many shrubs may be kept within the area allotted to them, but for top performance, others require more space than the average city or suburban lot affords. Hence, a big-scale rose like *Rosa helenae*, 12 to 15 feet tall, with its clusters of small white single flowers followed by orange fruits, belongs in a park or on a private estate. This rose was named for Mr. Wilson's wife.

Korean Boxwood   *Buxua microphylla koreana*

The dwarf boxwood or "edging box," *Buxus sempervirens suffruticosa*, which has been cultivated in gardens for more than two centuries, often suffers serious winter damage in northern New England, and requires protection, particularly in late winter. It remained for "Chinese" Wilson to introduce a new species, *Buxus microphylla koreana*, from the area near Seoul in central Korea. After ten years of testing, he felt that it was one of his best Korean importations and such it has proved to be. Korean boxwood is of ironclad hardiness, grows and propagates with ease, making a most attractive hedge, and requires a minimum of care. True, the foliage turns somewhat yellow-green in winter, but this is a minor fault in comparison with its hardiness, since it is unharmed even after exposure to below zero temperatures for extended periods. It averages 2 feet in height. The variety *B. microphylla japonica* is taller, to 4 feet when mature. Boxwood edgings or hedges are most appealing when allowed to assume a billowy appearance rather than be subject to severe shearing. This treatment makes for easier maintenance as well.

Korean Stewartia   *Stewartia koreana*

Summer-flowering trees are few in number and none are more appealing than the stewartias. E. H. Wilson constantly championed two species for garden use, the Japanese stewartia, *S. pseudocamellia*, and the showy stewartia, *S. ovata grandiflora*, but he did not live long enough to see his own introduction from Korea come into maturity in America. In July, it produces the largest flowers of all the kinds grown—single, white, fringe-petaled blooms accentuated with a generous mass of golden yellow stamens. They resemble single camellias, measuring about 3 inches in diameter when fully open, and, in early summer, they are a delight to the eye as the large pearl-like buds unfold. This tree is often multistemmed, branching in a pleasing shrublike manner near the ground. Another distinctive feature is the flaking bark which reveals shades of pink, green, gray, and brown as it peels. This characteristic, typical also of the lacebark pine, the paperbark maple, the sycamore, and the paper birch, adds a new dimension to the beauty of trees, especially in winter. In summer, too, they have eye appeal. Tree bark was a characteristic of the landscape about which Wilson liked to talk.

Broad-spreading but upright in its branching, Korean stewartia has smooth, oval leaves which take on orange-red tones in autumn. Although comparatively slow growing, it may reach 30 to 35 feet or more when mature. It flourishes in the best of moist loam on the acid side. Alas, it remains a rare tree in American gardens since nurserymen have failed to propagate it in quantity, if at all. Dr. Donald Wyman of the Arnold Arboretum and other horticulturists have bemoaned this fact, since the Korean stewartia is a true aristocrat among small trees.

Kurume Azalea   *Azalea*

Little wonder that E. H. Wilson waxed poetic in describing the Kurume azaleas which he had seen and photographed in Japan. The plants were single-stemmed and flat-topped, resembling tailored trees and revealing a high degree of cultural perfection. One old plant which particularly intrigued him was suggestive of the art of bonsai. The flat-topped form is the favorite method of treatment with commercial growers today, but many specimens of surprising beauty, developed by professional gardeners under glass, are more billowy and irregular in form, even if bulkier. This was a notable characteristic of many of the plants in the Ames Collection at North Easton, Massachusetts. Kurume azaleas grown in gardens from the Connecticut–New York border south, particularly in New Jersey, Pennsylvania, and throughout the South, make a brilliant display. Varieties are numerous and a number have double flowers. Plants are heavily twigged with small, glossy evergreen foliage. The list of varieties appears in chapter 4.

Moyes Rose   *Rosa moyesi*

The reddest of all wild roses, Moyes rose has been utilized in hybridizing because of its rich color. Seen primarily in the gardens of rose enthusiasts, it attracted nationwide attention at the Breeze Hill Garden of Dr. J. Horace McFarland, noted rosarian of Harrisburg, Pennsylvania, who championed the wild or species roses

Japanese dogwood in full flower (GEORGE TALOUMIS)

Branch of the Chinese form of Japanese dogwood
(*Cornus kousa chinensis*) (GEORGE TALOUMIS)

and shared his experience and love of the rose with E. H. Wilson. A superb single flower with a mass of golden stamens in the center, it makes a spectacular display. Plants grow 6 to 8 feet tall, blooming in June followed by showy orange-red fruits in autumn. This species, frequently attributed to Wilson, had been introduced earlier by the Vilmorin nurseries in France, but Wilson found the variety *R. moyesi rosea* and brought it home.

Omei Rose   *Rosa omeiensis*

On his first jaunt to China, Wilson sent back seed of this rose, conspicuous for its fernlike foliage, heavily spined stems, and pear-shaped red fruits, borne on yellow stalks, rather than for its small, white, single flowers. Plants reach 10 to 12 feet in height, spreading widely as they mature. The Omei rose had been discovered on Mount Omei in 1886, by an English missionary, Rev. E. Faber, hence the name. As with many Chinese plants, there were in the herbarium at Kew countless records and descriptions of trees and shrubs, discovered by various travelers, which had not been introduced into cultivation. It seems to have remained for "Chinese" Wilson to accomplish this task. What value the curious foliage and showy fruits of this rose may have in the estimation of some hybridizer remains to be seen. The work of plant breeders who pursue their science quietly and without fanfare makes it difficult to determine, sometimes for decades, whether or not some obscure plant may contribute to the development of an outstanding hybrid. Such has been the case with a number of rose species.

Paperbark Maple   *Acer griseum*

When Ernest Wilson discovered the paperbark maple in western China in 1901, the rage for decorative trees among gardeners, in both England and America, was centered on the Japanese cut-leaf maples with their brightly colored foliage. It is easy to imagine his pleasure when he found this unusual species with "cinnamon-red bark, exfoliating like that of the river birch." In the wilds of China, at an altitude of 7,300 feet, he saw mature specimens 60 feet high with a girth of 7 feet. Curiously enough, in cultivation, it is comparatively slow in growth and has proved to be well suited to the home garden. Ideal in scale for the small property, it is a tree with year-round eye appeal. After thirty years of growth, it develops into an open, round-headed specimen, about 20 feet tall. The compound foliage, made up of three segments, is refined in texture.

Wilson was later to learn that his new maple was difficult to propagate because the embryos in the seeds failed to develop. In England it did not become available for nearly twenty-five years after it was introduced. For more than fifty years it has remained a rarity in America until recently, when the Wayside Gardens propagated it in quantity. Now that it is more readily obtainable, it is hoped that gardeners will make wider use of the paperbark maple. It is a tree for full sun and requires no special culture, provided the soil is well drained.

Pearl Bush   *Exochorda giraldi wilsoni*

A choice flowering shrub, valued for its racemes of 2-inch, white, single flowers which appear at tulip time, pearl bush is by no means common. Fortune introduced it first to England in 1846, and Wilson brought back seed of *E. giraldi wilsoni* in 1907.

Fruits of *Cornus kousa chinensis* (GEORGE TALOUMIS)

Hard pruning produces a shapely, heavily-flowered shrub which may reach 10 feet or more as it matures, or it may be kept considerably lower with skillful use of the shears.

Pink Anemone Clematis   *Clematis montana rubens*

This handsome clematis caught on with gardeners from the very early days of its introduction. Its soft pink flowers (deeper in color, rosey-red, at the bud stage and when first unfolded) and the delicate bronzy-reddish tones of the new growth have transformed many an arbor and garden wall into a bower of loveliness in May, when tulips are at their best. The noted landscape architect, Beatrix Ferrand, grew it in her garden at Bar Harbor, Maine, and wrote: "The south window frame on which *C. montana rubens* grows looks like the frontispiece to an old gardening book." This is a vigorous climber, somewhat rampant, spreading to 20 feet or more, with individual blooms, squarish in shape, measuring nearly 2 inches across. At the height of its glory, the flower clusters of pink anemone clematis literally shroud whatever support they clamber on. E. H. Wilson was exceedingly proud of this "child" of his travels, as he was also of the white form of the species, which bears his name *C. montana wilsoni*.

Clematis montana was introduced to Great Britain in 1831 by Lady Amherst, a noted patron of horticulture and wife of the governor-general of India at the time. However, the two varieties which Wilson found have proved hardier in cold climates than the type, a strong point in their favor, to the great pleasure of their introducer. He sent home seeds of another small flowering kind, *C. tangutica obtusiuscula*, distinctive for its miniature, Chinese-lantern-like flower.

Clematis, as every good gardener knows, likes its feet in the shade and its head in the sun. A sweet soil is needed, one to which lime has been added (a generous handful dug into the soil at planting time). Pruning is important with clematis since some kinds bloom on new wood, while others, like the forms of *C. montana*, flower on the growth of the previous season. Prune after flowering to control growth. If the stems are given a protective wire collar at the point where they emerge from the soil, "die-back" will be less likely to occur. The showy seed pods which look like silken tassels are an added premium of the clematis tribe. See chapter 8 for E. H. Wilson's thoughts on the many worthwhile kinds.

Primrose Jasmine   *Jasminum mesnyi*

One of the first plants which Wilson collected and sent to England was the primrose jasmine, originally classified as *J. primulinum*. He lived to see it widely adapted to gardens in warm climates. Although he resided in New England for twenty-five years, his vision of the best plants for American gardens embraced the entire country, in a very personal way. The primrose jasmine is a vine of exceptional beauty, bearing single, lemon-yellow flowers, nearly as large as a half-dollar, which appear, on gracefully arching branches, from February to April. Well-grown specimens make superb cascade effects, ideal for a site above a wall, where they can spill over the top in lavish profusion. As a conservatory plant, the primrose jasmine has special merit.

Unfortunately it is truly a tender plant from the hardiness viewpoint, and gets nipped, even in many parts of England. In the warm sections of Europe, in Australia, and on our own West Coast, it has proven truly outstanding. In colder sections, it is a greenhouse plant grown in tubs, trained as a standard.

A tall, white trumpet lily (*Lilium formosanum wilsoni*), which blooms in October on stems often 6 feet tall, was collected and introduced by E. H. Wilson on his trip to Formosa. This lily is one of the easiest to raise from seed. (P. E. GENEREUX)

Fruits of the tea viburnum (*Viburnum setigerum*) (GEORGE TALOUMIS)

Privet Honeysuckle   *Lonicera pileata*

Where a low evergreen or semievergreen hedge is needed in sun, or more especially in shade, the privet honeysuckle is an ideal choice. It is equally adaptable as a shrubby ground cover for a slope. Allowed to develop naturally, the horizontal branches make dense growth, eventually reaching about 2 feet and spreading twice as wide. When clipped or pruned informally, plants are easily kept much more compact. Neither the fruits nor the flowers are conspicuous. Rather it is the neat, oval, glossy foliage and the pleasing habit of growth that gives this Chinese bush honeysuckle its appeal. Specimen plants seem to belong in large rock gardens, as accents near pools, or wherever the effect of a broad mass of horizontal growth is desired. Like all the honeysuckles, it is of the easiest culture, requiring no special care. Unquestionably, it will be planted more extensively, as it becomes more easily available in the trade.

Lonicera nitida is a taller-growing species, reaching 4 to 5 feet, similar in many ways but more untidy in growth.

Rhododendron

The rhododendron, the king of shrubs, held a very special place in the heart of E. H. Wilson. He it was who unlocked the door to that great treasure house of wild or species rhododendrons in western China. Similarly, he scanned the Chino-Tibetan borderland for new kinds. In later years he was to be followed by Reginald Farrer, George Forrest, Joseph F. Rock, Frank Kingdon-Ward, and others who trekked through the wilderness of China in search of more species. However, it was Wilson who first astonished the horticultural world by the number of kinds he introduced—nearly eighty, half of which were new to science. During his lifetime, he saw sixty of his introductions in cultivation in England, but, with one exception, all proved too tender for cold New England. Had he lived another twenty years, great would have been his satisfaction at the strides made in rhododendron culture in Oregon and Washington. Many of his discoveries flourish there, and some of them have become as important in hybridizing in the Northwest as they have in England. Wilson talked and wrote at great length about these handsome evergreen shrubs and continually pointed out the fact that the harsh climate of the northeastern United States, particularly in March, is often extremely trying for the successful culture of rhododendrons, particularly when they are not grown in protected locations. The principles which he set forth on rhododendron culture were more broadly based on a wider range of observations than hitherto had been furnished to amateur gardeners in America. No other living person knew the genus more intimately than E. H. Wilson, and the vagaries of the New England climate during the past forty years have borne out his convictions. Many of his finest rhododendrons now in cultivation in America are restricted to the gardens of Oregon, Washington, and northern California, where the winters are much milder than those of New England.

Schumann Abelia   *Abelia schumanni*

Few gardeners know this species of abelia; rather, it is important as one of the parents of a hybrid form, the variety Edward Goucher. A highly ornamental shrub usually with semievergreen foliage in the Northeast, but more characteristically a broad-leaved evergreen, or nearly so, in warm climates, it makes an attractive specimen or it may be used as a border plant. Sometimes, it is planted as a hedge, because it lends itself readily to shearing. The various abelias have value not only for their glossy foliage but for their refined textural effect. The tubular flowers, less than an inch in diameter, which appear in clusters from July through September, may be soft pink, white, or lavender-purple, according to the kind grown. All the abelias are somewhat tender in the colder regions of the Northeast but from New York City south, they are widely planted.

Shore Juniper   *Juniperus conferta (J. littoralis)*

Tracking down plants suited to every conceivable kind of situation was of prime concern to "Chinese" Wilson. He knew that coastal gardens needed sand binders and brought home a Japanese juniper in 1914. Since he had seen it carpeting large areas of the Japanese coast, where the plants at times were covered with sea water, he felt that his newly discovered juniper would be a boon to gardening on Cape Cod, on the Long Island coastline, and along the entire Eastern seacoast. Low-growing, the shore juniper hugs the ground developing a dense mat in dry, sandy sites. However, it has not been widely propagated and therefore is not easy to obtain. Unfortunately, many worthwhile plants of proven merit are either scarce or unobtainable, and one can only hope that increased demand will make possible their availability in the years ahead.

Tea Crab Apple   *Malus hupehensis*

A picturesque flowering tree, the tea crab apple (originally classified as *M. theifera*) rates as one of E. H. Wilson's outstanding introductions. Its zigzag branching habit, one of its distinctive attributes, gives it wide appeal. Wilson described the "plumes of flowers" as creating "a sight for the gods" when he saw this tree in the wilds of Hupeh province with its wealth of pink and white bloom. Averaging 15 to 20 feet in height at maturity, it forms a loose, open head. Both its size and its general aspect commend it for the small garden. The yellowish-red fruits appear in autumn. Peasants in the mountain regions of central and western China gathered and baled the leaves of this tree for sale to produce what they called "red tea," which is actually a rich brown color. On more than one occasion. Wilson found it "very palatable and thirst quenching." All of the Oriental crab apples are hardy, long-lived, and of easy culture. The various kinds vary considerably in size and shape, and the right kind in the right location makes all the difference in a garden.

Tea Viburnum   *Viburnum setigerum*

On the whole, viburnums are among the most useful of shrubs for gardens large or small, in sun or shade. For the most part, they are of the easiest culture, disease-free, and seldom troubled by insects, with the exception of aphids which have a liking for certain kinds. Wilson's introductions of this tribe included nearly twenty distinct kinds. He knew their merits, even in the wild, and realized what they would contribute to garden embellishment. One of his favorites was the tea viburnum, *V. setigerum*, of which he wrote: ". . . a tall, rather narrow shrub with erect stems, long dark green, rather leathery leaves, and small white flowers. Not until the autumn does it stand forth as possessing conspicuous merit. Then with its hanging clusters of large egg-shaped, orange-red to scarlet fruits it profoundly flaunts its charms, and none can pass it by." On Mount Omei, one of the five sacred mountains of China, it grows abundantly. There, the Buddhist monks infuse the leaves to make a sweet tea, "famed for its medicinal qualities," which they sell to pilgrims who come to the mountain to pay homage. Mature plants reach a height of 10 to 12 feet, but this loose, open-growing shrub may be kept much lower by pruning. Unlike many of the species which develop into a big-scale foliage mass of dense habit, this is a graceful plant of open growth, making bold tracery against a wall or fence. It thrives in full sun. The bright orange-fruited variety *V. setigerum aurantiacum* is the form offered by most nurserymen.

Tripterigium   *Tripterigium regeli*

Professor Sargent referred to this plant as a "dud" at the Arnold Arboretum, since it did not flourish there. He gave a seedling to his student Beatrix Farrand, whose great garden, Reef Point, at Bar Harbor, Maine, was noted for its choice plants, many of which were not expected to be hardy in the cold climate of Frenchman's Bay. Tripterigium, a member of the bittersweet family, bears its sweetly scented, small white flowers in great trusses, often 3 feet long. These show to notable advantage against the shiny foliage and reddish stems. Of it Mrs. Farrand wrote: "In July the whole side of the house is as murmurous with bees as any English lime tree walk." In growth, this vine is as vigorous and rampant as bitter-sweet but, unlike it, needs ample moisture to flourish. To be sure, the large glossy leaves are somewhat coarse because of their size, but the early summer flowering habit of tripterigium and the rapid cover which it makes are strong points in its favor, provided there is room for it to spread. It flourishes in full sun and endures windy sites with impunity, making it an ideal plant for seaside gardens. As yet, it has not been widely planted in the Northeast.

Wilson Magnolia   *Magnolia wilsoni*

High in the mountains of the China-Tibetan borderland Wilson found a magnolia which was later named for him, *M. wilsoni*. It is a wide-branching, open-growing, big-scale shrub or small tree, too tender for the cold Northeast but cultivated as a choice woody plant in West Coast gardens. The twigs are purplish-brown and the narrow, tapered, glossy foliage is covered with silky-brown hairs on the under side. Fragrant white flowers, 5 to 6 inches across, marked with a conspicuous ring of rich red stamens, appear in May and June in California gardens. Cucumberlike fruits with showy red seeds add an ornamental touch in autumn. Mature plants may reach 25 feet and spread nearly as wide. Specimens have been known to begin flowering at 4 feet.

HERBACEOUS PERENNIALS

Wilson closed his eyes to nothing that grew or displayed a colorful flower. He had an eye for plant forms as well, and even while trudging up a steep slope in western Hupeh or making his way through the underbush on the Tibetan border, he could visualize how this or that choice herbaceous plant might fit into a border at home in Gloucestershire, or in the more formal plantings at Kew, or in a New England dooryard. Woody plants were his prime concern, but he introduced also a number of worthwhile perennials.

Before World War II, a number of nurseries propagated and sold a wide array of hardy perennials, and a few specialists featured the rarer kinds. In addition, gardeners on private estates were constantly raising new kinds from seed obtained from England, France, and other countries. Consequently, visits to private gardens and attendance at flower shows enabled dedicated amateurs to become familiar with what was new and rare. Scarcity of labor and increased cost in the 1940's wiped out many sources of choice perennials and rock plants. The same was true of many little-known woody plants. However, English gardens did not suffer in quite the same way so that a goodly number of the herbaceous perennials which Wilson introduced are still available in the British Isles. The following list includes those best known and a few that are comparatively rare.

Anemone (Windflower)   *Anemone hupehensis*

In Hupeh, Wilson found a species of anemone about 2 feet tall with pink flowers which was named *Anemone hupehensis*. Hybridizers crossed it with the taller Japanese form and created the lovely September charm and other named kinds. Somewhat fickle about being moved, these choice plants require a year or two to get established. Give them a soil rich in humus with the best of drainage and partial shade. Where they are happy, they persist for years, bringing to the early autumn garden a note of freshness.

The vine-leaved windflower, *A. vitifolia*, 18 to 24 inches tall with white flowers, is another of his introductions. It is grown in English gardens.

Astilbe, False Spirea   *Astilbe davidi, A. grandis*

These two are tall growers, 4 to 6 feet high in their native heath, but somewhat lower in cultivation unless grown in moist loam. Noted for their long, airy plumes of flowers and stately stems, they make a striking accent in partly shaded areas, where all the astilbes seem to flourish best.

Chinese Rhubarb   *Rheum alexandrae*

This plant, which Wilson referred to as medicinal rhubarb, is a curious exotic. The inflorescence, made up of pale yellow bracts overlapping one another like tiles on a roof, rises on stout stems 3 to 4 feet above the shiny, dark green leaves, 1 foot or more in length. It prefers a moist soil and benefits from heavy feeding with barnyard manure. Occasionally it is grown in English gardens, as a curiosity in the herbaceous border.

Meadowrue   *Thalictrum dipterocarpum*

Not only the handsomest and the tallest but also the richest color of all the meadowrues is *T. dipterocarpum*, which flowers at the height of the lily season and makes a delightful companion for the trumpet types and the various aurelian hybrids. Plants grow 3 to 6 feet tall, depending on the soil and the length of time they have been established, although 8 to 10 feet was not unusual in China. The lavender-purple flowers with showy yellow stamens are arranged in loose sprays on sturdy stems above lacy foliage resembling that of the maidenhair fern. Full sun or light shade suits it. It is by no means common nor as widely planted as its attributes merit.

Silverdust Primrose   *Primula pulverulenta*

Primroses attracted Wilson's eye and he was responsible for the introduction of a goodly number. The best known and most widely grown is the silverdust primrose, *P. pulverulenta*, so called for the whitish meal covering the stems. This is no diminutive plant, but rather one of the candelabra group, so called because the flowers are arranged in tiers, with stems 2½ feet or more in height. Colors are pink, red, white, crimson, or purple, depending on the form grown, since hybridizers have developed several strains and numerous varieties. The leaves are narrow, often 1 foot long, forming a handsome rosette from which the flower stems emerge. This is a plant for moist soil, particularly a bog garden or along a stream.

P. cockburniana is distinctive for its large, orange-red flowers, borne in whorls, on 12-inch stems. Other species include *P. chungensis, P. veitchi, P. vittata,* and *P. wilsoni.*

Violet monkshood   *Aconitum carmichaeli (fischeri)wilsoni*

A tall, late-flowering perennial with violet-blue, helmet-shaped flowers, gracefully arranged in compact spikes on wiry stems to 6 feet or more in height, it makes a fitting companion for Wilson's variety of the Formosa lily. Both flower in September and October.

White Mugwort   *Artemisia lactiflora*

A rather striking perennial, it flaunts its showy plumes of creamy-white fragrant flowers on 3-foot stems, in August and September. White mugwort makes a good back border plant or it can be used among shrubs for its showy effect when perennial flowers are not numerous. Notably hardy and easy to grow, it multiplies rapidly, spreading by underground stems sometimes to the point of becoming weedy. The finely cut, dark green foliage is another asset.

Yellow Chinese Poppy   *Meconopsis integrifolia*

A rarity in America, it is grown as a biennial or short-lived perennial in English gardens. See description in chapter 17.

Lilies   *Lilium species*

Although woody plants were his special interest, E. H. Wilson is known the garden world over for lilies, especially the regal which have been described in detail in chapter 10. Among his finds was *L. davidi*, originally named *L. thayerae* in tribute to Mrs. Bayard Thayer of Lancaster, Massachusetts, a noted patron of horticulture. This lily had been discovered by Père David, nearly fifty years earlier, but Wilson rediscovered it in 1904 and introduced it. A striking species with reddish-orange blooms, spotted black when in full flower, it towers to 6 feet. In recent years, hybridizers have used it to develop notable hybrids.

Wilson it was who aided in making known the showy *L. henryi*, named for Dr. Augustine Henry. This lily is widely grown as are many of its improved forms; as with so many species, it has been utilized extensively in the past two decades by lily hybridizers to produce an outstanding new race of hybrid lilies. Nothing would have pleased Wilson more than to have witnessed the development of the "new" lilies in America, Australia, and elsewhere.

When gathering bulbs of the regal lily in western China, he found still another which he called Mrs. Sargent's lily. *L. sargentiae*, in tribute to the wife of his beloved "chief." This is a great, white, fragrant trumpet with rose-pink coloring on the outer petals; it has proved invaluable to hybridizers in developing the Aurelian hybrids. It blooms later in summer than the regal lily and produces bulblets in the axids of its leaves. A stately lily, often 5 to 6 feet tall, it is reliably hardy and disease-resistant.

Another white trumpet lily gathered by Wilson was *L. leucan-thum chloraster*, now considered identical with *L. centifolium*. The opinion has been expressed that the lovely Green Mountain hybrids with noticeable greenish shading on the outer side of the petals may be selections from the variety Wilson introduced.

From Formosa, he brought another white trumpet lily which bears its blooms in September and October. *L. formansum wilsoni*, which holds its bloom aloft wiry stems, 6 feet or more in height, is easily raised from seed.

Books by
Ernest H. Wilson

America's Greatest Garden. Boston: The Stratford Co., 1925.
Aristocrats of the Garden. Boston: The Stratford Co., 1926.
Aristocrats of the Trees. Boston: The Stratford Co., 1930.
The Cherries of Japan. Cambridge, Mass.: University Press, 1916.
China—Mother of Gardens. Boston: The Stratford Co., 1929.
The Conifers and Taxads of Japan. Cambridge, Mass.: University Press, 1916.
If I Were to Make a Garden. Boston: The Stratford Co., 1931.
The Lilies of Eastern Asia. London: Dulau and Co., 1925.
A Monograph of Azaleas. With Alfred Rehder. Cambridge, Mass.: University Press, 1921.
More Aristocrats of the Garden. Boston: The Stratford Co., 1928.
A Naturalist in Western China. 2 vols. New York: Doubleday, Page and Co., 1913.
Plant Hunting. 2 vols. Boston: The Stratford Co., 1927.
The Romance of Our Trees. New York: Doubleday, Page and Co., 1920.

Bibliography

Anderson, A. W. *How We Got Our Flowers*. London: Benn Ltd., 1956.

Bean, W. J. *Trees and Shrubs Hardy in the British Isles*. 2 vols. London: John Murray, 1950, 1951.

Bretschneider, E. *History of European Botanical Discoveries in China*. 2 vols. Leipzig, 1962.

Coats, Alice M. *Garden Shrubs and Their Histories*. London: Vista Books, 1963.

Cox, E. H. M. *Plant-Hunting in China*. London: Collins, 1945.

Farrington, E. I. *Ernest H. Wilson, Plant Hunter*. Boston: The Stratford Co., 1931.

Grant, John A., and Grant, Carol L. *Trees and Shrubs for Pacific Northwest Gardens*. Seattle: Dogwood Press, 1943.

Hadfield, Miles. *Gardening in Britain*. Newton, Mass.: C. T. Branford Co., 1962.

Hadfield, Miles, and Hadfield, John. *Gardens of Delight*. London: Cassell, 1964.

Li, H. L. *The Garden Flowers of China*. New York: Ronald Press, 1959.

McFarland, J. Horace, and Stevens, G. A., eds. *The American Rose Annual, 1931*. Harrisburg, Pennsylvania: The American Rose Society, 1931.

Pim, Sheila. *The Wood and the Trees: A Biography of Augustine Henry*. London: Macdonald and Co., 1966.

Rehder, Alfred. *Manual of Cultivated Trees and Shrubs*. New York: The Macmillan Company, 1940.

Sargent, C. S. Editor. *Plantae Wilsonianae*. 3 vols. Cambridge, Mass.: Harvard University Press, 1911–1917.

Siren, Osrold. *Gardens of China*. New York: Ronald Press, 1949.

Thomas, Gertrude Z. *Richer Than Spices*. New York: Alfred A. Knopf, 1965.

Veitch, James H. *Hortus Veitchii*. London: James Veitch and Sons, Ltd., Chelsea, 1906.

Waley, Arthur. *Translations from the Chinese*. New York: Alfred A. Knopf, 1941.

Wright, Richardson. *Gardener's Tribute*. Philadelphia: J. B. Lippincott, 1949.

Wright, Richardson. *The Winter Diversions of a Gardener*. Philadelphia: J. B. Lippincott, 1934.

Wyman, Donald. *The Arnold Arboretum Garden Book*. New York: Van Nostrand, 1954.

Wyman, Donald. *Shrubs and Vines for American Gardens*. New York: The Macmillan Company, 1953.

Wyman, Donald. *Trees for American Gardens*. New York: The Macmillan Company, 1951.

Index